Engineers

Corrosion Control in the Chemical Process Industries

Corrosion Control in the Chemical Process Industries

by C. P. Dillon

MCGRAW-HILL BOOK COMPANY

*New York   St. Louis   San Francisco   Auckland   Bogotá
Hamburg   London   Madrid   Mexico   Montreal
New Delhi   Panama   Paris   São Paulo   Singapore   Sydney
Tokyo   Toronto*

Library of Congress Cataloging in Publication Data
Dillon, C. P.
  Corrosion control in the chemical process industries.

  Includes index.
  1. Chemical plants—Equipment and supplies—
Corrosion. I.   Title.
TP155.5.D55   1986   660.2'83   85-19778
ISBN 0-07-016940-3

  234567890   D   8932109

ISBN 0-07-549275-X

The editors for this book were Betty Sun and Dennis Gleason, the
designer was M. R. P. Design, and the production supervisor was
Teresa F. Leaden. It was set in Caledonia by The Saybrook Press,
Inc.

Printed and bound in Canada by John Deyell Co.

To

Severn M. Frey, Works Chemist, Retired
Union Carbide Corp., Texas City, Texas

Who first introduced me to the fascinating subject of
corrosion control in the chemical processes.

Contents

SECTION 4   CORROSIVE ENVIRONMENTS / 139

Preface

Corrosion *control* is the real industrial need. The concept of corrosion control embraces a broad range of activity from the complete prevention of corrosion through various stages and degrees of protection to simple acceptance of the corrosion situation as it exists, depending upon economic decisions tempered by safety and other considerations.

Troubleshooting and failure analysis of corrosion problems should be secondary to proper materials selection and appropriate corrosion control measures in the design stage. Proper materials selection entails not only elements of design and operation but also provision for corrosion monitoring, inspection, and predictive, or at least preventive, maintenance.

Such efforts must be squarely based on corrosion *technology*, i.e., the reduction to engineering practice of scientific knowledge. Modern advances in materials and corrosion science must be applied at the practical level through adequate interpretation and communication.

The purpose of this book is to introduce the fundamental concepts of corrosion control to working engineers, scientists, and supervisors in the chemical, petrochemical, and other process industries, particularly. The approach chosen discusses fundamental considerations, corrosion phenomena and their mechanisms, the several aspects of corrosion control, attributes of common materials and their corrosion characteristics, and the corrosive nature of common environments.

I am indebted to Professor Ellis Verink of the University of Florida for reviewing much of the text in its first draft and making valuable suggestions for revision, correction, and expansion. I am also indebted to my many colleagues and associates, especially those of Union Carbide Corporation and Aramco, who encouraged me in the preparation and publication of this book.

C. P. DILLON

Corrosion Control in the Chemical Process Industries

CHAPTER 1

Introduction

1.1 PURPOSE

Corrosion is the deterioration of a material, or of its properties, as a consequence of reaction with its environment, as described further in Chapter 4. *Corrosion control* consists of one or more measures (e.g., materials selection, inhibition, painting, cathodic protection, and special design features) which will diminish the corrosion rate or permit its toleration in specific circumstances. The elements of corrosion control are discussed in detail in Section 5.

The primary purpose of corrosion control in the chemical process industries is the reliable, continuous manufacture of products for profit. The production and profits depend upon the economical selection of materials of construction and the applicable corrosion control measures, and on the reliability of the manufacturing equipment. These depend in turn upon effective communication along a chain of personnel, beginning with the materials and corrosion scientists and continuing through various engineering disciplines, purchasing, inspection, construction, operations, and maintenance personnel. It is essential that the people concerned, from management and the scientific and engineering staff down to the craft supervisors, understand at least the fundamentals of materials and corrosion control if a *safe* and productive operation is to be realized.

1.2 THE COST OF CORROSION

Several studies of the cost of corrosion in developed countries put the figure in the range of 3 to 4% of the gross national product (GNP). In the United States,

1

a recent estimate for the total cost of corrosion is about $80 billion per year. Of this amount, perhaps $55 billion is *irreducible*. The breakdown of materials because of corrosion cannot always be avoided, nor is it always desirable or economical to do so. Well-engineered systems already represent the optimum combination of construction materials and appropriate corrosion control measures, so that there is no possibility of further economies unless there is a breakthrough in technology. For example, the corrosion of UNS S31603 (Type 316L) equipment during the lifetime of an acetic acid plant simply represents one of the costs of doing business. There may be no more economical material of construction, but the equipment is ultimately destroyed by corrosion.

The remaining $25 billion of the total $80 billion is considered to be a *reducible* cost, savings from which could be effected by better application of existing technology. The loss occurs largely, it is thought, as a result of a lack of effective communication; it represents a summation of engineering mistakes.

Hidden costs which have not yet been fully comprehended and addressed include those arising from excessive use of energy and from the wasteful use of materials which are, or soon will be, in short supply. A nation which has no domestic source of chromium, nickel, or manganese should be on guard against waste of these critical elements by corrosion, mechanical loss, or misapplication.

Environmental considerations also enter into the hidden costs of corrosion. In the real world, one is always seeking a reasonable compromise between considerations for the quality of life (e.g., in terms of atmospheric pollution and the pollution of water sources) and what can reasonably be asked of a manufacturing facility from an economic standpoint.

1.3 METHODOLOGY

The basic method of corrosion control is the selection of the proper material(s) of construction and of appropriate means of protection against *unacceptable* rates of attack.

The proper material of construction is the one which is optimum in terms of initial cost, maintenance cost, and durability when evaluated in terms of specific accounting procedures, taxes, depreciation, and the time value of money. One must accept the ultimate loss of materials as an economic reality when corrosion can only be slowed and not prevented.

Selection of the proper materials of construction includes considerations such as cost, proper design and fabrication, operation, and maintenance. A material may be corrosion-resistant in its own right or may require one or more corrosion control measures (e.g., painting, inhibition, electrochemical protection) to prevent it from breaking down.

Because of human error or unforeseen circumstances, early failures of equipment are always possible. These early failures must be guarded against by proper inspection procedures, priorities, and schedules.

When failures do occur, a failure analysis may be required. Determining the reason for failure and the exact mechanism by which failure occurred is necessary if one is to select a suitable alternative material or to take counter-measures against recurrence.

In view of these considerations, this book is organized as follows:

Section 1: Fundamental factors—covering basic considerations, factors in materials selection, and procedures for the same

Section 2: Corrosion—covering corrosion mechanisms, phenomena, and testing

Section 3: Materials—covering the use of various metals and alloys and the complement of nonmetallic materials

Section 4: Corrosive environments—covering the corrosion characteristics of the natural elements (water, air, and soil); of acids, bases, and salts; of high-temperature exposures; and what are appropriate materials for such exposures

Section 5: Elements of corrosion control—the economics of corrosion control; use of materials, linings, and coatings; control of the environment; electrochemical techniques; inspection and failure analysis

To make this book as effective a working tool and guide as possible for the people responsible for protection of chemical and other process plants or facilities, I have included a number of reference tables and figures. For the reader who desires additional depth of understanding, most chapters are accompanied by a listing of recommended readings pertinent to the subject discussed.

1.4 RESOURCES

There are a large number of resources available to support the processes of materials selection and corrosion control. They include the following.

1.4.1 People

Professional Contacts

Professional contacts are found both in-house and outside the company. They may be professionals (e.g., corrosion and materials engineers, engineering specialists, designers) or simply people who have experience in and a personal concern with the matter at hand (e.g., purchasing agents or buyers, equipment negotiators, operations personnel, maintenance workers, inspectors). As long as proprietary information is not jeopardized, the same type of people, even in a competitive company, are inclined to share their knowledge in the areas of materials and corrosion.

Consultants

Independent consultants are available, usually for a modest fee in relation to what they have to offer in terms of experience and judgment. Some consultants may be affiliated with a manufacturer, usually because they were associated in some way with development of one or more products (e.g., corrosion-resistant castings). This in no way reflects on their objectivity, but indicates that they are only a step removed from the vendor's own technical service department.

Technical Service Departments

The technical service departments of the major producers of corrosion-resistant materials have long been of tremendous help in the resolution of corrosion-related problems. Such departments are the primary source of information on physical and mechanical properties and corrosion characteristics of specific materials.

Unfortunately, there is a growing tendency for manufacturers to dispense with this type of service, because it is perceived more as a promotional or public relations type of effort than one which contributes specifically to the "bottom line." More and more, the burden of collecting and collating technical data has fallen upon the user rather than the individual manufacturer or vendor.

1.4.2 Organizations

Following is a listing of some additional sources of information.

Technical Societies

NACE—THE CORROSION SOCIETY
P.O. Box 218340

Houston, TX   77218
(713) 492-0535
Originally organized as the National Association of Corrosion Engineers, this is the leading technical society in the fields of corrosion, corrosion prevention and control, and materials selection for corrosive services. It supports a variety of research and educational efforts and maintains liaison with other organizations with activities in these areas. The technical arm of NACE is the Technical Practices Committee, comprising more than 40 group and unit committees concerned with writing standards and exchanging information in specific industries or particular areas of concern. NACE standards consist of recommended practices, materials requirements, test methods, and other documents which reflect the state of the art for a variety of corrosion control and/or materials selection problems.

THE AMERICAN SOCIETY FOR TESTING AND MATERIALS (ASTM)
1916 Race Street
Philadelphia, PA   19103
(215) 299-5400
ASTM is the primary source of specifications relating to corrosion-resistant materials and various kinds of corrosion tests. Various parent committees are concerned with specific types of materials (e.g., A-1 on iron and steel, B-2 on nonferrous alloys, B-5 on copper and its alloys), while a special committee, G-1, governs a group of subcommittees concerned strictly with corrosion phenomena. It should be noted that specifications have a legal standing not usually accorded to standards.

THE AMERICAN SOCIETY FOR METALS (ASM)
Metals Park, OH   44073
(216) 338-5151
This organization is concerned with technology in the metallurgical fields, including corrosion.

THE AMERICAN SOCIETY OF MECHANICAL ENGINEERS
(ASME)
345 East 47 St.
New York, NY   10017
(212) 705-7739
ASME is responsible for administering the Pressure Vessel Code, which governs the use of metals and alloys in many industrial applications.

THE AMERICAN INSTITUTE OF CHEMICAL ENGINEERS (AIChE)
343 East 47th St.
New York, NY   10017
(212) 705-7338
AIChE includes a division concerned with materials technology in the chemical process industries.

THE AMERICAN WELDING SOCIETY (AWS)
550 Le Jeune Road
Miami, FL   33135
(305) 443-9353
The AWS has a proprietary interest in corrosion effects related to welding processes.

THE AMERICAN NATIONAL STANDARDS INSTITUTE (ANSI)
1430 Broadway, New York, NY   10018
(212) 354-3300
ANSI is the governing organization for many documents relating to materials
selection, especially piping.

Any technical society which deals with materials of construction must have
at least some interest in the control of deterioration of these materials under
the influence of natural or artificial environments.

Trade Associations

Trade associations are organizations formed to promote the proper and profitable utilization of specific types of products and are subsidized by all or most of
the major manufacturing companies concerned. Among the organizations
concerned with corrosion and materials selection are the following:

THE AMERICAN IRON AND STEEL INSTITUTE (AISI)
1000 16th St. N.W.
Washington, DC   20036
(202) 452-7100

STEEL FOUNDERS SOCIETY OF AMERICA*
Cast Metals Federation Building
455 State Street
Des Plaines, IL   60016
(312) 299-9160

THE AMERICAN PETROLEUM INSTITUTE (API)
1220 L Street N.W.
Washington, DC   20005
(202) 682-8000

THE AMERICAN WATER WORKS ASSOCIATION (AWWA)
6666 Quincy Ave.
Denver, CO   80235
(303) 794-7711

THE SOCIETY OF THE PLASTICS INDUSTRY (SPI)
355 Lexington Ave.
New York, NY   10017
(212) 573-9400

THE COPPER DEVELOPMENT ASSOCIATION (CDA)
405 Lexington Ave.
New York, NY   10017
(212) 246-1201

---

*The Steel Founders Society absorbed the Alloy Casting Institute, origin of ACI designations
for cast stainless steels, in 1970.

THE TECHNICAL ASSOCIATION OF THE PULP AND PAPER INDUSTRY
(TAPPI)
P.O. Box 105113, Technology Park
Atlanta, GA 30348
(404) 446-1400

THE ALUMINUM ASSOCIATION
818 Connecticut Ave. N.W.
Washington, DC 20005
(202) 862-5100

THE CHLORINE INSTITUTE
70 West 40th St.
New York, NY 10018
(212) 819-1677

NICKEL DEVELOPMENT INSTITUTE
15 Toronto Street
Suite 402
Toronto, Ontario
M5C 2E3
(416) 362-8850

Manufacturers

Although the availability of technical service is diminishing, the manufacturer is likely to be the most reliable source of information on proprietary materials. This is particularly true of manufactured items and composite materials. Further, for many items, such as valves, pumps, and compressors, there is a list of manufacturer's standard materials which may limit availability, especially as regards potential alternates.

Historically, the major suppliers of alloys, plastics, and coatings have been repositories for a large amount of both laboratory and field corrosion data and experience. They are reliable sources of information, especially as to where *not* to use their materials.

1.4.3 Literature

Journals

Certain journals are devoted specifically to the scientific aspects of corrosion, (*Corrosion, Journal of the Electrochemical Society*) or the technology of corrosion and materials (*Materials Performance, Metal Progress, Welding Journal*). Others have peripheral interests evident in particular articles or specific sections (*Chemical Engineering Progress, Petroleum Refiner, Hydrocarbon Processing*). Trade journals like *Plant Engineering* and *Maintenance Engineering* are also often useful sources of information.

Abstracts

Professional abstracting services offer publications which summarize both domestic and foreign articles on corrosion and related matters. The two major such publications are *Corrosion Abstracts* (published by NACE) and *Corrosion Prevention and Inhibition Digest* (published by ASM).

Manufacturers' Literature

An excellent starting point for many corrosion and materials investigations is manufacturers' literature. Most major manufacturers offer brochures which summarize the properties, including corrosion resistance, of their products. Among the more sophisticated presentations available is the *Corrosion Engineering Bulletin*, published by the International Nickel Company. Useful information is also available from the Huntington Alloys Division, Cabot Corporation; Ampco Metals; Cartech; and many other manufacturers, especially information concerning their proprietary products. For products which are produced by a large number of companies (e.g., the 300 series of austenitic stainless steels), there are, of course, a large number of summaries available.

RECOMMENDED READING

Atkinson, J. N., and Van Droffelaar, H.: *An Introduction to Corrosion Control*, NACE, Houston, 1982.

Copson, H. R., and LaQue, F. L.: *Corrosion Resistance of Metals and Alloys*, Reinhold, London, 1963.

Fontana, M. G., and Greene, N. D.: *Corrosion Engineering*, 2d ed. McGraw-Hill, New York, 1978.

Speller F. N.: *Corrosion—Causes and Prevention*, McGraw-Hill, New York, 1951.

VanDelinder, L. S.: *Corrosion Basics—An Introduction*, NACE, Houston, 1984.

SECTION 1

Fundamental
Considerations

CHAPTER **2**

Basic Considerations

The five basic considerations in corrosion control for the chemical process industries are cost, safety and reliability, energy considerations, materials conservation, and environmental factors. Although these are discussed separately below, there are inevitable interdependencies among them. All aspects must be considered in identifying, analyzing, and correcting a potentially corrosive situation.

2.1 COST

In seeking the optimum materials of construction (see also Chapters 3 and 33) in whatever combinations of initial cost, corrosion resistance, amenability to corrosion control, and life, the selection is inevitably compromised to some extent. It is not economical to design for unlimited life. Management will require a financial justification that will include not only the cost of labor and materials but also the cost of downtime and the aspects of safety and environmental control. Unforeseen or uncontrolled hazardous failures must be precluded. This entails not only proper materials selection and design but also predictive (or at least preventive) maintenance, based upon adequate monitoring and inspection procedures.

2.2 SAFETY AND RELIABILITY

In addition to the economics of materials selection and operation, corrosion control relates to several aspects of safety and reliability. One must consider not only the immediate safety of the equipment as it relates to profitable operation but also the short- and long-term effects upon plant equipment and personnel and even upon the local community.

The selected corrosion control solution must be considered in relation to

- Fire hazards
- Explosion hazards
- Brittle failures
- Mechanical failures
- Release of toxic, noxious, or other hazardous materials, except with adequate safeguards (e.g., scrubbing systems)

Fire and explosion are the most dramatic incidents of corrosion failures. One should be aware of the hazards inherent not only in the leakage of process fluids because of corrosion failures but also because of the nature of some corrosion products themselves. Some of the problems to keep in mind are

- Pyrophoric iron sulfides and certain sulfur-based corrosion products of zirconium become red-hot on exposure to air or oxygen.
- Explosive compounds are formed by reaction of some corrosion products (e.g., those of copper, silver, or mercury) with acetylene.
- Explosive silver azides are formed from reaction of ammonia or amines with silver salts.
- Certain organic compounds (e.g., diacetyl peroxide) become explosive on drying.
- Any organic materials can react explosively with powerful oxidizing agents, such as perchloric acid.

Be aware of corrosive situations that are made worse by poor control of process variables, actual or potential. Some things to watch out for include

- Unanticipated temperature or pressure excursions within the process equipment. Added to normal corrosion, such excursions can be disastrous. Temperatures may rise because of the failure of a cooling apparatus or from exotherms occasioned by contamination (as from the inadvertent ingress of alkaline substances into acrylic esters).
- Contamination of a process stream, such as water leaking into a chlorinated hydrocarbon or chloride contamination of an organic acid, may cause rapid unexpected attack.

- Recycling a process stream previously sent to sewer (e.g., introducing ferric ions, increasing chloride levels).

Other items which the corrosion engineer should be aware of (items that might seem unrelated to corrosion inspection, control, and remedy) include

- Unscheduled shutdowns which may sometimes cause corrosion, especially if they preclude special protective measures prescribed for normal operations to neutralize corrosive species (e.g., alkaline washes for stainless steel equipment in polythionate service).

- Hazardous materials, themselves noncorrosive, which might be released to the atmosphere. It is important to recognize that some materials *become* corrosive on exposure to atmospheric moisture (hydrogen chloride, chlorine). Poisons (hydrogen sulfide, phosgene, methyl isocyanate) or carcinogens [polychlorinated biphenyls (PCBs), vinyl chloride] must be contained.

Table 2.1 Specific Hazards and Related Protective Measures

Hazard	Remedy
Localized Failures	
External corrosion of steel under wet insulation	Heavy-duty industrial coating under insulation
External corrosion of steel chlorine piping at pipe supports	Pipe slides; plastic sheathing; heavy-duty coatings
Localized corrosion of underground gas lines	Coatings plus cathodic protection
Erosion-corrosion of steel sulfuric acid piping	Reduced velocity; long-radius ells; substitute materials
Special Effects in Corrosion	
Selective dissolution of alloy constituents	Proper alloy selection
Specific hydrogen phenomena	Alloy selection; environmental control
Cracking Phenomena	
Mechanical	
Nil ductility (e.g., steels at low temperature, superferritic stainless steels)	Limit thickness; minimize flaws and notches
Fatigue	Avoid sharp discontinuities; lower applied stress; shot-peen; autofrettage
Corrosion-Related	
Stress corrosion cracking (SCC)	Materials selection; stress relief
Hydrogen-assisted cracking (HAC)	Materials selection; hardness control
Liquid metal cracking (LMC)	Materials selection
Corrosion fatigue	Avoid sharp discontinuities, etc. (as for fatigue); materials selection

It is the duty of the corrosion engineer to anticipate and prevent corrosion failures related particularly to such potential dangers.

Examples of some specific hazards and related preventive measures are given in Table 2.1 (see also other sections relative to specific materials and environments).

Misapplications of conventional materials may also be hazardous, e.g., steel drain plugs in alloy pumps, wrong welding rod (AISI Type 347 rods in AISI Type 316L equipment), failure to blank off nonresistant items during chemical cleaning (e.g., stainless steel–trimmed valve from inhibited HCl, copper alloys from ammoniated citric acid, aluminum components from alcohols or chlorinated solvents).

It should be evident that careful selection, design, and operation are of the utmost importance to ensure safety and reliability and that equipment must be carefully inspected at suitable intervals. Inspection techniques are discussed in detail in Chapter 38.

2.3 ENERGY CONSIDERATIONS

Industry has always had to consider the availability of fuel and cooling water in selecting plant locations, in addition to the basic considerations of raw materials and transportation. It takes 10 to 15 tons of water to produce 1 ton of gasoline or sulfuric acid; several hundred tons for each ton of ammonia, steel, paper pulp, or rayon; several thousand tons per ton of aluminum.

The quality and amenability to treatment of fuel and water resources has not always received proper consideration. Fuel quality considerations include inherent corrosion problems such as vanadium contamination in oil stocks and indirect environmental effects such as sulfur dioxide emissions from high-sulfur coal, which is one of the causes of acid rain.

Water must be available in sufficient quantity and either be of an inherently suitable quality or be amenable to economical treatment against scale and corrosion, as for cooling purposes or steam generation.

The cost of energy for a proposed plant or process must be accurately appraised, including steam losses. The mnemonic "TILT" is often used to remind one to consider traps, insulation, leaks, and tracing, these being the major source of wastage of steam.

2.4 MATERIALS CONSERVATION

In the current economy particularly, certain elements such as chromium, nickel, and manganese are in critical supply (especially in the United States).

Because these are essential in the manufacture of corrosion-resistant and high-temperature alloys, every consideration must be given to their possible recovery and reuse. This will not always be possible, but because the high alloys are usually used where they are in fact suitably resistant, much of the domestic usage can be recovered by adequate salvage and recycle plans.

In the past, the free enterprise system has promoted the entrepreneurial manufacture and sale of products pretty much without regard to the long-term needs of the economy. With present-day knowledge of the finite nature of resources, elements in critical supply should be conserved for important applications and discouraged from use unless they contribute to the real service life. For example, stainless steel trim on kitchen or other appliances can be replaced with substitute materials of equally aesthetic appearance.

2.5 ENVIRONMENTAL FACTORS

Concern for the quality of air and of effluent industrial water goes far beyond the immediate concerns relative to safety and toxicity, as discussed in Section 2.2. Atmospheric pollutants include corrosive species such as sulfur dioxide, oxides of nitrogen, hydrogen sulfide, and hydrogen chloride, as well as those which can be either autocorrosive or have adverse catalytic effects upon other contaminants (e.g., coal dust). Many organic vapors contribute to overall pollution, increasing health hazards in terms of eye irritation or pulmonary problems.

Effluent water must not only be free of biocides, carcinogens, and other objectionable species, particularly in streams which might contaminate a municipal water supply, but even "thermal pollution" may be objectionable. Thermal pollution occurs when a cooling-water discharge raises the ambient temperature of the receiving body of water, with possible adverse effects on commercial fishing, for example.

In developing countries, it is obvious that some compromise must be effected between the need for industrial growth and concern for environmental quality. However, care must be taken that such pollution as can be tolerated temporarily does not cause irreversible damage.

It is unfortunately true that many industries in developed countries grew to considerable size without an adequate appreciation of the damage they were inflicting on the environment. Originally, such damage was seen by all concerned as a necessary price to pay for industrial growth and job opportunities. In today's climate, such industries must be pressured to clean up their atmospheric and aqueous effluents with all deliberate speed and with adequate consideration of the economic demands entailed. Most reputable firms today willingly embrace even multimillion-dollar environmental control programs, once the need becomes apparent, if they are permitted to do so at a rate that will not destroy them in a competitive market.

A substantial amount of the corrosion and materials engineer's technical input to a project may be concerned with its possible environmental impact, and this in turn may have a substantial influence on the economics of materials selection, as discussed in Chapter 4.

CHAPTER 3

Factors in Materials Selection

The major factors to be considered in materials selection are cost, physical and mechanical properties, availability, fabricability, corrosion characteristics, and amenability to corrosion control. Although the reader with an engineering background will already be familiar with the properties of engineering materials, the following discussion will aid in recalling their relation to corrosion problems.

3.1 COST

Although the initial cost of materials has an important psychological effect, it is essential that the *true* (rather than first) cost be considered. The true cost of process equipment includes materials, labor of fabrication and installation, annual maintenance, salvage value, and cost of corrosion control, if any. In comparing alternatives, a common basis is their *equivalent uniform annual cost*, which permits comparison of different lives and different categories of expenditure. The concept is explained in detail in Chapter 33 on the economics of corrosion control.

3.2 PHYSICAL PROPERTIES

Some physical properties are more important than others, and they are generally less important than mechanical properties from the engineering standpoint. However, they should be taken into consideration as required because they do have some influence on corrosion in some instances.

3.2.1 Specific Gravity

Specific gravity (sp gr) is the ratio of mass per unit volume to that of water, whose sp gr = 1 gram per cubic centimeter (g/cm^3). It is a factor in the strength-to-weight ratio, in ease of physical handling of equipment, and in coverage per unit weight by metallic coatings. A given weight of aluminum applied to a given area of steel substrate will give a thicker protective coating than will the same weight of zinc, for example (approximately 2.5 times thicker). However, zinc is preferred as a sacrificial coating (e.g., hot-dipped galvanizing), whereas aluminum coating is preferred as a barrier for high-temperature applications (e.g., "Calorizing").

3.2.2 Thermal Conductivity

Thermal conductivity is a measure of the capacity of a material to conduct or transfer heat. It is of importance primarily in heat exchanger design. Thermal conductivity is greater in pure metals than in their alloys. However, from an engineering standpoint, the thermal conductivity of the metal per se is often overridden by surface film effects in practical applications. Because a metal surface transferring heat to an environment will sometimes corrode at a higher rate than the same metal simply immersed at equivalent temperature, it is sometimes necessary to use different materials for calandria tubes or heating coils than for the vessel proper (e.g., silver coils in Type 316L acetic acid tanks, Type 316L coils in aluminum tank cars for monoethanolamine).

3.2.3 Thermal Expansion

Thermal expansion is expressed as a decimal part of an inch per inch (a millimeter per millimeter) per unit of temperature [e.g., 11.7 millionths of an inch per inch per degree Celsius, as for pure iron at 20°C (68°F)]. The practical significance of thermal expansion lies in the stresses caused by *differences* in expansion between different components of equipment (e.g., tubes vs. shell in a heat exchanger), and in the necessity of making provision for the elongation or contraction of engineering structures, as in replacing metal with plastic piping.

Thermal expansion problems are usually associated with improper design but can have an inherent influence on corrosion problems. For example, it is impractical to thermally stress-relieve steel vessels clad with austenitic stainless steels because the difference in thermal expansion will still leave the cladding in tension and susceptible to SCC.

3.2.4 Melting Point or Range

Pure elements have melting *points*, but most engineering materials have a melting range rather than a distinct melting point. The practical significance of this relates largely to weldability (e.g., a material with a *narrow* melting range is more difficult to weld with a structurally sound weldment). "Hot-short" cracking, which is caused by the presence of low-melting-point constituents at the grain boundaries, can be a problem in hot-forming as well as welding. Hot-short cracks may in turn become focal points for the inception of corrosive attack (e.g., SCC, corrosion fatigue, pitting).

3.2.5 Magnetic Properties

The magnetic properties are rarely an engineering concern, except as they relate to identification, methods of inspection, or removal of particulate matter from a product stream, such as "tramp" iron or mill scale.

3.2.6 Modulus of Elasticity

Although a physical property, the *modulus of elasticity* (Young's modulus) is the ratio of stress to strain below the yield (approximately 30 million for many steels and ferrous alloys).

3.3 MECHANICAL PROPERTIES

3.3.1 Tensile Strength

The ultimate, or tensile, strength of a material is a primary engineering concern. It is a measure of the load that a material can sustain more or less indefinitely. This property can be changed radically either by cold-work or heat treatment (or both), depending upon the nature of the material.

3.3.2 Yield Strength

A few materials have a definite yield point, at which there is a temporary drop in stress with an increase in strain. Most engineering alloys are characterized by an arbitrary *yield strength* (e.g., at 0.2% offset), above which they will no longer behave in an elastic manner. A value of five-eights of the yield strength is often used as the basis for mechanical design.

The yield point, tensile strength, and modulus of elasticity are illustrated in Figure 3.1, a stress-strain diagram for a hypothetical alloy. In the process of developing the data for such a diagram, one can also obtain a measure of ductility, as noted below.

3.3.3 Elongation and Reduction in Area

Elongation and reduction in area are complementary measures of the ductility of a material. *Elongation* is expressed as the amount that a material will stretch, due to applied stress, over some defined unit length before breaking under a tensile load. *Reduction in area* is the corresponding diminution in cross-sectional area at the fracture. Greater elongations are associated with greater reduction in area (i.e., "necking down"). Conversely, the smaller the value for each, the less ductility the material has exhibited. Ductility (and

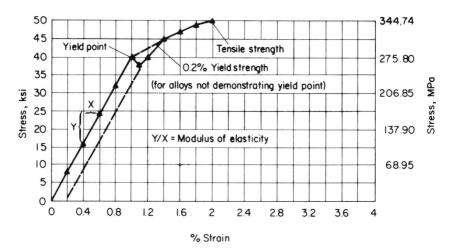

Figure 3.1   Stress-strain diagram.

toughness, see below) is an important consideration in mechanical design, especially under conditions of tensile loading.

Notch sensitivity is an important auxiliary consideration. An otherwise ductile material may nevertheless break in a brittle fashion if it is notch-sensitive. For example, threaded pipe connections in a "rimmed" steel may break off rather easily, even though the parent metal of the pipe has good ductility in the unnotched condition.

3.3.4 Toughness

Toughness is the ability to withstand impact; it is related in a general way to ductility. There are, however, many engineering materials which lose their toughness with decreasing ambient temperature to a degree that is determined by thickness. This dependency on thickness indicates that toughness under impact is not a true physical or mechanical property. It is discussed under mechanical properties because it is an important element in mechanical design. Ordinary carbon and low-alloys steels, as well as ferritic stainless steels, change from ductile to brittle fracture modes, under impact, with decreasing temperatures.

Toughness is evaluated primarily by means of high-impact tests, using standardized specimens (e.g., Charpy V-notch), which measure the absorption of energy of a given thickness of material at a given temperature. The values at different temperatures are then delineated in a nil ductility transition temperature (NDTT) diagram (Figure 3.2). Other types of tests (e.g., drop-weight and tear tests) have also been devised to study this phenomenon.

Selection of some materials, such as superferritic stainless steels, for their outstanding corrosion resistance in some applications may be limited to thin-walled components such as heat exchanger tubes because of the danger posed by NDTT of heavier-walled components.

3.3.5 Hardness

Hardness, or resistance to indentation, is related in a general way to strength and to abrasion resistance. It may be increased by either cold-work or heat treatment (or both), depending upon the nature of the material. It is expressed in arbitrary units (Brinell hardness number, Rockwell B or C), depending upon the type of indenter employed and the static applied load used in the particular hardness test.

Hardness constitutes a corrosion problem where there is a specific relationship between internal stresses and corrosion activity, as in sulfide stress cracking (Chapter 8).

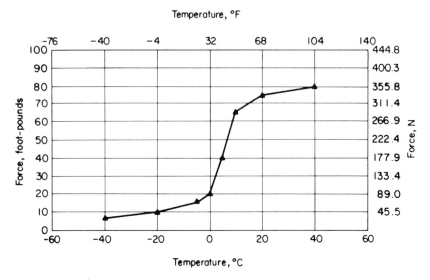

Figure 3.2   Nil ductility transition temperature diagram.

3.3.6 Fatigue Strength

Fatigue strength is the ability of a material to withstand repeated alternations of stress at some specific stress level. An S-N curve can be derived that describes the number of cycles (repetitions) of alternating stress which can be withstood at specific levels of stress (Figure 3.3).

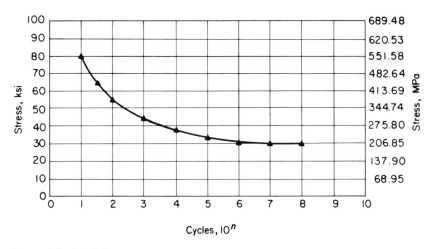

Figure 3.3   S-N fatigue curve.

In a general way, fatigue strength increases with increasing yield strength (and hardness, which has a rough correlation with yield strength), at least until notch sensitivity develops to counteract the benefit of higher strength. For example, an SAE 4130 steel has optimum fatigue strength at a hardness of about Rockwell C 35, above which it is harder and stronger but also less reliable in a situation of cyclic stress (due to notch sensitivity).

The *endurance limit* is that stress level at which (or below which) the material will endure cyclic stress indefinitely. However, in the simultaneous presence of corrosive action, there is *no* endurance limit. In cases of corrosion fatigue, the S-N curve continues to drop with increasing cycles of repetition; no endurance limit is to be found.

3.4 CODES AND REGULATIONS

Two specific codes and a number of standards and specifications are of interest.

3.4.1 ASME Boiler Code

Historical incidents of pressure-vessel failures, notably of steam boilers, led to the development of regulatory codes governing their design and inspection. The current ASME code is intended to ensure that proper materials, design, fabrication, and inspection are utilized in both fired and unfired pressure vessels, in the hope of precluding unforeseen failures. New materials and designs must receive prior approval before being used in a plant. Analogous codes have been developed in other countries for the same purposes.

3.4.2 ANSI Piping Code

A similar code has been developed by ANSI in regard to process piping.

3.4.3 Specifications and Standards

As discussed in Chapter 1, specifications are documents legally prescribing certain requirements as to composition, mode of manufacture, physical and mechanical properties, freedom from defects, etc. The ASME and ANSI codes refer in detail to certain ASTM product specifications.

Although standards lack the legal stature of specifications, they are accepted both nationally (ANSI) and internationally [the International Standards Organization (ISO)] as documents embodying a voluntary consensus. In representing the "state of the art" as to what is a good and reliable way to achieve a specific end result, they are invaluable in engineering practice. In addition to the NACE standards already mentioned, other standards are available from such technical organizations as API, SAE, AISI, and ACI.

Individual companies or corporations also develop engineering standards which reflect their experience and needs.

3.4.4 Unified Numbering System

Many trade organizations formerly had their own systems for codifying materials (e.g., SAE had a numbering system for steels, AISI for stainless steels, CDA for copper alloys, AA for aluminum alloys). These have been adapted to or replaced by a unified numbering system (UNS), developed jointly by ASTM and SAE [1]. The UNS for the most part incorporates the older numbering codes. For example, the former AISI 304 is now UNS S30400; copper alloy CDA 706 is UNS C70600; nickel alloy 200 is UNS N02200. In the long run, the UNS should replace the older designations (trade names and historical names), which were often misleading.

3.5 FABRICATION CHARACTERISTICS

The types of products available in specific alloys and their response to routine working and joining operations are important considerations.

3.5.1 Available Products

The practical usefulness of materials of construction may be limited by available form. Practically speaking, some metals or alloys are not available as castings (e.g., tantalum), whereas other materials are available only in cast form (e.g., silicon cast irons) and cannot be purchased as heat exchanger tubes, for example.

Following is a brief discussion of the more common forms in which metals and alloys are sold.

Castings

A casting is a product made by pouring molten metal into a mold. Pumps, valves, and furnace tubing are examples of products commonly manufactured in this manner.

Forgings

A forging is a cast ingot which has been hammered or pressed into shape under intense heat. Forgings are used for aircraft landing gear, high-pressure parts, hubbed tubesheets, and other massive components in which one needs a more homogeneous structure than can be obtained by casting alone.

Wrought Products

In one context, this term is applied to the final product deriving from *working* (i.e., rolling, drawing, or extruding) an ingot to a relatively massive final product, such as bar stock. The term *wrought* is an older English form of the past participle of the verb "to work." We also use the word "wrought" to denote the small, relatively equiaxised microstructure resulting from such a working, so the term also applies to flat products.

Flat Products

Flat products include plate, sheet, and strip, which are used either as materials for the fabrication or lining of tanks and vessels or as a form from which other products (e.g., clad plate, welded pipe, welded tubing) are manufactured.

Skelp is a flat product destined for the manufacture of pipe or tubing by rolling and forming it longitudinally and welding the edges together, with or without filler metal.

3.5.2 Heat Treatment

Metals and alloys are subjected to heat treatment for a variety of reasons. Usually, the heat treatment is intended to control metallurgical, mechanical, or corrosion characteristics or to effect thermal stress relief. Some of these treatments are discussed in detail later, when we discuss specific materials or phenomena.

Metallurgical characteristics of steels are discussed in more detail in Chapter 11. For the moment, it can be noted that normalizing ensures homogeneity of structure. The grain size of metals and alloys may be controlled for specific purposes, such as to obtain improved low-temperature properties.

The complex interplay between strength and ductility in many steels is controlled almost entirely by the sequence of hardening and subsequent drawing or tempering to effect a suitable compromise between hardness and ductility or toughness.

Thermal stress relief is commonly employed in many applications either for mechanical reasons (e.g., to minimize internal triaxial stresses) or to improve resistance to environmental cracking or corrosion fatigue.

Homogenization and other effects associated with heat treatment may have a profound influence on corrosion resistance, such as of aluminum alloys in certain atmospheric exposures, of certain austenitic stainless steels in environments conducive to environmental cracking, and of corrosion-resistant castings in aggressive environments.

3.5.3 Forming Characteristics

Forming characteristics are of primary concern to the manufacturer. The corrosion/materials engineer, however, should at least be aware of certain problems.

Hot shortness, for example, is a problem both in manufacture or forming and in welding operations. Hot shortness is a cracking tendency encountered when mechanical stress is applied in a critical temperature range, due to a low-melting-point constituent at the grain boundaries or a phase having reduced strength at elevated temperatures. Silicon bronzes, nickel-molybdenum alloys, stabilized austenitic stainless steels (e.g., Type 347), and "duplex" (i.e., mixed austenite-ferrite structure) stainless steels are notorious in this regard.

This undesirable characteristic not only limits hot-formability, as, in forming dished heads, but also shows up as cracking during or after welding under conditions of restraint.

3.5.4 Welding or Joining

Soldering and brazing techniques use low-melting alloys to join the metal parts, without actually melting the parent metal. Lead- and tin-based alloys comprise the soft solders, while hard solders are alloys with copper, nickel, or silver bases. When used to join nonferrous metals above 425°C (800°F), but below the melting range of the parent metal, the process is called *brazing* rather than soldering.

Welding

In a general way, the term *welding* includes any method of joining metals by the application of heat. In its original connotation, it included pressuring or hammering the metal in order to facilitate the joining and induce recrystallization across the joint. In current terminology, the concepts of soldering (e.g., *tinkering*) and brazing are excluded; welding means that the pieces are heated until molten and fused at the joining interfaces of the parent metal.

Pressure welding, which derives from the blacksmith trade, may still be employed for specific products, such as butt-welded pipe. There are still some complicated automatic butt-welding processes used in manufacturing. However, most of the welding which will be encountered by the engineer in shop or field will be one of the processes discussed below.

1. *Gas Welding.* In this process, a heating torch (e.g., oxyacetylene) provides the heat for melting both the appropriate filler metal and the edges to be joined. Except for repair welding of some high-temperature castings, this process is rarely used today in industrial plants. Furthermore, it is completely unsuitable for most corrosion-resistant alloys.

2. *Stick Electrode Welding.* *Stick welding*, or as it is more properly called, *shielded metal arc welding*, employs a wire core covered with a special coating as the electrode (Figure 3.4). Coalescence is effected by an electric arc between the coated electrode and the work. The hot, molten weld deposit is shielded from the atmospheric oxygen by the decomposition of the flux coating, while the electrode wire itself provides the filler metal.

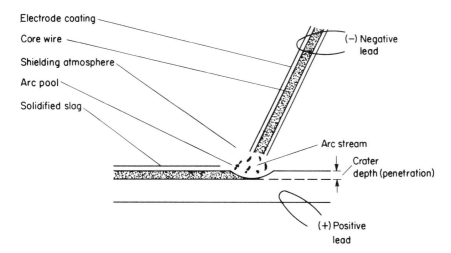

Figure 3.4 Shielded metal arc welding—straight polarity.

Either ac or dc current can be employed in this as in other arc-welding techniques. In dc welding with straight polarity, as shown, the electrode is negative and the work positive; current flows from the work through the arc to the electrode. In reverse polarity, the current flow is in the opposite direction and can lead to stray current corrosion (often called *electrolysis*) if an adequately sized return to the dc source is not provided (as described in Chapter 5, Section 5.2).

3. *Gas Metal Arc Welding*. This process, often abbreviated as GMAW or MIG (metal inert gas), uses a consumable metal electrode but replaces the flux coating with a shield of inert gas flow (e.g., helium, argon, carbon dioxide). The gas composition must be carefully selected and controlled for the alloy composition to be welded. For example, carbon dioxide is not suitable as a shield for a low-carbon stainless steel to be used in corrosive service because of the probable carbon pickup by the molten metal. Reverse polarity is routine for this type of welding, and stray current corrosion problems have been encountered in the welding of buried stainless steel piping, for example. *Short-arc welding* is a special type of GMAW, using a very fine wire which deposits weld metal by short-circuit transfer.

4. *Submerged Arc Welding*. This process uses a consumable wire electrode also. However, the arc is struck through, and the molten weldment protected by, a pool of molten flux.

5. *Gas Tungsten Arc Welding*. This process, abbreviated as GTAW or TIG (tungsten inert gas), employs an inert gas shield (as with GMAW) but around a nonconsumable tungsten electrode. The weld metal is provided either by the work itself (making an *autogenous* weld) or is supplied through a separate wire feed.

Filler Metals

There are many different filler metals designed to meet specific needs. It is important to remember that the filler metal (and its coating, if any) is designed to deposit an appropriate weld metal composition. This is usually (but not always) a close match to the parent metal. Also, alloying elements are sometimes introduced via the coating; a chemical analysis of the wire, stripped of its flux coating, is not necessarily representative of the composition of the weld deposit.

Examples of weld rods *not* identical with the parent metal to be joined are

1. Type 347 rod (18−8Cb) is used to weld Type 321 (18−8Ti) stainless steel, because titanium does not transfer well across the arc.
2. Type 308 rod (19−9) is used in welding Type 304 (18−8) stainless steel to enrich the alloy content of the weld and minimize depletion by oxidation effects.

3. Type 309 (25−12) or 310 (25−20) rod is used to weld carbon steel to 18−8 stainless steel, to ensure an alloy-rich weldment of suitable ductility.

4. Alloy 600−type rods of high nickel content are used for a number of bimetallic joints, to ensure ductility, impact properties, and corrosion resistance.

Welding Positions

The orientation of the proposed weld affects the choices of certain variables, because of the influence of gravity on the molten weld metal. Down hand (flat) position makes the weld from the upper side of near-horizontal work. In the *vertical* position, the axis of the weld is upright. In the overhead position, one is welding from the bottom side of horizontal work (e.g., from inside the roof of a tank). *Penetration*, which is the depth of the fusion zone beneath the surface of the work, may be adversely affected in overhead welding particularly.

Joints and Welds

Five types of joint design (butt, corner, lap, edge, and tee) are illustrated in Figure 3.5, and four types of welds (fillet, groove, bead, and plug) are shown

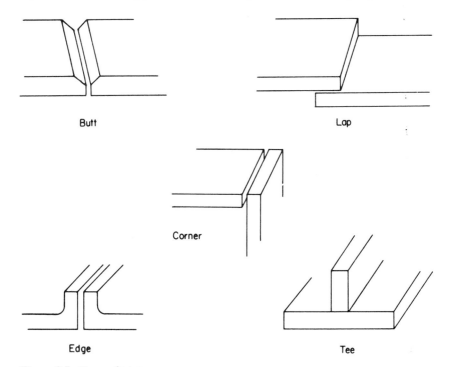

Figure 3.5 Types of joints.

in Figure 3.6. The anatomy of a grooved butt weld is shown in Figure 3.7 to indicate especially the fusion zone (FZ) and the heat-affected zone (HAZ). The latter, particularly, is often of great significance from a corrosion standpoint.

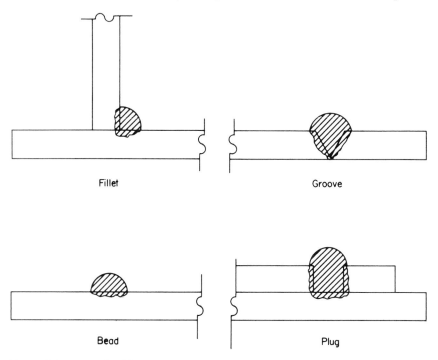

Fillet

Groove

Bead

Plug

Figure 3.6   Types of welds.

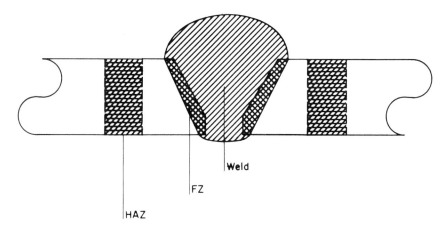

Weld

FZ

HAZ

Figure 3.7   Weld, fusion zone (FZ), and heat-affected zone (HAZ).

Weld Defects

There are several types of weld defects (or faults) which are of concern mainly with regard to mechanical integrity, such as warping and brittle behavior.

The contours and finished surface not only have aesthetic importance but also affect the application of paints or coatings for corrosion protection. Several other types of defects may affect mechanical integrity and the initiation or promotion of corrosion phenomena. These include the following:

1. *Lack of Penetration* (Figure 3.8).   This can be a focal point for accumulation of corrosive species (e.g., of caustic in steam lines) or a site to initiate concentration cell corrosion, environmental cracking, or corrosion fatigue.

2. *Porosity* (Figure 3.9).   Potential site(s) for pitting, cracking, or other corrosion phenomena.

3. *Slag Inclusion*.   Residues of welding flux in the form of slag may corrode out in certain environments, leaving sites with the same potential for problems as derive from weld porosity.

4. *Weld Cracking* (Figure 3.10).   This may initiate fatigue, brittle failure, or environmental cracking, or act as a site for initiation of corrosion phenomena.

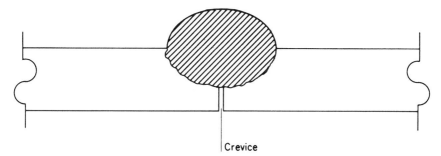

Crevice

Figure 3.8   Lack of penetration.

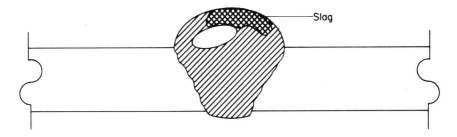

Slag

Figure 3.9   Weld porosity.

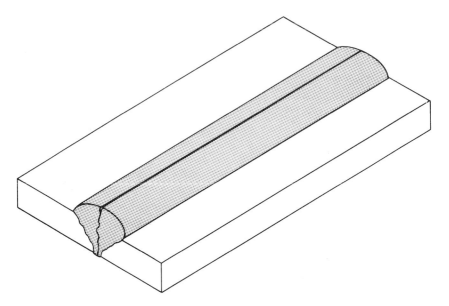

Figure 3.10 Weld cracking.

The stresses left in weldments are not defects because they are an inherent part of the cooling of the molten weldment under restraint; but they are conducive to cracking phenomena. Stresses should be reduced in many process applications by appropriate thermal or mechanical stress relief to combat both mechanical problems and corrosion phenomena.

3.5.5 Machining Characteristics

Machinability of an alloy varies with its structure, tendency to work-harden, and response to lubrication and cooling. The severity of various machining operations is rated from mild (e.g., sawing) to severe (e.g., internal broaching, which is a multiple shaving operation).

Sulfur is the element most commonly added to improve the machinability of ferrous alloys. Unfortunately, this leads to hot-short cracking in the free-machining grades of austenitic stainless steels if welding operations are attempted, as in repairing a pump shaft which has cracked from fatigue.

In addition, the iron or manganese sulfides formed can act as focal points for pitting-type corrosion. In a similar fashion, pools of lead in free-machining copper-based alloys are susceptible to localized attack in some environments.

3.5.6 Surface Finish

Finish-machined parts in rotating equipment such as pumps and compressors are often polished for improved mechanical operation. The internal surfaces of vessels may be ground or polished to minimize sticking (e.g., in the handling of polymeric resins), although the benefit is often transitory in nature. When surfaces are ground rather than polished, as in finishing of welds in tanks and vessels, high superficial tensile stresses can be induced. Such stresses increase the susceptibility to environmental cracking. Surface grinding should be done with care and, if possible, before the final stress-relieving heat treatment.

3.6 CORROSION CHARACTERISTICS

The susceptibility of a metal or alloy to the various forms of corrosion, which are discussed in detail in Chapter 6, obviously enters into the matter of materials selection. It is better that the metal suffer a general or uniform attack at some predictable corrosion rate than undergo localized corrosion such as pitting. A relatively uniform rate of attack permits the intelligent use of a corrosion allowance in the mechanical design of process equipment.

Even more insidious than localized corrosion are subsurface corrosion phenomena (dealloying, intergranular corrosion) and cracking phenomena (corrosion fatigue, environmental cracking).

Various types of phenomena associated with the effects of atomic hydrogen may also be of great concern, depending on the specific materials and environments.

3.7 AMENABILITY TO CORROSION CONTROL

Corrosion control, which is discussed in more detail in Section 5, often affects materials selection. One must be familiar with the measures that may be or are required for a particular material of construction.

Aside from simply accepting some reasonable rate of corrosion (which is the most practical approach in some cases), corrosion control may involve any or all of the five major approaches. These are

1. A change of materials

2. A change in environment

3. Use of barrier coatings

4. Application of electrochemical techniques

5. Specific design features

The amenability to corrosion control of the materials selected is an important factor in achieving safe, reliable, and profitable operation.

REFERENCES

1. *Metals & Alloys in the Unified Numbering System*, 3d ed., SAEHSJ1086 (also ASTM DS56B), Society of Automotive Engineers, Warrendale, Pa., June 1983.

RECOMMENDED READING

ASME Handbook: Metals Engineering, McGraw-Hill, New York, 1965.

Current Welding Practices, American Welding Society, New York, 1965.

Gillett, H. W.: *The Behavior of Engineering Materials*, Wiley, New York, 1951.

Jastrzebski, Z. D.: *The Nature and Properties of Engineering Materials*, 2d ed., Wiley, New York, 1977.

CHAPTER **4**

Materials Selection Procedures

The ultimate purpose of this book is to aid the process industry engineer in arriving at the optimum materials of construction for the necessary corrosive service, either by personal selection or by working with a professional corrosion engineer. It must be remembered that the term *corrosive service* holds different connotations for different people. However, whether the problem involves only product contamination or the more aggressive conditions of water-side corrosion or chemical processes, it is a corrosion problem for the parties concerned. Unfortunately, many corrosion problems are perceived only after the fact, the engineer or maintenance workers in the plant then becoming immediately concerned with recognition and understanding of corrosion and metallurgical phenomena and the economics of repairing, refurbishing, or replacing equipment.

It is only common sense that the major effort toward selection of the best materials of construction and any accompanying corrosion control measures be made in the design stages. This effort properly lies within the province of the professional corrosion/materials engineer, if such is available. However, for companies or plants who do not have such staff available, it often falls upon the design engineer, or even the design engineer's maintenance counterpart or the operating department head. Also, materials selection decisions for maintenance purposes are often made at the plant level.

4.1 MATERIALS CONSIDERATIONS

Selection of optimum materials of construction involves consideration of a number of materials-related factors, the materials-environment interactions, and the problems inherent in specific types of equipment.

4.1.1 Optimum Materials

The optimum materials are those which provide the lowest cost-to-life ratio when corrected for tax rates and accounting procedures (see Chapter 33) and which incorporate certain aspects of safety, health, and environmental considerations, and reliability. The desired end result includes profitable operation with a minimum of unscheduled shutdowns and regularly scheduled refurbishing or replacement.

4.1.2 Factors in Materials Selection

The major factors in materials selection, such as cost, physical and mechanical properties, and fabricability have been described in the previous chapter. In addition, one must know and understand the response of the material to corrosion, particularly its susceptibility to localized forms of attack such as pitting, crevice corrosion, or environmental cracking, as described in Section 2.

Besides these factors, which are intrinsic to the materials, there are such extrinsic factors as the ASME code or other regulatory controls, amenability to one or more of the five types of corrosion control (as required); probable response to fire, explosion, or temperature or pressure excursions; and the economic considerations.

4.2 MATERIALS-ENVIRONMENT INTERACTIONS

The characteristics of the basic materials of construction are discussed in detail in Section 3. The corrosion characteristics of many common environments are covered in Section 4, and corrosion control measures are the subject of Section 5.

If the probable behavior of the material under consideration is not known with confidence, it must be ascertained either from the information resources previously described (Chapter 2) or by appropriate corrosion testing (Chapter 9).

4.3 SPECIFIC EQUIPMENT

Not only do certain materials forms have limitations (e.g., some alloys can only be cast and, while suitable for valves and pumps, do not lend themselves to pipe or vessel fabrication), but specific types of process equipment have characteristic corrosion and materials problems inherent in their design.

Rotating equipment has a greater incidence of problems related to galvanic corrosion, wear, and fretting because of the necessity of running one metal against another under load. Heat exchangers have bimetallic corrosion problems in many instances, as well as hot-wall or condensation corrosion inherent in their operation. Distillation or extraction columns have problems of corrosion and materials selection associated with the presence of distinctly different environments at different locations in the same vessel. Pumps and valves are not necessarily available in the same materials as the associated piping and are subject to a higher incidence of velocity effects. These and other considerations enter into the final materials selection process.

4.4 PROCEDURES AND COMMUNICATIONS

Despite the complexity of these factors, which may require a skilled professional to "pull it all together," the biggest problem seems to lie in adequate documentation and communication of the final requirements. For new project design, particularly, the specific procedures and their associated documentation can be conveniently divided into three phases: *the definition of technology, the definition of facilities*, and *construction and start-up*.

4.4.1 Definition of Technology

The definition of technology (DOT) entails a full description of the process, its chemistry, and its conditions. This is essential for new processes, and should be developed as early as possible, in conjunction with the research and development department or other originating source. (*Note:* While it is apparent that a formal DOT is not required for replication of existing processes, one should always consider the fact that *exact* replication rarely occurs. Minor changes in operating conditions, or even associated utilities, may affect materials selection.)

A preliminary materials selection is usually based on the following considerations:

1. *Ingredients.* The major and minor constituents of each process stream, including trace contaminants, pH, and degree of aeration.

2. *Process Changes*. Possible deviations from the prevailing chemistry or ordinary conditions of temperature and pressure; also, aberrations associated with start-up or shutdown conditions.

3. *Contaminants*. The possible effects of inadvertent contamination of a feedstock or raw material, or the influence of species entering or building up through a recycle stream, condenser leaks, etc.

4. *Catalysis*. The positive or negative effects of metal ions which may affect either the chemistry of the process itself or the product quality.

A thorough consideration of these factors will aid in deciding what further corrosion or process investigations might be required before a final decision can be made. Sometimes, the appropriate questions can be resolved through laboratory tests of various kinds. At other times, a *pilot plant* operation might be indicated before one can reasonably start design of a full-scale unit.

4.4.2 Definition of Facilities

The definition of facilities (DOF) establishes the necessary kind, size, and number of the various types of equipment, and their physical layout at the plant site. A considerable amount of standardization can be achieved in consideration of the plant site, utilities, and auxiliary services. The plant location preestablishes the atmospheric conditions (which govern the selection of paint systems, insulation, and corrosion-resistant bolting, for example) and the kind and quality of utilities. The latter consist of cooling water, fire-control water, potable water, steam, and steam condensate. Soil conditions establish the corrosion control requirements for underground piping, tanks, etc. By standardizing as much of the materials selection as possible for the specific plant site, the engineer is able to consider in more detail the actual process requirements.

Wastewater streams are a special problem, since they reflect the specific contamination by process effluent(s), as discussed further in Chapter 18. Trace amounts of organic species in wastewater can profoundly affect the behavior of plastics and elastomers used in piping, gaskets, valve diaphragms, etc.

The process requirements demand optimum materials of construction (and related design considerations) for pressure vessels, heat exchangers, valves, piping, pumps, tanks, and instrumentation. These requirements must be adequately documented in complete flow diagrams called *P&IDs* or *P&CDs* (*process and instrumentation* or *process and control diagrams*). The P&ID should include reference specifications and standards, as well as process stream compositions and conditions. Also needed are descriptive *equipment lists* and *line lists*, *criteria* (which describe what one is trying to accomplish), and the *engineering standards* (which describe how the criteria are to be effected).

4.4.3 Construction and Start-up

The P&ID and related lists and standards must be complete and must be capable of adequately transmitting the specified requirements to the equipment negotiators, buyers, vendors, fabricators, subcontractors, and inspectors involved in construction and start-up.

To obtain adequate quality assurance, fracture toughness requirements must be established (Chapter 6), inspection methods and criteria spelled out (Chapter 38), and a materials identification procedure (MIP) provided.

The MIP may include alloy verification (by spot test or other qualitative or quantitative analytical procedures) and such qualification tests as may apply [e.g., the ASTM A-262 tests for intergranular corrosion (IGC) in 18−8 stainless steels].

Water-quality requirements, temperature limitations, and procedures must be established for hydrostatic testing, "dummy running" (i.e., start-up of distillation columns on water only), tank settling, and wet-lay-up procedures.

Welding standards may be required, and weld quality and finish requirements are needed, especially for equipment to be internally coated. Procedures for preservice chemical or physical cleaning of equipment must be established, and provision made for disposal of resultant wastes in accordance with environmental quality requirements.

Assistance should be rendered during start-up as to the proper installation and operation of any necessary corrosion control measures and the monitoring or on-stream inspection (OSI) of the equipment and materials selected.

4.5 CONCLUSION

The principles enumerated above comprise only a thumbnail sketch of the process of materials selection. More detail will be found in the forthcoming NACE publication on this subject. However, the following chapters provide insight into the corrosion aspects, materials characteristics, behavior of the major corrosive environments, and the application of specific corrosion control methods.

RECOMMENDED READING

Corrosion Data Survey, 2 vols., NACE, Houston, 1984.

Inco Corrosion Manual, The International Nickel Company, New York, 1973.

SECTION **2**

Corrosion Considerations

CHAPTER **5**

Corrosion Mechanisms

There has been as yet no final agreement on the definition of corrosion, on either a national or international level. One school wants to restrict the term to corrosion of metals, in which the transfer of electrons is necessarily involved. A second school wishes to apply the term to any and all materials of construction. The latter seems to have history in its favor, because the word "corrosion" has historically been used in reference to the deterioration of concrete, for example, as well as metals and alloys. For our purposes, I have elected to stay with the second school of thought.

5.1 DEFINITION

Corrosion is the deterioration of a material of construction *or of its properties* as the result of exposure to an environment. We include the deterioration of properties because there may be, for example, a loss of ductility without any material loss or dimensional changes. Corrosion may entail weight loss, weight gain, or changes in physical or mechanical properties. Sometimes, there may be no obvious change in the appearance of the artifact.

5.2 ELECTROCHEMISTRY OF METALLIC CORROSION

5.2.1 Fundamentals

Corrosion entails the conversion of a metal from the atomic to the ionic state, with the loss of one or more electrons. This *anodic* reaction produces a positively charged metal ion and free electrons, in accordance with the reaction

$$M^0 \rightarrow M^+ + ne$$

for example,
$$Fe^0 \rightarrow Fe^{2+} + 2e$$

From the chemical standpoint, corrosion is by definition the anodic reaction and an *oxidizing process* because it involves the loss of electrons. However, changes in properties due to corrosion, such as hydrogen embrittlement, result from the concurrent cathodic process.

Just as a battery will not function until the two terminals are connected through an external circuit, the anodic reaction cannot proceed without a corresponding *cathodic* reaction, which is a *reduction* process. The electrons released by the anode travel through the external circuit and react with some species at the surface of the cathode. In aqueous solutions, this reaction is the reduction of hydrogen ions (i.e., protons) to atomic hydrogen.

$$H^+ + e \rightarrow H^0$$

or reduction of both hydrogen ions and molecular dissolved oxygen to water or hydroxyl ions

$$2H^+ + \tfrac{1}{2} O_2 + 2e \rightarrow H_2O$$

or

$$H_2O + \tfrac{1}{2} O_2 + 2e \rightarrow 2OH^-$$

The driving force that makes metals corrode arises from the energy input required to smelt them from their ores to the metallic state. The order of corrosion resistance to natural environments can be roughly defined by the relative tendency to exist as a metal in the natural state. Gold and silver are found free in various geographical locations, but iron is found only as the ore (e.g., iron oxide, also known as hematite, Fe_2O_3).

Table 5.1 lists some commonly used metals in order of diminishing amounts of energy required to reduce them from their ores. The more reactive or anodic materials are at the top, while the less-reactive, or "noble," metals are at the bottom of the list.

Table 5.1 Metals by Order of
Energy Required for Smelting

Most Energy Required	Potassium
	Magnesium
	Aluminum
	Zinc
	Chromium
	Iron
	Nickel
	Tin
	Copper
	Silver
	Platinum
Least Energy Required	Gold

As with the dry cell or battery, there are five conditions which must be fulfilled before corrosion can occur:

1. There must be an electrical potential difference (i.e., voltage) between the anode and cathode to drive the reaction.

2. There must be an anodic reaction.

3. There must be an equivalent cathodic reaction.

4. There must be an electrolyte present for the internal circuit, i.e., an environment which will conduct electricity, such as a saline water.

5. There must be an external connection or circuit; i.e., a direct electrical contact between the electrodes. (In single-metal corrosion, the metal itself constitutes the external circuit between discrete anodes and cathodes, as described further below.)

Even when all these conditions are fulfilled, corrosion may be stifled by polarization.

Polarization is a change in potential as the result of current flow (Figure 5.1). Either the anodic or cathodic reaction (or both) may become polarized, but cathodic polarization is more common in natural environments, such as water. Anodic polarization occurs when the corrosion products are insoluble in the environment (e.g., an accumulation of lead sulfate on lead immersed in dilute sulfuric acid). An example of cathodic polarization is the accretion of molecular hydrogen at the cathode (as with steel in deaerated water); the hydrogen being neither evolved (as with steel in dilute acid) nor oxidized (as in aearated water). The accumulation of unreacted hydrogen as a film not only physically retards current flow (changing the internal circuit resistance) but also shifts the potential of the cathode.

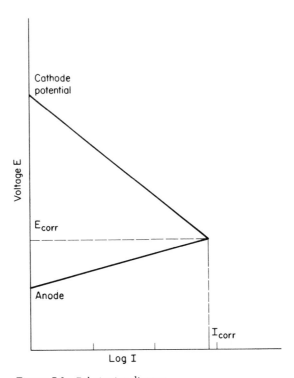

Figure 5.1 Polarization diagram.

5.2.2 Single-Metal Corrosion

When a single metal or alloy corrodes in a homogeneous environment, the discrete anodes and cathodes are microscopically tiny spots on the metal surface. Any particular site does not remain an anode or cathode, but changes back and forth from one capacity to another, giving an overall effect of a uniformly corroding surface. Under these circumstances, the factors and functions analogous to an electrical battery are as follows:

Voltage. The difference in energy levels between discrete anode and cathode sites on the metal surface

Electrodes. Specific discrete anode and cathode sites

Electrolyte. The corrosive environment

External Circuit. The metallic continuity between the anode and cathode sites

Even with a single metal, there may be abnormal potential differences between specific sites. These can arise from differences in metallurgical structures, from different degrees of cold-work, or from different levels of residual stress. In such cases, there exists a *nonuniform* metal surface exposed to the environment, the potential difference driving the corrosion reaction.

In other cases, part of the metal surface may either have or acquire a surface film with a different solution potential than the metal itself. (As we will see further below, this condition becomes similar to two-metal, otherwise known as bimetallic or galvanic, corrosion.) This film can develop in service, such as the lead sulfate film on lead, or may be the result of prior treatment, such as the mill-scale, or "magnetite," film, Fe_3O_4, on hot rolled steel.

It is also possible to have a uniform metal surface but a nonhomogenous environment. A common example is the oxygen concentration cell, in which oxygen becomes depleted in a crevice or other shielded area (Figure 5.2). Such a cell can be easily demonstrated in the laboratory by immersing twin steel electrodes in an aqueous solution divided by a semipermeable membrane, with nitrogen bubbling through one side and air through the other. Either a voltage difference or current flow can be measured, and it will be observed that the oxygen-starved electrode is the anode. Note that corrosion occurs where the oxygen is absent. Although essential to the corrosion mech-

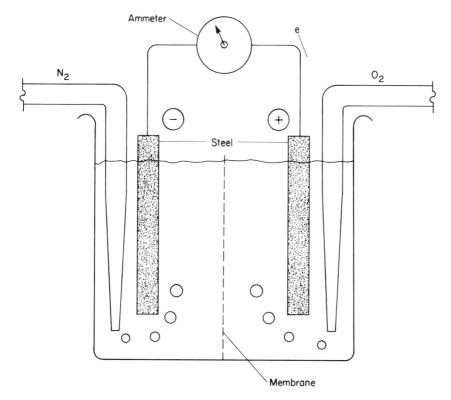

Figure 5.2 Oxygen concentration cell: lab demonstration.

anism, its function is that of a cathodic depolarizer; the oxygen-rich electrode is the cathode and does *not* corrode.

5.2.3 Two-Metal (Galvanic) Corrosion

The accelerated attack which occurs on one metal as a consequence of being in electrical contact with another in a corrosive environment is a matter of common observation. Sir Humphrey Davy, over 200 years ago, reported the accelerated corrosion of rudder irons as a consequence of installing copper sheathing on wooden hulls to protect them from marine borers. Aluminum screens are locally corroded if installed with steel or brass screws. Cast iron and steel waterboxes on copper-alloy condensers suffer accelerated attack in cooling water.

When extraneous factors are held constant, the difference in corrosion tendency between different metals can be quantitatively determined by measuring their individual corrosion potentials against a reference half-cell electrode. (A standard half-cell is one with reproducible open-circuit potential, e.g., calomel or mercury−mercuric chloride, copper−copper sulfate, silver−silver chloride, etc.; see Figure 5.3). Such values are often corrected to a value against a theoretical standard hydrogen electrode (SHE).

When the open-circuit potential is determined under standard conditions [i.e., for a pure metal in a 1 M solution of its own ions at 25°C (77°F)], the electromotive series is obtained (Table 5.2). This simply rates metals in order of decreasing (less negative) activity. Such series predict the tendency of one metal to displace another. The fact that one metal is more noble (cathodic or less negative) than another is easily demonstrated. For example, a piece of steel dipped into a copper sulfate solution will suffer corrosion, but an electrochemical equivalent of copper will appear as copper plating by a process known as *cementation*. Likewise, silver will plate out on copper from a silver nitrate solution. In each case, the more anodic metal displaces the ions of the more cathodic metal from solution, becoming plated with the more noble metal in the process. The anodic reaction is the oxidation of the base metal; the cathodic reaction is the reduction of the ions of the more noble metal.

When metals and alloys are arranged in order of diminishing negative potential in a real-world situation such as in seawater, a galvanic series is obtained (Table 5.3). Such a series can be constructed by immersing different metals in a liquid environment and rating them in order of increasing corrosion resistance. Such a series may also be constructed in a more quantitative manner. The open-circuit potential of the metals and alloys can be measured against a standard reference electrode, using a high-resistance voltmeter. The readings can then be converted to the values against a SHE, as also shown in Table 5.3. The driving voltage of a galvanic couple is the difference between

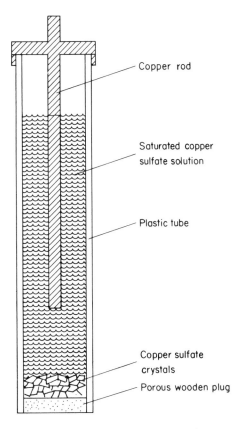

Copper rod

Saturated copper
sulfate solution

Plastic tube

Copper sulfate
crystals

Porous wooden plug

Figure 5.3 Copper–copper sulfate reference
half-cell.

the open-circuit potentials of the members. For example, there is about 0.4 V
potential between steel and copper in water.

In common practice, the galvanic series is taken to be that established for
seawater. It should be noted, however, that while this galvanic series is
generally applicable to many natural waters, it does not *necessarily* apply.
Also, significantly different chemical environments will have their own galvanic series.

It is interesting to note the radically different position of titanium, for
example, in the two types of series. It is strongly anodic in the electromotive
series because of its reactivity, but is among the most cathodic in the galvanic
series for seawater because of its rapid polarization by formation of a passive
film. From a practical standpoint, its behavior in the real world of aqueous
solutions is more relevant. *Passivity* is a condition in which a relatively active
metal assumes more cathodic characteristics, either temporarily (as with

Table 5.2 Electromotive Series

Metal	Ion Formed	Potential, vs. SHE
Potassium	K	−2.92
Magnesium	Mg	−2.40
Aluminum	Al	−1.70
Zinc	Zn	−0.76
Chromium	Cr	−0.56
Iron	Fe	−0.44
Cadmium	Cd	−0.40
Titanium	Ti	−0.34
Nickel	Ni	−0.23
Tin	Sn	−0.14
Lead	Pb	−0.12
Hydrogen	H	0.00
Copper	Cu	+0.34
Silver	Ag	+0.80
Platinum	Pt	+0.86
Gold	Au	+1.36

Table 5.3 Galvanic Series in Seawater

	Metal or Alloy	Voltage, vs. SHE*
Active (anodic)	Magnesium	−1.49
	Zinc	−0.81
	Cadmium	−0.64
	Aluminum	−0.61
	Steel	−0.38
	18−8 SS (active)	−0.36
	Lead	−0.32
	Tin	−0.27
	Admiralty Metal	−0.12
	Hydrogen	0.00
	Copper	+0.02
	Nickel	+0.10
	Monel	+0.13
	Titanium	+0.14
	18−8 SS (passive)	+0.15
	Silver	+0.16
	Graphite	+0.49
	Platinum	+0.50
Noble (cathodic)	Gold	+0.50

*To convert SHE to saturated calomel electrode (SCE), add −0.24.

steel in strong nitric or sulfuric acid) or permanently by virtue of oxidized films (e.g., aluminum, titanium, stainless steels). The word "permanently" is somewhat misleading because the film can be removed either chemically or mechanically, with the metal thereby becoming active. This is why the stainless steels are shown in two positions in the galvanic series, one as active and one as passive, although the latter is the more permanent and prevailing condition.

The fundamental relationships in a galvanic cell are expressed by Ohm's law

$$E = IR$$

where E is the voltage in volts, I the current in amperes, and R the resistance in ohms. If one measures the current flowing in a galvanic cell, it will be proportional to the amount of metal corroded per unit time, in accordance with Faraday's law

$$W = ITZ$$

where W is the weight lost, I the current in amperes, T the time, and Z the electrochemical equivalent of the metal, proportional to (1) strength of current flowing, (2) duration of current, and (3) the chemical equivalent weight of the corroding metal.

In any galvanic couple, the metal near the top of the series will be the anode, suffering accelerated attack, while the other will be the cathode and be protected, suffering less corrosion that it would as an individual freely corroding metal. This beneficial galvanic effect is called *cathodic protection* (CP) and is discussed briefly in section 5.2.4 below and in detail in Chapter 37.

Assuming bimetallic contact in a corrosive environment, three major factors control the actual amount of corrosion: the relative areas of the electrodes, the geometry of the internal circuit, and polarization. (*Note:* the resistance of the electrolyte is also an important factor, as we will see in considering corrosion in soil in Chapter 19. However, it is of less practical importance under immersion conditions in electrolytes.)

In accordance with Faraday's law, the amount of current determines the amount of anodic metal which will be dissolved. [It happens that 1 A of dc flowing for 1 year will dissolve about 20 lb (9 kg) of steel; so too will 8760 A flowing for 1 h.] In most cases of galvanic corrosion in natural environments, the system is under *cathodic control*; the amount of current is determined by the area of the cathode. Consequently, in total immersion it is not particularly harmful to put a bronze bolt in a large steel plate, whereas a steel rivet in a large copper plate will be corroded at a catastrophic rate. (This effect would be less noticeable in low-conductivity steam condensate than in highly conductive seawater, as mentioned above.) It is axiomatic that high cathode-to-anode area ratios should be avoided wherever possible.

The geometry of a couple can affect current flow because the current will flow through the easiest path. For example, the galvanic corrosion of a steel waterbox is caused by the face of the bronze tubesheet and the tube ends. Only the first four to six tube diameters of the internal surface of the tubes can enter into the circuitry of the couple. The rest of the tube internal diameter is simply too far away, electrically speaking, to enter into the circuitry (Figure 5.4).

Normally, the controlling cathode is depolarized (e.g., by dissolved oxygen), allowing corrosion to proceed, as governed by the factors described. Otherwise, hydrogen will accumulate on the cathode, setting up increased resistance as well as a back electromotive force, and diminishing the galvanic corrosion. No significant galvanic corrosion will occur in anaerobic seawater, for example, barring other depolarization effects. Cathodes are also frequently polarized by calcareous deposits (i.e., calcium and magnesium salts), as we will see later in discussing water chemistry (Chapter 8).

It should be emphasized once again that each chemical environment (if significantly different from water or from dilute aqueous solutions) will have *its own galvanic series.* The relationships shown in the galvanic series, in Table 5.3, which is based on seawater, may become quite different in other environments. Magnesium is cathodic to steel in hydrofluoric acid. Steel can

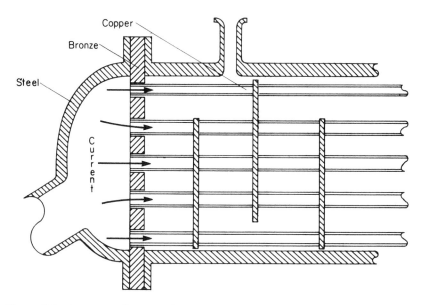

Figure 5.4 Geometric effects in galvanic corrosion of steel waterbox by copper alloy tubes and sheet.

become cathodic to stainless steel in hot caustic, for example. Even zinc can become cathodic to steel in hot water of certain specific chemistry (of Section 18.7.3, p. 157).

5.2.4 Cathodic Protection

CP is a practical utilization of galvanic corrosion. In the early 1940s, an investigation was made as to the practicality of protecting steel in seawater by attaching zinc or magnesium anodes to it. The inexpensive sacrificial anodes would corrode, affording protection to the steel. In so doing, the current generated also plated out calcareous deposits from the seawater, building a partially protective coating and effectively reducing the area of the cathode, thereby limiting the current demand. It was also determined that the same effects could be achieved by supplying dc from an external source such as a battery, rectifier, or generator, using either metal scrap or inert but conductive anodes of carbon or silicon cast iron, for example.

The major impetus for CP came after World War II, when the process was commercially applied to underground pipelines. Underground steel tends to be corroded, especially by low-resistivity (i.e., high-conductivity) soils. From a practical standpoint, the steel should be coated or wrapped to reduce the current demand to that required by "holidays" (i.e., breaks or defects) in the coating.

The steel can then be economically protected either by sacrificial anodes or by driven anodes, utilizing an external dc source. (In practice, the dc is often provided by rectifiers, which convert ac to dc.) The choice between sacrificial and driven anodes will be dictated by economics, geometry, and possible damage to surrounding structures by stray currents (i.e., so-called electrolysis).

Electrolysis is corrosion of a buried or immersed structure due to stray dc from some external source. The current leakage from a dc motor, welding machine, or rectifier will corrode steel at the rate of about 20 lb/A-yr (9 kg/A-yr). (Naturally, the smaller the area from which the steel is lost, the higher the corrosion rate.)

The problem was first observed around electrical railways, whose current was supplied from an overhead wire, or trolley, and was supposed to return to its source along the track or third rail. If the current found it easier to return to source on buried steel pipe (e.g., a water line or sewer system), it would protect the pipe at the point of entry but cause corrosion at the point of discharge via the soil to the power source. Similarly, ship hulls have been damaged during reverse-polarity welding operations when the welding machine was ashore and inadequate electrical returns were provided (or where the return connections were faulty). In either case, the current simply found it easier to return to source through the hull-seawater interface than through the return leads, causing severe hull damage. Welding austenitic stainless steel pipe in place for underground applications has resulted in similar problems, in the form of severe localized pitting.

5.2.5 Anodic Protection

There are particular cases in which current flow *from* the metal can be beneficial rather than causing electrolysis. Some combinations of metals and environments lend themselves to *anodic protection* (AP), which requires that the anodic metal be dependent for its corrosion resistance on an insoluble film which can be reinforced and maintained by the oxidizing effect of an impressed anodic polarization.

The classical examples of AP are in storage of concentrated sulfuric acid in steel tanks (to reduce iron contamination of the acid) and in stainless steel coolers for the strong acid. AP *absolutely* requires professional design and operating supervision, as corrosion by electrolysis may ensue if the proper potentials are not maintained. Obviously, power failures will permit corrosion to proceed when external power sources are employed for either CP or AP.

The advent of microcomputers has expanded the application of electrochemical control. Not only are CP and AP handled in a more sophisticated manner today, but other applications are also in use (e.g., prevention of environmental cracking in pulp and paper plants by constant control of open-circuit corrosion potential of the austenitic stainless steel equipment).

CHAPTER **6**

Corrosion and Metallurgical Phenomena

The ability to recognize and distinguish different corrosion, metallurgical, and mechanical phenomena is an important part of failure analysis and, by extension, of corrosion control decisions. In this chapter, we will discuss the three groups of phenomena in an introductory manner. Certain subgroups are of sufficient importance to warrant more detailed discussion in their own right, and are covered in more detail in subsequent chapters. Inevitably, as noted in the discussion below, there is a certain amount of overlap between some types of phenomena.

6.1 CORROSION PHENOMENA

Although there is not total agreement even among experts, it is generally accepted that there are basically eight forms of corrosion. (These, as given in current literature, are derived from those originally expounded by Fontana.) NACE Handbook 1, *Forms of Corrosion—Recognition and Prevention*, lists these as follows:

1. General (uniform) corrosion
2. Localized corrosion
3. Galvanic corrosion

4. Cracking phenomena

5. Velocity effects (erosion-corrosion, cavitation, fretting)

6. IGC

7. Dealloying

8. High-temperature corrosion

The eight forms of corrosion can be divided into three categories:

Group I   Those readily identified upon visual examination (forms 1,2, and 3).

Group II   Those which may require supplementary means of examination (forms 5, 6, and 7).

Group III Those which usually should be verified by microscopy, optical or SEM, although they are sometimes apparent to the naked eye (forms 4 and 8).

The individual phenomena are illustrated schematically in Figure 6.1 and are defined further below.

6.1.1 Definitions

Group I Forms

1. *General Corrosion.*   General, or uniform, corrosion is characterized by an even, regular loss of metal from the corroding surface. All metals are subject to this type of corrosion under some conditions, such as atmospheric rusting of steel or dissolution of zinc by dilute acid. It is the most desirable form of attack because it lends itself to predicting the life of equipment. It is observed in both single-metal and bimetallic corrosion (form 3 below).

2. *Localized Corrosion.*   Localized corrosion is the type in which all or most of the attack occurs at discrete areas. These may be relatively large but shallow, as with the "corrosion lakes" encountered in oil and gas equipment. However, pitting, with its intense localized attack, is of greater consequence. Pitting may occur on a boldly exposed surface, due to weak points in a surface film, or by local cell action under deposits. *Crevice corrosion* is a particular form of pitting which occurs between faying surfaces (e.g., in threaded or flanged connections), usually due to oxygen concentration cell effects.

3. *Galvanic Corrosion.*   Also known as bimetallic or two-metal corrosion, galvanic corrosion is accelerated attack occasioned by electrical contact between dissimilar conductors in an electrolyte. The accelerated corrosion is suffered by the anodic member of the couple (e.g., steel in the iron-copper cell in seawater) and depends on their relative position in the

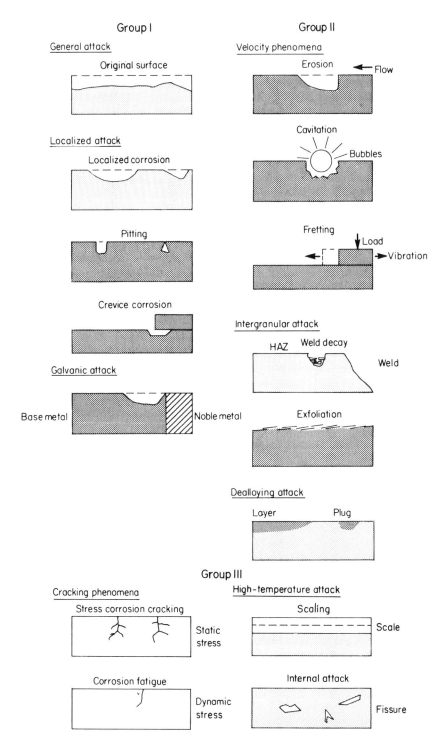

Figure 6.1 Eight forms of corrosion (mechanics of attack). (From NACE Handbook 1, *The Forms of Corrosion Recognition and Prevention.* Reproduced with permission.)

pertinent galvanic series and the relative areas and geometry of the two electrodes. Galvanic corrosion can also be caused by conductive films such as mill scale and by conductive nonmetallic cathodes such as carbon or graphite).

The distinctions among Group I forms refer primarily to the distribution of attack (i.e., general, localized, or confined to the anode of a galvanic couple). Groups II and III below are categorized by the *morphology* of attack, which is usually localized in nature but in some instances may be fairly general.

Group II Forms

5. *Velocity Effects.* Velocity effects comprise erosion-corrosion, cavitation, and fretting. *Erosion-corrosion* is attack accelerated by high-velocity flow or impingement. There is actually a family of phenomena ranging from purely mechanical such as abrasion and wear to the corrosion-related type in which an otherwise protective film of corrosion products is swept away by the flow conditions. In all cases, there is a distinctive flow pattern (e.g., copper in water or steel in steam).

Cavitation is a distinctive form of velocity attack caused by the implosion of bubbles formed where the local pressure in the flowing liquid drops below the vapor pressure. One observes a porous, gouged effect quite unlike the flow lines of erosion-corrosion. Cavitation is observed on ship propellers, pump impellers, and on the internal bore of water-cooled compressor rods. Its mechanical aspects can be demonstrated (e.g., by ultrasonic vibration of glass in distilled water), as can its electrochemical features (e.g., response to corrosion inhibition and CP).

Fretting is another form of corrosion associated with motion, in this case between mating surfaces under load and subjected to vibration. This induces the tearing away of small particles which are subsequently oxidized or otherwise corroded between the faying surfaces. A typical example is the fretting of automotive wheel bearings if the vehicles are inadequately supported during rail shipment.

6. *IGC* is preferential attack at the grain boundaries of a metallic structure. In some cases, whole grains may fall out (e.g., "sugaring"). The attack may be general if an artifact is improperly heat-treated or localized in the HAZs of welds (e.g., the so-called weld decay of certain austenitic stainless steels).

7. *Dealloying corrosion* is the selective removal of one metallic constituent of an alloy. Also known as *parting corrosion*, it is exemplified by the dezincification of yellow brass. (Note that *layer-type* dezincification corresponds to general attack, while *plug-type* corresponds to pitting.) Another manifestation is the graphitic corrosion (sometimes erroneously called *graphitization*) of gray cast iron. Typically, the selective dissolution of an alloy constituent seriously weakens the metal structure without necessarily changing the apparent physical dimensions.

Group III Forms

4. *Cracking phenomena* include both the corrosion-related environmental cracking and the mechanical-electrochemical fatigue. *Environmental cracking* comprises three forms of attack which involve the brittle cracking of a metal or alloy under the combined effect of a tensile stress and a *specific* corrodent. The three forms are

- **a.** *Stress Corrosion Cracking (SCC).* An anodic process exemplified by the chloride SCC of stainless steel.
- **b.** *Hydrogen-Assisted Cracking (HAC).* A cathodic process exemplified by sulfide stress cracking of hardened steel by hydrogen sulfide.
- **c.** *Liquid Metal Cracking.* A fissuring process exemplified by the action of mercury on cold-worked brass.

Fatigue is the brittle cracking of an otherwise ductile material induced by numerous repetitions of a cyclic stress. It becomes corrosion fatigue when a *nonspecific* corrodent aggravates the situation and eliminates the endurance limit, as previously described in Chapter 3.

8. *High-Temperature Corrosion.* This includes a variety of phenomena which involve conversion of the metal to a metallic compound. The most common product is the metal oxide, but other conversions (e.g., halides, sulfides, carbides, nitrides) are possible. Reactions may occur on the metal surface or within the structure of the metal itself, as discussed further in Chapter 30.

6.2 METALLURGICAL PHENOMENA

There are two metallurgical phenomena which, although not corrosion-related, are nevertheless important in materials selection.

6.2.1 Nil Ductility

Nil ductility is the phenomenon in which an otherwise ductile metal or alloy becomes distinctly brittle with decreasing temperature, as discussed briefly in Section 3.2.4, and shown in Figure 3.2. Steels are particularly susceptible to this phenomenon, but so are such corrosion-resistant alloys as the low-interstitial ferritic stainless steels. The exact nil ductility transition temperature (NDTT) will vary primarily with thickness of the material but is also influenced by compositional variables and heat treatment. Special impact tests have been devised which are used to determine the NDTT for a particular set of conditions, including flaw size (which can be very critical).

6.2.2 Hot-Short Cracking

Hot-short cracking is the microfissuring which occurs under tensile stress at elevated temperatures (as when welding under restraint), due to low-melting constituents at the grain boundaries. When a metal is hot-worked or welded, these low-melting constituents separate (even though the metal itself is well below its melting range) and leave a network of microfissures. These usually develop quickly into visually detectable macrocracks as well. Hot-short cracking bears a distinct resemblance, upon microscopic examination, to environmental cracking in an intergranular mode. However, it is usually detectable immediately after occurrence by such methods as dye-penetrant or ultrasonic inspection. Columbium-stabilized stainless steels, silicon bronzes; and nickel-molybdenum alloys are particularly susceptible to hot-short cracking.

A more detailed discussion of the most important phenomena will be found in later chapters. Although we have made passing reference to specific materials, I will now introduce common materials of construction before discussing certain corrosion phenomena in detail.

RECOMMENDED READING

Corrosion Handbook No. 1. *The Forms of Corrosion Recognition and Prevention,* NACE, Houston, 1982.

CHAPTER **7**

Sensitization and Weld Decay

These topics are of special interest because of the unhappy consequences of IGC in process equipment. Together with environmental cracking (Chapter 8), they are the primary concern in many corrosion applications.

The term *sensitization* is used broadly to describe the susceptibility to IGC which results from exposing a metal or alloy to a critical temperature range (as in heat treatment or welding). Sensitization may be general (as when an entire item is improperly heat-treated) or localized (as by spot heating or welding).

The most common form of localized sensitization occurs in the HAZ adjacent to welds that results from the temperature gradient between the cold parent metal and the molten weld. The resultant IGC of the HAZ in certain environments is commonly known by the misnomer of "weld decay." (Such a term should have been reserved for those incidents in which the weld *itself* is selectively corroded, as with S31603 in some organic acid services.) Figure 7.1 shows a schematic diagram of the location and nature of the so-called weld decay in a HAZ.

The problems of sensitization and weld decay are experienced most commonly in the austenitic stainless steels (see Chapter 12), as discussed further below. However, they are also encountered in certain high-nickel alloys, and occasionally in other metallic materials.

When an austenitic stainless steel of the 18-8 variety with moderate carbon content (e.g., S30400; 0.08% carbon maximum) is heated in the temperature range from 425°C (800°F) to 815°C (1500°F), the dissolved carbon migrates to

Heat-affected zones

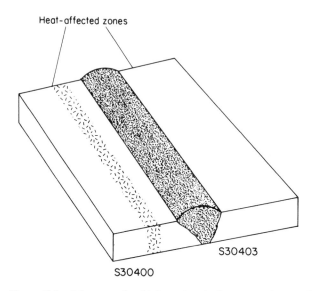

S30403

S30400

Figure 7.1   Schematic of weld decay (IGC) of 18−8 stainless steel.

the grain boundaries and precipitates as chromium carbides. This leaves a chromium-depleted zone of diminished corrosion resistance around each individual grain, resulting in a susceptibility to IGC *in certain environments* (not all, by any means). Exposure to this critical sensitizing temperature range can be the result of improper annealing, inadequate quenching from a solution-anneal, slow cooling during thermal stress relief, hot-working (e.g., spinning a dished head), or from heating during welding or forming operations.

It is important to note that the environment must be specific for this form of attack. Oxidizing acids like nitric acid and acids containing oxidizing agents (e.g., sulfuric or phosphoric acid containing ferric or cupric ions) are highly specific for this type of attack. So too are hot organic acids such as acetic acid and formic acid process streams. Seawater and other high-chloride waters cause severe pitting in sensitized areas, but low-chloride waters such as potable water do not, except in particular situations, for example, as might occur under the influence of bacterial action.

Originally, sensitization and weld decay of the 18−8 stainless steels were combatted by alloy additions of titanium, columbium, and columbium-tantalum mixtures. This practice continues today to some extent and is also employed with higher alloys like the superstainless steels (although lowering the carbon content is also utilized, as further discussed below).

Adding titanium or columbium in amounts equal to 5 or 10 times the carbon content, respectively, permits the alloy to precipitate titanium or columbium carbides (in lieu of chromium carbides) during sensitization heat exposures. The carbon is still precipitated, but without diminishing the chromium content of the grain boundaries. S32100 (18−8Ti) and S34700 (18−8 Cb) were thus derived from the basic 18−8 stainless steel (S30400).

Two problems exist with this approach. Titanium does not transfer well across a welding arc, thus losing much of its effectiveness in multipass welding or crosswelding. Although columbium does not have this deficiency, the columbium carbides (as also titanium carbides) can be redissolved by the heat of welding, especially with alloys of higher nickel content. Consequently, multiple-pass welding or cross welding can first redissolve titanium or columbium carbides and then permit chromium carbide precipitation in the *fusion* zone (*not* HAZ). This can result in a highly localized form of IGC known as *knife-line attack* (KLA), observed particularly in alloys like S34700 and NO8825.

With the development first of low-carbon ferrochromium and later with modern improved steel-making processes, it became possible to manufacture 18−8 stainless steels of much lower carbon content. When the carbon content is held to less than about 0.030%, chromium carbide precipitation can still occur upon sensitization, but in such small amounts that no significant chromium depletion occurs. Modern low-carbon alloys (e.g., S30403, S31603, S31703) are practically immune to weld decay. They will, however, become sensitized upon *prolonged* heating in the sensitizing range, such as in service, or during very prolonged stress relief. Graphs are available which depict the time-temperature-transition characteristics of such alloys. From a practical standpoint, they can usually be welded, hot-formed, and even thermally stress-relieved without sensitization occurring.

The newer superstainless alloys often combine stabilization (e.g., titanium or columbium additions) *and* very low carbon contents. The high-nickel alloys such as N10276 combine carbon control with control of specific ratios of other critical elements.

Both composition and thermal history may require verification other than that provided by the manufacturers' records. There are specific quality assurance tests developed and standardized for the evaluation of susceptibility to IGC. Note that these are more reliable than chemical analyses (which only show composition) because they verify the proper *distribution* of the alloying elements and their derivative species. For the 18−8 stainless steels, these tests are exemplified by ASTM A-262, with its various practices. Practice A is a screening test, employing an electrolytic oxalic acid etch combined with metallographic examination. The other practices involve exposure, after sensitization, to boiling 65% nitric acid, 10% nitric−3% hydrofluoric acid, acidified ferric sulfate or acidified copper sulfate plus copper, depending upon specific alloys and applications of interest. Similar ASTM tests have been developed for other, higher-alloy stainless steels, ferritic stainless steels, high-nickel alloys, etc.

Although in common parlance the terms sensitization and weld decay have been used primarily in regard to stainless steels, it should be noted that other metals and alloys are susceptible to IGC as a result of either carbide or other intermetallic compound precipitation or to pre-precipitation effects.

Aluminum alloys may suffer a type of IGC known as *exfoliation* because of the leaflike appearance of the surface when corrosion proceeds along the grain boundaries in the direction of cold-working. Aluminum alloys may actually swell, increasing in thickness because of the retention of high-volume corrosion products within the metallic structure.

The weld HAZ of carbon steel piping can be attacked in strong sulfuric acid. Admiralty Brass (C44300) may suffer IGC in certain types of water. Monel (Alloy N04400) may suffer IGC in hydrofluoric or chromic acids. Hastelloys B (N10001) and C (N10002) can suffer IGC because of the precipitation of molybdenum-rich phases, although this can be prevented by alloy modification. Alloys N06600 and N06625 are susceptible in some environments. Zirconium (R60701) suffers weld decay in hydrochloric acid or sulfuric acid environments contaminated with ferric ions.

CHAPTER **8**

Environmental Cracking

Environmental cracking is a form of localized corrosion in which tensile stress and corrosion have a mutually accelerating effect, causing cracking of a susceptible material in a specific environment. The failure entails *brittle* cracking, usually of an otherwise ductile material. It should be noted that environmental cracking is not confined to metals and alloys; many plastics can suffer this type of attack.

8.1 METALLIC MATERIALS

Almost all metals and alloys are subject to environmental cracking in certain environments. The *specificity* between material and environment is a key feature, unlike corrosion fatigue (which lacks this relationship). Also, unlike fatigue, the stresses are most often of a static rather than a dynamic nature. (However, cyclic stresses can cause environmental cracking, or environmental cracking can initiate fatigue in the presence of cyclic stresses.)

Environmental cracking of metals and alloys can be divided into three categories:

1. *Stress Corrosion Cracking (SCC).* This is an anodic process (i.e., one which can be alleviated by CP), exemplified by the chloride SCC of austenitic stainless steels.

2. *Hydrogen-Assisted Cracking (HAC).* This is a cathodic process, induced by nascent atomic hydrogen and hence aggravated by CP. It is exemplified

by the sulfide stress cracking (SSC) of hardened steels in "sour" (i.e., hydrogen sulfide–bearing) service.

3. *Liquid Metal Cracking (LMC).* This is the result of liquid or molten metal on a stressed metal (e.g., the effect of mercury on high-strength copper alloys).

All three of these types of environmental cracking meet the definition we have given in the lead paragraph, but corrosion fatigue does not.

8.1.1 Stress Corrosion Cracking

SCC is an electrochemical process and usually occurs in only mildly corrosive environments. A highly stressed area, not necessarily the point of maximum stress, becomes anodic to the adjacent metal. The large cathode-to-anode area ratio causes rapid penetration along the stressed areas, which may comprise either grain boundaries or transgranular slip planes. The anodic dissolution, together with the tensile stresses tending to pull the metal apart, causes rapid cracking.

The stresses must be tensile in nature. (*Compressive* stresses, such as result from shot-peening, are actually used to combat SCC.) The tensile stresses may be residual in nature (as from cold-work, restraint during welding, or uneven cooling) or applied, as from mechanical loading. A common example is the stress due to differential thermal expansion, as of 18–8 stainless steel tubes in a steel-shelled exchanger. Tube bending and tube rolling are common sources of stress in heat exchangers, while forming and welding are the source of stresses in vessels.

The principal factors involved in SCC are the magnitude of the tensile stress, the nature of the environment, the characteristics of the material, and the length of time or duration of the exposure. These factors interact, and their relative importance varies with the conditions of exposure. The rapidity of failure may vary from a few hours (or even minutes, in extreme cases) to periods of many years.

The most effective means of combatting this type of attack is to select materials of construction which are not susceptible to SCC in the environmental conditions anticipated. This is not always possible. Economic considerations may dictate the use of a susceptible material, or one may not be able to anticipate the presence of agents specific for SCC (especially where they need be present only in trace amounts).

A practical means of alleviating, if not preventing, this type of corrosion is thermal stress relief. The item of equipment is heated to a suitable temperature, held for about 1 h per inch (2.5 cm) of thickness (but usually not less than 2 h), and *slowly* cooled. This will normally double or treble the life of equipment. It will not usually prevent SCC altogether, because it is impossible to eliminate stresses completely from operating equipment.

Mechanical stress relief, as done by controlled shot-peening, is also a useful option, especially for rotating equipment which may not be amenable to thermal stress relief because of distortion effects.

8.1.2 Hydrogen-Assisted Cracking

HAC is caused by access of atomic hydrogen to a susceptible metal surface. Most often, this is caused by the corrosion process itself, in the presence of some agent which prevents the oxidation or dimerization of the nascent atomic hydrogen. In practice, susceptibility is most often associated with the internal stresses of a hardened steel. The most common agent, which is found under anaerobic conditions and is also specific for poisoning the dimerization of atomic hydrogen, is hydrogen sulfide. However, very hard and highly stressed alloy steel can suffer HAC even in salt air, simply from hydrogen generated at the cathodes. Characteristically, the danger of HAC or SSC, unlike SCC, diminishes rapidly with only moderate increases of temperature (above 80°C).

HAC is aggravated by any situation which tends to promote the ingress of atomic hydrogen, as in CP or when the susceptible material might serve as a cathode in a galvanic couple.

For steels particularly, the most common form of control is to restrict the hardness of equipment, e.g., to below Rockwell C 24 or thereabouts, depending upon the specific alloy. NACE Standard MR-01-75 gives the accepted criteria for equipment in sulfide service.

8.1.3 Liquid Metal Cracking

LMC, also called *liquid metal embrittlement*, is environmental cracking caused by penetration of molten metal along the grain boundaries of a metal or alloy under tensile stress. One common example is the effect of mercury on brass or other highly stressed or high-strength copper alloys. In this case, even mercury salts in aqueous solution are inimical, because of cathodic reduction of the mercury ions to metallic mercury. A mercuric nitrate solution can be used to check for residual stresses in yellow brass. Mercury vapors, such as might arise from broken thermometers or blown manometers, have caused failure of silicon bronze and aluminum bronze process equipment.

At elevated temperatures, molten lead, cadmium and zinc have caused problems with process equipment, especially when fabricated from austenitic stainless steel. Molten copper will cause LMC of steel, as in welding of copper-clad steel vessels. A nickel sulfide eutectic will cause LMC of nickel-based alloys if there is sulfur contamination of weldments, for example.

8.1.4 Specific Materials

The susceptibility of specific alloy groupings to the three types of environmental cracking are shown in Table 8.1 and discussed briefly below.

Magnesium Alloys

Magnesium alloys which contain aluminum or zinc to improve mechanical strength for aircraft construction may be subject to SCC in atmospheric exposures. The cracking is predominantly transcrystalline. A solution of sodium chloride containing sodium chromate is used as a quality assurance test for alloy evaluation and is said to correlate well with atmospheric exposures. Being anodic to other engineering metals and alloys, magnesium is not subject

Table 8.1 Susceptibility to Environmental Cracking

Material	SCC	HAC	LMC
Magnesium	$Cl^- + CrO_4^{2-}$	—	Na, Zn
Lead, cadmium, zinc	$Cl^- +$ Ox. agents	—	Hg, Na, Sn, Zn
Steel			
Soft	OH^-, NO_3^-, CN^- CO_3^{2-}, NH_3, $CO-CO_2-H_2O$	—	Cd, Cu, Pb, Sn, Zn
Hard	OH^-, Cl^-	H^0, H_2S	Cd, Cu, Pb, Sn, Zn
Stainless			
Martensitic	OH^-	H^0, H_2S,Cl^-	?
Ferritic	OH^-, Cl^-	—	?
Austenitic	OH^-, Cl^-	—	Al, Cd, Cu, Pb, Zn
Austenitic, sens.	$S_2O_6^-$, O_2-H_2O	—	?
Copper alloys	NH_3, NO_3^-, steam	H^0	Hg
Nickel alloys			
Nickel	OH^-	—	S
Monel	OH^-, $HF + O_2$	H_2S	S
Inconel	OH^-	—	S
Alloy 625	OH^-	H_2S-Cl*	S
Alloy C276	OH^-	H_2S-Cl*	S
Titanium	HNO_3, Cl^- (300°C)	Methanol	Cd, Pb, Sn, Zn

*Severely cold-worked plus cathode in a galvanic couple.

to HAC. I am not aware of any reported LMC, but mercury could be expected to cause problems, if encountered.

Aluminum Alloys

Aluminum alloys containing more than 6% magnesium or 12% zinc are subject to SCC in both atmospheric and water exposures, although low alloys and commercially pure aluminum are resistant. Cracking is usually intergranular and has been studied extensively. Salt solutions containing oxidants are specific for this type of attack and are used as quality assurance tests. HAC is not reported. LMC is probably possible, but mercury contamination usually leads to amalgamation and general corrosion, as in acetic acid storage tanks.

Steel

Steel is subject to SCC, HAC (when hardened), and LMC. The most common SCC agent is caustic, the attack being erroneously named *caustic embrittlement* (see Chapter 24). Steels also suffer SCC on exposure to nitrates, concentrated nitric acid, dilute nitric acid plus manganese dioxide, anhydrous ammonia, and by mixtures of carbon monoxide – carbon dioxide – water vapor at elevated temperatures.

At hardnesses above Rockwell C 22, steel suffers HAC by sour environments (i.e. SSC), cyanide, and thiocyanate solutions.

LMC has occurred as a result of exposure to molten copper, as in brazing, and in welding copper-clad equipment.

Stainless Steels

Stainless steels are susceptible to all three types of environmental cracking, depending upon their type and condition. SCC is encountered with martensitic, ferritic, and austenitic grades in hot caustic. SCC of the 18−8 austenitic grades has been reported in a wide variety of environments, from foodstuffs to industrial waters and chemicals. In most instances, this is due to the ubiquitous chloride ion. Usually, the SCC is transgranular and multibranched for 18−8s in both chloride and caustic environments, but *may* be intergranular if the metal structure is sensitized.

SCC of 18−8 stainless steels is very sensitive to chloride ion concentration, pH, and temperature. High chloride concentrations and low pH are a deadly combination. 18−8 stainless steels can suffer SCC in a matter of hours in boiling 42 to 45% magnesium chloride solutions.

Heat transfer is an important variable. Stainless steel will often tolerate simple immersion in hot water, yet suffer SCC if used to cool another stream with the same water. SCC of 18−8 condenser tubes is a common experience. A rule of thumb in condenser design is to permit not more than a 50°C (122°F) tubewall temperature. Note that vapor spaces where salts and deposits can accumulate are very dangerous. Alternate exposure to steam and water is particularly conducive to SCC.

SCC is electrochemical in nature. Complete deaeration of water (which removes the cathodic depolarizer, oxygen) has been effective in some applications (e.g., for 18−8 waste heat boilers). CP has been useful in such applications as sacrificial metallic coatings on stainless steel tube inlets. Industrial-type potentiostats are now being employed in some processes in an attempt to maintain the materials at a nonsusceptible level of potential.

External stress corrosion cracking (ESCC) of 18−8 stainless steel equipment is occasioned by chloride contamination of the surface (e.g., under insulation). The chlorides may derive from the insulation itself or may be deposited from the atmosphere or by spillage of water or aqueous solutions. A practical solution is to *paint* the exterior with a chloride-free paint system (e.g., a modified silicone or epoxy).

Stainless steels with a higher nickel content (e.g., S31254, N08825, N08020) are resistant to chloride SCC but not against caustic. A mixed austenite-ferrite structure (e.g., S32900) is helpful against chlorides, but not entirely reliable. A thorough discussion of how to prevent environmental cracking is found in the MTI Manual No. 1, *Guidelines for Control of Stress-Corrosion Cracking of Nickel-Bearing Stainless Steels and Nickel-Base Alloys.*

The martensitic grades can suffer HAC in the hardened condition. In addition to sour service, salt-laden atmospheres can crack 14% chromium grades, as was observed in attempts to use these steels in lighter-than-air craft.

LMC is occasioned mostly by zinc contamination, as in attempts to weld galvanized steel to stainless and contamination by zinc vapors from galvanized hardware during fire. However, lead, bismuth, cadmium, and aluminum are also possible hazards.

Lead

Lead and its alloys are susceptible to SCC in lead acetate solutions. HAC and LMC are not practical problems.

Copper

Copper and its alloys, when hardened by cold-work, are susceptible to SCC (even pure copper). The high-strength alloys, like silicon and aluminum bronze, are notorious in this regard. Brasses and bronzes are particularly subject to SCC by ammonia (i.e., the so-called season cracking) and by steam. Nitrates and nitrites can also cause cracking, although this may entail cathodic reduction to ammonium ions.

I know of only one reported instance of HAC, which was due to the action of an impressed current CP system on a naval bronze ship propeller.

LMC of copper alloys is usually due to mercury contamination.

Nickel

Nickel and its alloys are quite resistant to environmental cracking. However, even nickel itself (N02200) can suffer SCC in concentrated caustic at temperatures of the order of 300°C (575°F). Alloy 400 (N04400) suffers SCC by hydrogen fluoride vapors in the presence of air, as well as in hot caustic or caustic-contaminated steam.

HAC was encountered in a severely cold-worked Monel expansion joint on exposure to a sulfide-contaminated alkaline steam condensate, under the simultaneous influence of a galvanic couple with a steel liner.

LMC of Alloy 400 by mercury vapors has been reported.

Titanium

Titanium suffers environmental cracking in red fuming nitric acid and in anhydrous alcohols. In the latter case, halide contamination will further aggravate the situation.

Zirconium

Zirconium reportedly may suffer environmental cracking in the presence of iodine.

8.2 PLASTICS

Both thermoplastic and thermosetting resin materials can suffer cracking from mechanical, chemical, and ultraviolet effects. However, environmental cracking has the same specificity as described for metals and alloys, although it is not, of course, electrochemical.

The polycarbonates are notoriously susceptible, failing by SCC even in atmospheric exposure in industrial areas. The polyolefins are cracked by detergents, wetting agents, and organic solvents (notably ketones and esters). SCC of polypropylene has been reported in silicone oils. Polysulfones may crack even in vapor exposures of ketones and esters. Nylon can suffer SCC in both acids and alkaline solutions. ABS and polystyrene plastics are also reportedly susceptible in unspecified organic solvents.

RECOMMENDED READING

MTI Manual No. 1, *Guidelines for Prevention of Stress-Corrosion Cracking of Nickel-Bearing Stainless Steels and Nickel-Base Alloys*, Materials Technology Institute of the Chemical Process Industries, Columbus, OH, 1979.

MTI Manual No. 15, *Guidelines for Preventing Stress-Corrosion Cracking in the Chemical Process Industries*, Materials Technology Institute of the Chemical Process Industries, Columbus, OH, 1985.

CHAPTER 9

Corrosion Testing

There are many reasons for running laboratory and/or field corrosion tests and many considerations in their design and utilization. The purpose of the test must be clearly defined and understood. In some cases, *only* laboratory tests will suffice (e.g., quality assurance tests), while in others a test under service conditions is essential.

In the formulation of a corrosion test program, one must be aware of the metallurgical and corrosion characteristics of the metals and alloys of interest and of the strengths and weaknesses of nonmetallic materials.

9.1 MATERIAL FACTORS

9.1.1 Composition

The specific chemical composition of a material is a major factor in determining its corrosion behavior. In scientific research, it may be necessary to know the *exact* composition. In such cases, it is often desirable to obtain an independent analysis. However, in the case of metals and alloys, the composition should be available from the manufacturer. The *heat number* will identify the manufacturing lot, from which the manufacturer can provide the exact chemical composition.

More often, in ordinary engineering practice, it is sufficient to know the *generic composition* (i.e., if the material is S30400, S31603, etc.). Normally, minor variations *within commercial composition limits* are not the cause for aberrations in service performance (although this is the first thing the novice tends to look for; e.g., Is the alloy on the low side of the commercial limit for chromium or molybdenum, for instance?).

9.1.2 Homogeneity

This characteristic cannot be quantitatively described, but it relates to the uniformity of composition across a plane surface. It is important to know whether a metal contains more than one phase (which might be subject to preferential attack). In cast stainless steel, for example, the amount of ferrite in the otherwise austenitic structure can have an important influence on corrosion (being detrimental in some environments but beneficial against SCC in others). Ferrite is indicated by a detectable magnetic permeability and can be quantitatively estimated. However, ferrite can be converted by heat treatment to the nonmagnetic *sigma phase*, which can still adversely affect corrosion behavior.

In wrought stainless steels, sensitization results in a nonhomogeneous structure susceptible to IGC but undetectable by conventional chemical analysis. Nonmetallic inclusions in metals and extraneous materials in non-metals can be focal points for corrosion damage.

9.1.3 Stress

Residual stress, as from cold-work, can affect general corrosion. It may be beneficial, as in the performance of cold-worked copper in vinegar service, but more often it is somewhat harmful, (as indicated by the reaction to acid etching of stamped engine block serial numbers which have been filed or ground off). Residual stress is, of course, very detrimental in services conducive to environmental cracking. Except for the stamped identification numbers on coupons, there should be no substantial residual stress involved in any corrosion test, unless one is studying environmental cracking. In such tests, the *applied* stress should be known at least in a semiquantitative manner.

9.1.4 Thermal History

The heat treatment of a metal or alloy should be known (or reestablished), as thermal history may have a profound effect on corrosion. Annealed, normalized, stabilized, sensitized, or stress-relieved items may behave quite differently, depending on the material and the environment.

Welding is a special case in point. The cast structure of a weld may have a different corrosion resistance than the wrought parent metal (either better or worse). The heat of welding may alter the resistance of the HAZs in the parent metal. Normally, the kind of welding (if properly performed) does not have a great influence, although there are exceptions.

Usually, testing of welded coupons is not recommended, because the thermal effects can neither be quantified nor reliably reproduced with various thicknesses of metals, number of weld passes, etc.

9.2 MATERIALS CHARACTERISTICS

The characteristics of metals are discussed in subsequent chapters (Section 3, Chapters 10 through 17). However, following is a listing, for easy reference, of specific phenomena associated with different classes of materials.

Aluminum alloys. General corrosion, pitting, IGC, exfoliation, SCC

Cast iron. General corrosion, graphitic corrosion

Steels. General corrosion, localized corrosion, SCC, HAZ effects, weld attack

Stainless steels. General corrosion, pitting, IGC, SCC, weld attack

Copper alloys. General corrosion, SCC, dealloying effects

Nickel alloys. General corrosion, IGC, SCC

Reactive metals. General corrosion, IGC, SCC, hydrogen attack

Rubber and elastomers. Softening, hardening, swelling, embrittlement

Plastics. Softening, hardening, swelling, SCC, embrittlement

Paints and coatings. Softening, swelling, crazing, loss of adhesion

9.3 LABORATORY TESTS

There are basically three types of laboratory tests, related to specific corrosion phenomena, quality assurance, and service behavior, respectively.

9.3.1 CORROSION PHENOMENA

Phenomena-related tests are intended to evaluate the relative resistance of metals and alloys (or of nonmetallic materials) to specific types of attack, e.g., SCC, IGC, pitting, or dealloying. In some cases, there are available standardized environments, coupons, or methodologies. These are used for alloy development and studies of materials-related variables. (Also see section 9.3.3.)

9.3.2 Quality Assurance

Quality assurance tests are standardized tests which are intended to give a quantitative evaluation of the resistance of metals and alloys to phenomena to which they are known to be susceptible unless properly formulated and heat-treated. Although manufacturers also perform such tests, it is more often the user who is evaluating the composition, homogeneity, and/or thermal history of a specific lot of material. This may be critical for materials to be used in aggressive chemical or petrochemical processes.

There are standard laboratory tests for dezincification of brass, exfoliation of aluminum, environmental cracking of a number of materials, and particularly for IGC of austenitic stainless steels.

The tests for IGC of 18−8 stainless steels are exemplified by ASTM A-262. This specification comprises a screening test (Practice A, Electrolytic Oxalic Acid Etch) and three other total immersion tests (Practices B, C, and D) based on boiling 65% nitric acid, 10% nitric with 3% hydrofluoric, and 50% sulfuric with ferric sulfate, respectively. Similar tests have been developed for the higher nickel alloys and other stainless steels.

9.3.3 Service Tests

Service-related laboratory tests may be divided into three categories:

1. Laboratory tests may be run in a number of preselected standard solutions in order to categorize new materials by direct comparison with older materials of known behavior.
2. The response of materials may be studied with respect to their probable behavior under conditions conducive to some specific problem (e.g., velocity effects, heat-transfer behavior) or phenomenon (e.g., IGC, SCC).
3. Predictive tests are those which attempt to establish the probable behavior of a material under known conditions, compared to other materials. For example, a test might be run to determine whether S31603 would probably be better than S30403 in a particular service.

Note: It is dangerous to try to *accelerate* a test by changing temperatures, velocities, or other conditions, as such changes may drastically alter the corrosion characteristics of the environment (e.g., boiling solutions becoming anaerobic).

9.3.4 Methodology

A typical laboratory test apparatus and details concerning recommended procedures are to be found in the NACE Standard TM-01-69 or its ASTM counterpart, ASTM G-31. A laboratory test may be of relatively short duration (e.g., from less than 24 h up to several weeks), because small coupons are used, which can be weighed very accurately. A small change in weight (e.g., a few tenths of a milligram) can be detected, which can be calculated as corrosion rate from the appropriate formula.

There are also electrochemical techniques which can be used to evaluate metals or phenomena, based on current-voltage relationships. Some techniques measure the corrosion current developed by small voltage changes, and from these data corrosion rates are indicated directly. Other techniques develop curves of the current flow caused by incremental changes in an applied voltage. The configuration of the curves indicates active or passive behavior and the corrosion potentials related to pitting, crevice corrosion, and SCC. Such tests should only be conducted and evaluated by trained professionals.

9.4 FIELD TESTS

There are a number of reasons for running field or in-plant corrosion tests in addition to (or in preference to) laboratory tests. It may not be possible to duplicate plant conditions in the laboratory, or very difficult to do so because of temperatures, pressures, flows, contaminants, etc. A field test is more reliable for comparing contemplated alternative materials with existing materials. Field tests are the best and often the only way to monitor the effect of process variables or changes.

There are pitfalls even in field testing. In addition to the materials-related factors discussed above, the test may not faithfully reproduce such factors as crevices, stresses, or weld-related phenomena. Also, even the field test can only imperfectly evaluate mechanical phenomena, localized corrosion, environmental cracking, heat-transfer effects, and intermittent process contamination. Nevertheless, there are a number of valuable and proven field-testing techniques, among which we can list the following.

9.4.1 Corrosion Racks

These are devices intended to hold corrosion coupons within process vessels or piping, usually in electrical isolation to prevent galvanic effects. Details can be found in ASTM Specification G-4. A brief description of some of the devices follows.

Bird Cage

The bird cage consists of major end pieces and support rods, within which are enclosed another rod carrying the corrosion coupons. Such a device can test a large number of coupons at one time. The disadvantage is that process equipment must be down and open (and otherwise prepared for safe entry) in order to install or remove the racks, which are exemplified by the old International Nickel Company corrosion racks.

Insert Racks

A more modern device consists of a rod and coupon assembly mounted on a welding disk and designed to be supported within an unused nozzle, with the coupons projecting into the process stream. Although the equipment must be out of service for installation and removal, the process only entails removal and replacement of a small [e.g., $1\frac{1}{2}$ to 2-in (3.75- to 5.0-cm)] flange.

Dutchmen

A *dutchman* is a disk which fits between two flanges (e.g., in a line or between a pipe-vessel connection), with the disk perforated so that it does not impede flow. The dutchman is usually used for somewhat larger flanges than the insert rack, usually with the coupons mounted sideways on a cross strip.

Slip-in Racks

Slip-in racks are designed for insertion in and removal from operating equipment without shutdown. They include a nozzle recess–packing gland arrangement so that the rod and coupons can be slid in through a full-port gate valve. For services above 2 MPa (300 psi), special high-pressure access devices are commercially available.

9.4.2 Corrosion Devices

These are corrosion-detection or corrosion-measuring devices which do not employ coupons. Among them we can list the following.

Bayonet Heat Exchangers

These are single-tube exchangers used to evaluate hot-wall or condensation effects within process equipment. (A metal transferring heat to or from an environment may corrode differently from the same metal in a simple immersion situation at the same temperature.)

Hydrogen Probes

Evolution of hydrogen is one indication of corrosion. Hydrogen probes vary from simple single-tube capillary devices (in which diffusion of atomic hydrogen results in dimerization and development of pressure, measured by a pressure gauge) to more sophisticated devices which detect hydrogen migrating to the outside of equipment by electrochemical techniques.

Electrical Resistance Probes

This technique utilizes Wheatstone bridge circuitry to measure corrosion rate through the increased electrical resistance over time of a single, exposed corroding element. The advantage of these probes lies in their ability to detect corrosion changes in a matter of hours, rather than obtaining the average change over a prolonged period, as with coupons. False readings are obtained if conductive films form (e.g., magnetite, iron sulfides, copper plating). The devices are effective in both liquid exposures (conductive or otherwise) and vapor phases.

Electrochemical Devices

In its crudest form, the electrochemical device is simply a galvanic couple, such as an alloy valve in, but electrically isolated from, a steel line, connected through either a voltmeter or ammeter. Significant changes in the observed value of potential or current indicate changes in corrosivity (e.g., acid ingress, a large change in pH, or process changes).

In more sophisticated form [e.g., polarization admittance instantaneous rate (PAIR) probes], minute voltage changes between paired electrodes measured against a working electrode result in current flow from which *instantaneous* corrosion rates can be obtained. These devices require an electrolyte as the corrosive medium and do not work in vapor phase. Also, oxidation-reduction reactions other than the corrosion process can give misleading results. A three-element probe can correct for the electrolyte conductivity.

Sidestream Apparatus

This is a device that permits diversion of a small side stream from a process to an apparatus in which corrosion racks or other measuring devices are inserted to appraise the result of process changes, inhibition, etc.,without disturbing the process itself.

Experimental Equipment

Obviously, experimental installations of pipe sections, valves, pumps, heat exchanger tubes (or even whole tube bundles) can be made. While these are the most reliable indicators of material performance, the logistics and planning for installation, removal, and evaluation can be difficult. Operations, maintenance and inspection personnel need to be completely dedicated to the effective use of such experimental installations if useful data are to be obtained.

9.5 CORROSION COUPONS

Both laboratory and field corrosion tests utilize corrosion coupons, sometimes of a standard size. A convenient form is a $1\frac{1}{2}$-in (38-mm) round coupon, about $\frac{1}{8}$-in (3-mm) thick, having a $\frac{7}{16}$-in (11-mm) center hole. These coupons will pass through a 45/50 ground-glass neck joint on a laboratory flask and will fit inside a nominal $1\frac{1}{2}$-inch (38-mm) piping tee or nozzle. Polytetrafluoroethylene (PTFE) or other nonconducting spacers are used to electrically isolate the coupons from each other, the rack, and the equipment.

9.6 COUPON EVALUATION

Corrosion coupons are carefully measured and weighed before exposure. After exposure, they are cleaned, dried, and reweighed (see NACE Standard TM-01-69, ASTM G-1, ASTM G-4) and the corrosion rates calculated.

$$\text{Penetration, ipy*} = \frac{534 \times \text{weight loss,}}{\text{Area, in}^2 \times \text{sp gr} \times \text{hours}}$$

One should also record special observations concerning pitting, crevice corrosion (e.g., under the spacer), SCC, dealloying, etc.

RECOMMENDED READING

Ailor, W. H., *Handbook on Corrosion Testing and Evaluation*, Wiley, New York, 1971.

*To convert inches per year to mils per year (mpy), multiply by 1000. To convert to SI units, millimeters per annum (mm/a), multiply inches per year by 13,563.6, or if calculating mils per year, substitute milligrams for grams.

SECTION 3

Materials

CHAPTER 10

Light Metals

10.1 STRUCTURE OF METALS

The following comments are generally applicable to all metals and alloys and serve as an introduction to the subject.

The atomic structure of an element consists of a nucleus containing neutral particles (neutrons) and positively charged particles (protons), surrounded by orbiting negative particles (electrons) (Figure 10.1). It is the potential loss of electrons that accounts for the electrochemical nature of corrosion.

A small orderly arrangement of atoms in a geometric configuration constitutes a *unit cell* (Figure 10.2), while an orderly stacking of unit cells forms a metallic crystal, or grain; the terms are synonymous.

In outward appearance, a metal or alloy is a homogeneous solid. Under the microscope, however, it is readily seen to consist of many individual crystals. Unless it is extremely pure, it will also be seen to contain constituents of different compositions (e.g., intermetallic compounds in certain aluminum alloys, different phases in steel, free graphite in cast iron).

10.2 MAGNESIUM

The two outstanding characteristics of magnesium are its very light weight (the density of approximately 1.8 being about two-thirds that of aluminum)

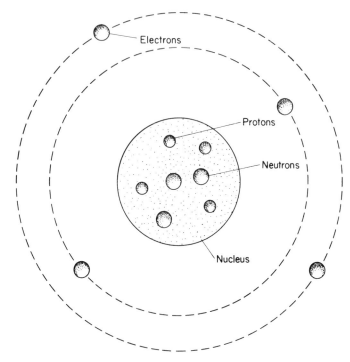

Figure 10.1 Atomic structure.

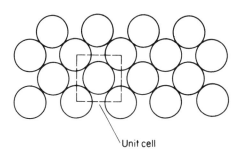

Figure 10.2 Unit cells.

and its highly anodic position in the galvanic series in water. It is anodic to all common engineering metals in aqueous environments.

Magnesium alloys may contain small amounts of aluminum, zinc, or tin. As a material of construction, magnesium alloys are used primarily for aircraft (engine parts, nose pieces, landing wheels, parts of the fuselage, oil and gas tanks), for moving parts in machinery (blowers), and in lightweight portable structures (ladders). For even mildly corrosive service, magnesium alloys may require anodizing (to reinforce the surface film) or painting, although magnesium drums and tanks are used for highly specific services such as phenol and methyl bromide. Surprisingly, it has good resistance to hydrofluoric acid, because of the insoluble corrosion product film.

Magnesium anodes are widely used in CP of steel piping or structures underground. Aside from the aircraft industry, magnesium is rarely encountered by the engineer concerned with materials of construction.

10.3 ALUMINUM AND ITS ALLOYS

10.3.1 General

Aluminum and its alloys are lightweight (density about 2.7, about one-third that of carbon steel), reasonably strong, and quite resistant to natural environments in spite of their anodic position in the galvanic series. (This resistance is due to the presence of a protective oxide film.) These materials are relatively easy to fabricate, available in most standard forms, and can be joined by most of the common methods of welding and brazing.

Commercially pure aluminum and its alloys are covered by the UNS, using identifying numbers derived from the older Aluminum Association designations. The general format is A9NNNN for wrought materials, A0NNNN for castings. As seen in Table 10.1, the second digit indicates the major alloying element. The third digit (the second N) indicates whether there are controls on impurities, and the last two are arbitrary holdovers from the older AA system. Alloys commonly used in the process industries include A93003, A95154, and A96061.

Table 10.1 UNS Numbers for Aluminum Alloys

Alloy No.	Example	Major Alloying Element
A91NNN	A91100	None, 99.00% aluminum minimum
A92NNN	A92020	Copper
A93NNN	A93003	Manganese
A94NNN	A94002	Silicon
A95NNN	A95154	Magnesium
A96NNN	A96063	Magnesium and silicon
A97NNN	A97001	Zinc
A98NNN	A98013	Miscellaneous (e.g., chromium)

10.3.2 Properties

Annealed aluminum alloys such as A91100 have mechanical properties of the order of 110 MPa (16,000 psi) tensile strength and 41 MPa (6000 psi) yield strength. These alloys can be hardened by cold-work (i.e., *strain-hardened*). Other wrought alloys can be heat-treated (i.e., *age-hardened* or *precipitation-hardened*). In such cases, the alloy designations carry a suffix, H for strain-hardened, T for tempered, i.e., precipitation-hardened followed by drawing to the desired hardness.

In the process industries, one does not look for anything stronger than, for example, A96061-T6. This indicates an alloy of about 310 MPa (45,000 psi) tensile strength, 276 MPa (40,000 psi) yield strength, and about 12% elongation. One of the strongest available heat-treated alloys is A97075, which can attain 572 MPa (83,000 psi) yield strength while maintaining 10% elongation. It is used exclusively for aircraft structures.

For most purposes, joining with the inert-gas-shielded welding processes, e.g., TIG (GTAW) or MIG (GMAW) is preferred, but shielded metal arc (SMA or stick electrode) is acceptable, and gas welding is permissible. Of course, in hardened alloys, the strength of the HAZ is drastically reduced by the annealing effect of the welding heat input.

Aluminum has excellent low-temperature properties with high impact strengths and is widely used in noncorrosive cryogenic services, such as gas treating and air separation.

10.3.3 Corrosion

Usually, corrosion resistance of aluminum in uncontaminated atmospheres is good. However, it will become unsightly after a time because of the initial rate of attack, which slows itself by development of a protective film. For architectural applications, an electrolytically induced film can be predeveloped by a process called *anodizing*. This gives a more aesthetically pleasing and stable surface.

The A92000 series of alloys (and the similar copper-bearing castings of the A02000 series) do *not* have good resistance. This is particularly evident in contaminated industrial or marine atmospheres. An insidious subsurface intergranular attack (exfoliation) develops, and corrosion proceeds along the grain boundaries of the cathodic copper-rich phases. The attack may not be evident on the surface, which may show only a frosted appearance, and the thickness of the metal may actually increase as a result of the corrosion products within the alloy structure. Aluminum alloys intended for industrial applications should contain not more than 2.5% copper.

Except for the copper-bearing grades, aluminum has good resistance to many natural waters, as witnessed by the use of aluminum boats even in seawater. However, aluminum is subject to pitting under stagnant conditions in saline waters, and under low-flow conditions even in some fresh waters, particularly as a heat-transfer surface (e.g., in heat exchangers).

In aqueous solutions, the situation is complicated by chlorides or other halides, deposits, and by the amphoteric nature of aluminum, which can be attacked by either acidic or alkaline environments. Because aluminum is anodic to most other common metals except zinc and magnesium, it is subject to attack by the ions of heavy metals (iron, copper, lead, mercury) due to cementation. Heavy-metal ions can easily be present, of course, in industrial waters, from corrosion of equipment upstream.

Many organic chemicals are fully compatible with aluminum. Aldehydes, ketones, esters, amines and organic acids, and anhydrides can be shipped and stored in aluminum as dry refined products. It should be emphasized, however, that some organic chlorides (i.e., chloroorganic compounds such as chloroform or ethylene dichloride) and alcohols can react catastrophically with aluminum, with attendant danger of fire or explosion due to hydrogen liberated in the corrosion process. In some such solvents, water may be an effective inhibitor. This is not universally true, however, as in the case of hydrolyzable organic chlorides (which simply liberate hydrochloric acid on warming with water).

Among the inorganic products, concentrated nitric acid and hydrogen peroxide are commercially handled in aluminum. The nonoxidizing acids, and alkalis or *aqueous* ammonia derivatives, are corrosive.

Even in relatively innocuous media, galvanic couples (except with zinc) must be avoided. Galvanized surfaces and zinc-pigmented coatings afford CP to aluminum. CP is also utilized in Alclad products, in which a surface layer of an anodic aluminum alloy corrodes sacrificially to prevent pitting of a more cathodic substrate.

In addition to the exfoliation previously described, some aluminum alloys (e.g., A97074) are subject to IGC of the weld HAZ in corrosive environments.

Environmental cracking is encountered only in the heat-treated high-strength alloys. Such cracking is a problem primarily in aircraft and marine structures seeking a high strength-to-weight ratio. A typical susceptible material is A97075-T6. However, the same alloy in the T73 temper has good resistance to environmental cracking, which illustrates once again the importance of sound materials engineering.

RECOMMENDED READING

The Metals Handbook, 9th ed., ASM Metals Park, OH, 1982.

CHAPTER 11

Iron and Steel

Commercial cast irons and steels are basic materials of construction for a wide variety of industries. We are not concerned with "pig" or ingot iron, nor with the now obsolete wrought iron (although it was once commercially important). The relatively pure low-carbon irons, such as carbonyl iron and electrolytic iron, are not structural materials.

11.1 CAST IRONS

Various types of cast irons are widely used, especially for pipe, valves, pumps, and certain mechanical parts. Cast iron is an alloy of iron, silicon, and carbon. The carbon content varies from about 1.7 to 4.5%, most of which is present in insoluble form (e.g., graphite) in this range. This definition adequately covers the unalloyed gray irons, white irons, malleable irons, and ductile irons.

11.1.1 Unalloyed Cast Irons

The most common form is *gray cast iron*. When the casting is allowed to cool slowly, the insoluble carbon precipitates as flakes of graphite, which are the outstanding feature of this material and which cause its typically brittle behavior (because the material fractures along the graphite flakes). Gray irons are quite soft and readily machinable. A typical microstructure is shown in Figure 11.1.

Figure 11.1   Microstructure of gray cast iron.

White iron is produced by rapid cooling of a gray cast iron of controlled composition, such as low silicon, high manganese, to produce an alloy that is hard, brittle, and practically unmachinable. The carbon is retained as a *dissolved* solid, in the form of iron carbides. White iron is used primarily for wear resistance. *Chilled iron* is a duplex material, having a wear-resistant white iron surface (produced by rapid surface cooling) over a comparatively tougher gray iron core.

A relatively ductile material called *malleable iron* can be produced by prolonged heat treatment of white iron. A 30-h treatment at 925°C (1700°F) followed by an equivalent period of slow cooling allows the graphite to precipitate as nodules rather than flakes. Ductility is therefore much less impaired, as compared to gray cast iron. Malleable irons have been used in fittings, machinery, tools, and automotive parts.

Another method of improving the mechanical properties of cast iron is through the addition of "inoculants." Minor additions of calcium silicide (in the proprietary Meehanite process) or of nickel plus ferrosilicon (the Ni-Tensyl process) cause the graphite to separate as fine flakes, rather than the coarser flakes of gray iron. This substantially improves ductility without significantly changing the chemical composition of the cast iron.

The best modern form of cast iron, having superior mechanical properties and equivalent corrosion resistance, is *ductile iron*. The addition of a small amount of nickel-magnesium alloy to cast iron causes the graphite to precipitate as *spheroids* rather than as flakes (Figure 11.2). This results in a ductility approaching that of steel. Ductile iron can be produced to have as much as 18% elongation, while some wrought carbon steels have no more than 20%. Ductile iron castings can also be produced to have improved low-temperature impact properties (i.e., low NDTT) by control of the phosphorus, silicon, and alloy content, and the thermal treatment.

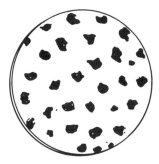

Figure 11.2 Microstructure of ductile cast iron.

11.1.2 Alloy Cast Irons

There are several types of commercially important alloy cast irons, in which the alloy additions substantially modify mechanical and physical properties as well as corrosion resistance.

Molybdenum.   Molybdenum may be added to improve strength or (with other alloying elements) to improve corrosion resistance in chloride media.

Silicon.   Silicon is added to cast iron in the range from 11 to 14% to produce an alloy with superior resistance to hot sulfuric acid (e.g., Duriron.). Small amounts of molybdenum or chromium are also sometimes added to improve resistance in the presence of chloride contamination.

Nickel.   Nickel is another common alloying element. Nickel is added in amounts varying from 0.5 to 6% in engineering-grade gray irons. At about 4.5%, it produces a martensitic gray iron with outstanding resistance to abrasion and wear (e.g., Ni-Hard). Austenitic, nonmagnetic gray irons containing 14 to 38% nickel, such as the several grades of Niresist, have outstanding resistance to corrosion and moderately high temperatures, as well as having very low coefficients of thermal expansion.

Copper.   Copper is a mild strengthener, increasing resistance to wear and to certain types of corrosion.

Chromium.   Chromium is added to cast irons in amounts varying from 0.15 to 1% to improve resistance to graphitic corrosion. In amounts from 1 to 1.5%, it is added to increase high-temperature oxidation resistance. In special alloys, up to 35% chromium may be added for resistance both to corrosion and high-temperature oxidation.

11.2 STEELS

Steel is an alloy of iron and carbon, containing small amounts of other alloying elements or residual elements as well. It is the presence of carbon and its effect upon response to heat treatment that change iron from a laboratory curiosity to an engineering material.

In the manufacture of steel, iron ore is reduced in a blast furnace to produce pig iron. Pig iron contains impurities (carbon, silicon, phosphorus, sulfur, etc.) which make it hard and brittle. It must be refined, and the alloy content controlled, in order to obtain suitable properties. A newer method of making steel is with the basic oxygen furnace, in which pure oxygen (rather than air) is blown through the molten metal. To prevent reaction of residual oxygen with dissolved carbon during solidification, steel may be "killed" (i.e., made to lie quietly in the mold) by addition of deoxidants such as silicon or aluminum. Killed steels are used down to −6°C (21°F) because of their improved NDTT as compared with ordinary steels.

11.2.1 Carbon Steels

Carbon steels are primarily iron and carbon, with small amounts of manganese. They are the workhorse material for structural members, sheet, plate, pipe, and tubing.

Steels that have been worked or wrought while hot will be covered with a black mill scale (i.e., magnetite, Fe_3O_4) on the surfaces, and are sometimes called *black iron*. *Cold-rolled* steels have a bright surface, accurate cross-section, and increased yield and tensile strength. The latter are preferred for bar stock to be used for rods, shafts, etc.

11.2.2 Principles of Heat Treatment

Carbon and low-alloy steels occupy an essential place among materials of construction, precisely because of the potential range of hardness, strength, and other mechanical properties. These are achieved primarily through heat treatment.

Iron has three allotropic crystal forms (alpha, gamma, and delta) which exist at different specific temperatures from room temperature up to the melting point and have different capacities for dissolving carbon.

A *phase diagram* (Figure 11.3) best illustrates the following discussion. We are concerned primarily with the alpha (ferrite; body-centered) and gamma (austenite; face-centered) crystal forms. Ferrite converts to austenite in the vicinity of 910°C (1670°F).

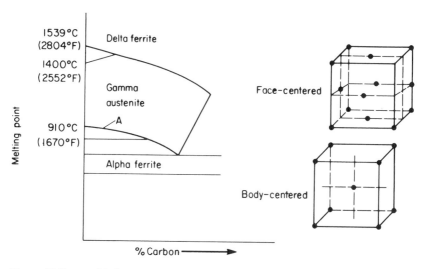

Figure 11.3 Simplified iron-carbon phase diagram.

The hardenability of steel is due to a combination of the allotropic transformation and the different solubility of carbon in the two crystalline forms of iron. In room-temperature ferrite, carbon is soluble only to about 0.008%, any excess being in the form of iron carbides (i.e., cementite). On the other hand, the austenite which is formed at high temperatures can dissolve up to about 2% carbon.

A typical carbon steel might contain about 0.30% carbon. At room temperature, about 0.29% of the carbon is dispersed in the ferrite structure as alternate platelets of cementite. The mixture of ferrite and cementite is called *pearlite*, because it has the appearance (under the microscope) of mother-of-pearl.

When such a steel is heated to the transformation temperature (point A in Figure 11.1), the austenite phase is formed and *all* of the 0.30% carbon dissolves. If the alloy is slowly cooled, the austenite reverts to ferrite and the pearlite is also re-formed. The process of heating and *slow* cooling is called *annealing* (or *normalizing*, at a somewhat lower temperature). There is little, if any, change in mechanical properties under these conditions.

However, if the heated steel in its austenite form is rapidly cooled (i.e., quenched), the reversion to ferrite is very rapid, while the precipitation of carbon is much slower. The carbon atoms then become entrapped in the ferrite lattice, stretching and distorting the structure. This gives a distorted, acicular structure called *martensite* (Figure 11.4), which is very hard and brittle. In this quenched condition, the material is at maximum hardness and strength and minimum ductility or toughness. In most engineering applica-

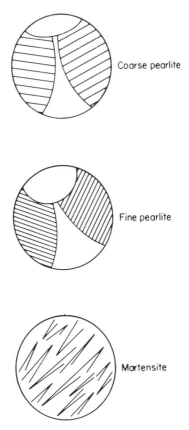

Coarse pearlite

Fine pearlite

Martensite

Figure 11.4 Microstructures of steel.

tions, a combination of toughness and strength is desired, so some compromise must be effected.

This compromise is attained by reheating the hardened steel to some temperature *below* the lower critical temperature of about 720°C (1330°F). This procedure is known as *tempering* or *drawing*, and allows the "logjam" of iron and carbon atoms to sort itself out. The higher the temperature and the longer the time, the more the iron and carbon revert from the martensite to the ferrite-pearlite structure. A quenched-and-tempered steel will have much higher strength and less ductility than an annealed or normalized steel, but lower strength and more ductility than the same material in the fully hardened condition.

In hardening a steel, the *rate* of cooling is critical. For a given composition, it is easier to completely harden (i.e., "through-harden") a smaller-diameter piece than a thicker one. The latter may retain a softer core than the outside

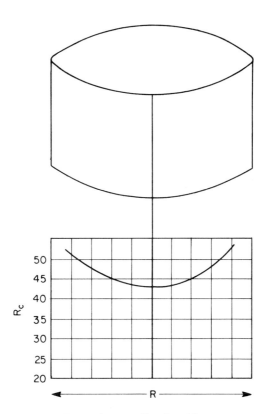

Figure 11.5 Hardness profile of steel bar.

surface, giving a hardness profile across the diameter (Figure 11.5), which may or may not be desirable for the intended end use.

11.2.3 Alloy Steels

Alloying elements, in small amounts, affect primarily the *rate* of cooling required to harden the steel. For example, with small additions of chromium, nickel, and molybdenum, heavier sections can be through-hardened. By the same token, a less drastic quenching medium (e.g., oil instead of water) can be used. More highly alloyed steels can be "quenched" in still air. Also, it should be remembered that, in welding, the weld proper and adjacent areas will be quenched by the mass of cold metal surrounding the joint, leading to hardening and residual stresses.

As a general rule, the dividing line between low-alloy and high-alloy steels is about 5% total alloying elements. Low-alloy steels were developed primarily to control response to heat treatment and extend mechanical properties. Their corrosion resistance is usually not significantly different from that of carbon steel. High-alloy steels are more often made for improved corrosion resistance, with the exception of a few specialty steels (e.g., Hadfield's Manganese Steel for abrasion resistance).

The effects of the individual alloying elements are as follows.

Carbon.   Carbon is the principal hardening element. In fact, the percentage of carbon can be estimated approximately from the maximum hardness induced by heat treatment.

Manganese.   Manganese is a deoxidizer and desulfurizer which also contributes to strength and hardness. A major purpose of desulfurizing steel is to improve hot-workability, since iron sulfides cause cracking (i.e., hot-shortness) during hot-working. Further, a manganese-to-carbon ratio of not less than 3:1 is beneficial for impact strength and NDTT.

Silicon.   Silicon is a principal deoxidizer. The amount of retained silicon will vary with deoxidation practices. A killed steel may contain as much as 0.6%, although structural steels usually have a range of 0.15 to 0.30% silicon.

Aluminum.   Aluminum is used to finish off the deoxidation reaction, and silicon-killed aluminum-finished steels are used at moderately low temperatures.

Phosphorus.   Phosphorus is primarily an impurity, decreasing ductility and toughness. A maximum phosphorus content of 0.04% or less is commonly specified.

Sulfur.   Sulfur is likewise undesirable, except where improved machinability is required. Manganese sulfides break up the chips during machining, but they have an adverse effect upon ductility and impact strength. Sulfur content is usually held to 0.05% or less, except in resulfurized free-cutting grades (which may contain from 0.1 to 0.3% sulfur).

Copper.   Copper is added only to improve resistance to atmospheric corrosion, which it probably does by scavenging sulfur. Only small concentrations of copper can be tolerated (not more than 0.2 to 0.3%) because of its low solubility and hot-short cracking or LMC effects.

The *major* alloying elements, which affect corrosion as well as metallurgical characteristics and response to heat treatment, are

Chromium.   Chromium is added to increase the depth to which thick sections can be hardened; to provide abrasion resistance; to provide higher hardness of carburized or carbonitrided surfaces; to improve corrosion and oxidation resistance; to improve resistance to high-temperature, high-pressure hydrogen; to improve resistance to high-temperature graphitization.

Molybdenum. Molybdenum is added to prevent graphitization and give close control of hardenability, while increasing high-temperature tensile and creep strength. It is used at about 0.5% concentration (often in conjunction with chromium), and is also effective in preventing temper embrittlement.

Nickel. Nickel is added to improve toughness (particularly NDTT), response to heat treatment, and corrosion resistance.

Vanadium. Vanadium is added to refine grain size and improve mechanical properties, as well as to increase the hardenability of medium-carbon steels.

A combination of two or more alloying elements usually imparts some of the characteristic good properties of each. Chromium-nickel steels develop good hardening properties with excellent ductility, while chromium-nickel-molybdenum steels develop even better hardenability with only a slight reduction in ductility. The carbide-forming elements such as chromium, molybdenum, and vanadium also increase resistance to hydrogen attack at elevated temperatures and pressures, under conditions which lead to embrittlement, blistering, or methanation of carbon steels.

11.3 NUMBERING

The traditional numbering system for steels was developed by SAE. A similar system was that of the AISI. Together with the numbering systems for other alloys, these have been assimilated into the UNS, as previously mentioned.

Each steel is assigned an identifying number consisting of a letter (usually G or K for carbon and low-alloys steels) and a five-digit number. The first two digits codify the major alloy additions, and the next two the carbon content (expressed in hundredths of a percent). The final digit encodes any special requirements. For example, a plain carbon steel of 0.20% carbon (SAE 1020) is numbered UNS G10200. G31300 is a nickel-chromium steel of 0.30% carbon, while G43NN0 is a chromium-nickel-molybdenum steel, and G61NN0 is a chromium-vanadium steel.

RECOMMENDED READING

"The Making, Shaping and Treatment of Steel," (United States Steel Corp., 1950).

Krauss, G: *Principles of Heat Treatment of Steel*, ASM, Metals Park, OH, 1980.

ASTM DS56B, *Metals and Alloys in the Unified Numbering System*, 3rd ed., ASTM 1983.

CHAPTER 12

Stainless Steels

The addition of a minimum of the order of 11% chromium to steel produces a stainless steel. There are many compositions of stainless steel belonging to different "families," from the basic 11 to 13% chromium steel to complex alloys containing chromium, nickel, molybdenum, copper, etc. Stainless steels are used in a variety of applications ranging from simple protection from iron contamination (e.g., of pure water, foodstuffs, or refined chemicals) to the most demanding corrosive chemical services.

12.1 THE NATURE OF STAINLESS STEEL

The addition of about 12% chromium to steel produces a synthetic "noble metal," with little tendency to react with most natural environments. The difference between stainless steels and the *true* noble metals of silver, gold, and platinum is that the nobility or *passivity*, as it is commonly called, of the stainless can be induced, reinforced, or removed by chemical or electrochemical reactions.

Passivity is a surface phenomenon, associated primarily with an oxide film or with adsorbed oxygen. Depending upon the stability, reactivity, and solubility of the film in a given environment, the stainless steels may be either passive or active. In the active condition, they may be less resistant than ordinary steel, for example, in hot caustic, molten salts, or reducing acids.

The passive protective film on stainless steels is formed by reaction with oxygen (which is why it resists most natural environments) or with oxidizing agents such as nitric acid. The film is removed by reaction with hydrogen or reducing agents, and is penetrated by some species, notably chloride ions. Stainless steels tend to be rapidly attacked by reducing acids or hot caustic, for example, and pitted (or cracked) by chloride environments, but they tend to resist nitric acid, other oxidizing acids, peroxides, etc. The film can also be mechanically removed, as by abrasion, wear, or erosion, but re-forms readily on exposure to air or aerated water.

Passivity is the normal condition for stainless steels, and they are usually several tenths of a volt *cathodic* to carbon steel in natural waters and aqueous solutions. Only under special conditions will they become active and then they are usually *anodic* to steel.

12.2 TYPES OF STAINLESS STEEL

In Chapter 11, we discussed the ferrite-austenite-martensite transformation in steel and alloy steels, based on the iron-carbon phase diagram. A similar diagram (Figure 12.1) is used to explain the phase transformations in iron-

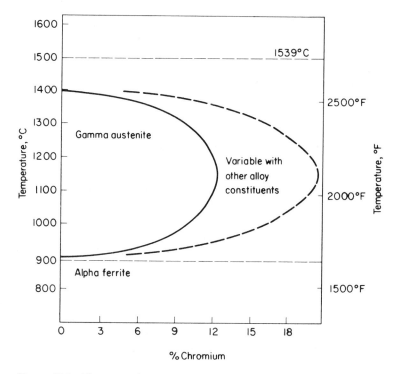

Figure 12.1 The gamma loop.

chromium and related alloys. When chromium is the only major alloying element and carbon is held essentially constant at a moderate value, the conditions under which martensitic stainless steels and ferritic stainless steels are formed is explained by "the gamma loop." (*Note*: Gamma is the Greek letter used to denote the austenite phase.)

As illustrated in Figure 12.1, an increase in temperature takes the alloy through the gamma loop up to about 12% chromium. Because they undergo the ferrite-austenite transformation, 12% chromium stainless steels can be hardened to a martensitic structure by cooling from above the transformation temperature. Above about 12% chromium (and the next level of alloying is usually around 17%), the alloy never passes through the gamma loop and therefore remains ferritic regardless of heat treatment.

If the chromium is in the 16 to 19% range and about 8% nickel is added, the phase diagram would show the gamma loop expanded to fill the diagram. Such "18−8" alloys are austenitic over the normal range of temperature, rather than ferritic or martensitic.

12.2.1 Martensitic Stainless Steels

Because of the combination of hardenability with stainless properties, the martensitic grades are of interest for cutlery, turbine blades, and high-temperature parts. Their high order of resistance to atmospheric corrosion, compared with steel, puts them into the stainless category, but they are of limited usefulness in process exposures, compared with the more highly alloyed grades. Exemplified by UNS S41000 and S42000, such alloys are somewhat difficult to fabricate by welding, requiring extensive pre- and postweld heating. This is because of their air-hardening characteristic. Their transformation rate is so sluggish that a quench in oil or water is not required for hardening, a slow air cool sufficing to effect the martensite formation.

The greatest weakness of the martensitic grades is a susceptibility to absorption of atomic hydrogen, resulting in HAC environmental cracking (Chapter 8), notably in sulfide environments. Their low-temperature impact resistance is also poor. When cooled rapidly from elevated temperature, they are susceptible to IGC (see Chapter 7).

12.2.2 Ferritic Stainless Steels

This class of alloys starts in the 15 to 18% chromium range, although they can go up to about 30%. Well outside the gamma loop, they are wholly ferritic. Note that both martensitic and ferritic grades are ferromagnetic, regardless of heat treatment.

The ferritic grades, exemplified by S43000, have corrosion resistance superior to the martensitic grades by virtue primarily of their higher chromium content. They are commonly used for nitric acid services, water, food processing, automobile trim, and architectural applications. Their high-temperature oxidation resistance is also good, and they are used for furnace and turbine parts. Their impact resistance and weldability are rather poor, even though they are not hardenable by heat treatment. Welding may result in brittleness and/or diminished corrosion resistance, unless proper pre- and postweld heat treatment is employed.

Ferritic stainless steels have poor impact resistance at low temperatures, sometimes even at relatively warm temperatures, as mentioned further below. They are not susceptible to hydrogen attack, but can suffer environmental cracking in caustic environments and, to a much lesser extent, in chlorides. On heating, as by welding, grain growth can occur, with attendant embrittlement. *Fast* cooling can lead to susceptibility to IGC.

Modern controlled melting and other improved practices have permitted development of a new group of "superferritic stainless steels." These are molybdenum-bearing variants with very low carbon (and nitrogen) contents. Such alloys (e.g., S44625, 26Cr−1Mo; S44800, 28Cr−4Mo) have superior resistance to chloride pitting and environmental cracking and improved general corrosion resistance in some environments, but they have some deficiencies in impact strength (e.g., high NDTT even at temperatures above 40°C) and weldability.

12.2.3 Austenitic Stainless Steels

This third group, which is characteristically nonmagnetic, is the most important for process industry applications. By virtue of their austenite-forming alloy additions, notably nickel and manganese, these stainless steels have the face-centered austenite structure from far below 0°C (32°F) up to near melting temperatures. They are not hardenable by heat treatment, but can be strain-hardened by cold-work. This also induces a small amount of ferromagnetism. (*Note:* In the cast varieties, a small amount of magnetism is deliberately induced, through an imbalance in austenite-forming vs. ferrite-forming elements, to improve casting characteristics.)

The garden-variety 18−8 austenitic stainless steels are exemplified by S30400. Such alloys have a rare combination of corrosion resistance, high-temperature strength and oxidation resistance, ease of fabrication and weldability, good ductility, and good impact resistance down to at least −183°C (−216.4°F). Their mechanical properties, in general, are excellent. Improved chemical resistance is obtained by molybdenum additions (e.g., S31600), and resistance to IGC by stabilization (e.g., S34700; 18−8Cb) or low carbon content (e.g., S30403, S31603).

When substantial amounts of nickel are replaced by manganese, an analogous group of alloys is formed, exemplified by the 9Mn−5Ni alloy, S20200. There are also *duplex* alloys (i.e., mixed ferrite-austenite structure), for improved corrosion resistance at some cost in fabricability (e.g., S32900). Other grades can be *precipitation-hardened* (e.g., S17400, S15700 or 15−7Mo) while retaining corrosion resistance similar to the S30400 or S31600.

Higher alloys, such as S30900 (25Cr−12Ni) and S31000 (25Cr−20Ni) are used for high-temperature applications and for welding 18−8 to steel.

12.2.4 Specialty Stainless Steels

Superstainless steels were developed to cope with corrosion in sulfuric acid and phosphoric acid services. These are exemplified, in the most modern form, by N08020 (20Cr−35Ni−3Mo−4Cu). Note the N (rather than S) designation. This is rather arbitrary, since the alloy contains *neither* more than 50% iron nor more than 50% nickel, because of the other additive alloying elements. Such alloys are also columbium-stabilized against IGC, but this is not entirely reliable in the event of multipass welding or prolonged heating (as in hot-working or stress relief), as described in Chapter 7.

In order to obtain improved resistance to chloride pitting and environmental cracking, a number of alloys have been developed which are intermediate between the 18−8s and N08020. Of considerable interest in brackish or saline waters, these have compositions of roughly 20Cr−25Ni−4Mo−2Cu or 20Cr−25Ni−6Mo.

Table 12.1 Wrought Stainless Steel Compositions

| UNS | Weight % | | | |
	Cr	Ni	C max	Other
S41000	11.5−13.5	—	0.15	
S43000	16−18	—	0.12	
S44600	23−27	—	0.20	
S30400	18−20	8−10.5	0.08	
S30403	18−20	8−12	0.030	
S32100	17−19	9−12	0.08	Ti 5 × C min
S34700	17−19	9−13	0.08	Cb 10 × C min
S31600	16−18	10−14	0.08	2−3 Mo
S31603	16−18	10−14	0.030	2−3 Mo
S31700	18−20	11−15	0.08	3−4 Mo
S31703	18−20	11−15	0.030	3−4 Mo
S30900	22−24	12−15	0.20	
S31000	24−26	19−22	0.25	
N08020	19−21	32−38	0.07	2−3 Mo; Cb 8 × C; 3−4 Cu

Table 12.2 ACI Designations for Stainless Steel Castings

ACI	Weight %		
	Cr	Ni (max)	Other
Ca-*nn**	11−13	1	Carbon
Cb-*nn*	18−21	2	Carbon
CD4MCu	25−27	6	Carbon, 2 Mo, 3 Cu
CF-8	18−21	11	Carbon, 0.08 max
CF-3	17−21	12	Carbon 0.03 max
CF8M	18−21	12	Carbon 0.08 max, 2−3 Mo
CF3M	17−21	13	Carbon 0.03 max, 2−3 Mo
CH-20	22−26	15	Carbon 0.20 max
CK-20	23−27	22	Carbon 0.20 max
CN7M	19−22	31	Carbon 0.07; 2−3 Mo; 3−4 Cu
HK-*nn*†	23−27	20	

* C indicates corrosion-resistant; *nn* is maximum carbon content.
† H indicates heat-resistant; *nn* is *middle* ± 0.05% of carbon.

12.3 ALLOY DESIGNATIONS

Table 12.1 lists the UNS designations for a number of commercially important stainless steels of various types. Table 12.2 lists the Alloy Casting Institute (ACI) designations for a similar grouping of corrosion- and heat-resisting castings (C and H, respectively), in which the number indicates the *midrange* of the carbon content (± 0.05%).

RECOMMENDED READING

Peckner, D., and Bernstein, I. M.: *Stainless Steels*, McGraw-Hill, New York, 1977.

"Stainless Steel 77," Climax Molybdenum Company, Pittsburgh, Pa., 1977.

Woldman, N. E.: *Engineering Alloys*, ASM, Metals Park, OH, 1979.

CHAPTER 13

Lead, Tin, and Zinc

These three metals are grouped together for discussion because they share an amphoteric nature (i.e., they can be attacked by both acids and alkalis), because they are all employed as metallic coatings, and because it is convenient to separate them from other nonferrous metals, such as copper and nickel, more commonly used in corrosive service.

13.1 LEAD AND ITS ALLOYS

Lead is a weak, heavy metal (almost half again as heavy as steel) which has difficulty supporting even its own weight. However, it has enjoyed widespread industrial use, particularly because of its resistance to sulfuric acid. In nature, it is usually associated with copper and silver.

13.1.1 Types of Lead

There are a number of lead alloys developed specifically to increase endurance limit and hardness (or ability to work-harden) and to prevent excessive grain growth.

Chemical lead is lead with traces of copper and silver left in it. It is not economical to recover the silver, and the copper content is thought to improve general corrosion resistance.

Antimonial lead (also called *hard lead*) has been alloyed with from 2 to 6% antimony to improve the mechanical properties. This is effective in services up to about 93°C (200°F), above which both strength and corrosion resistance rapidly diminish.

Tellurium lead has been strengthened by the addition of a fraction of a percent of tellurium. Because it will work-harden under strain, it has better resistance to fatigue failure induced by vibration.

There are also proprietary alloys, such as Federated Metals' Asarcon, to which copper and other elements have been deliberately added for improved corrosion and creep resistance. National Lead's Nalco has been alloyed specifically for improved corrosion resistance in chromic acid plating baths.

13.1.2 Forms

Lead is available in pipe, tubing, and valves, as well as sheet for process vessels. Sheet lead is also used as a membrane in acid-brick-lined vessels. Lead-clad steel plate is also available. Because it will not easily support its own weight, lead is subject to creep and *static fatigue*. Creep is characterized by stretching under constant load. Static fatigue is characterized by a "crazing" effect and, sometimes, by IGC.

For these reasons, lead vessels are usually externally supported by wooden or steel structures, or fabricated from clad metal (i.e., homogeneously bonded lead-clad steel). Since the steel supplies the mechanical strength in lead-clad steel, any grade of lead can be used as the cladding, at the discretion of the manufacturer.

13.1.3 Corrosion Resistance

Lead is an amphoteric metal susceptible to attack by both acids and alkalis under certain conditions. That it has excellent resistance in many environments is due largely to the insolubility of its corrosion products, which tend to form protective films in the appropriate services.

Lead tends to resist sulfuric, sulfurous, chromic, and phosphoric acids, and *cold* hydrofluoric acid (see Chapters 18 to 31 on specific environments). It is attacked by hydrochloric acid and nitric acid. It is also attacked by organic acids if they are dilute or if they contain oxidizing agents.

The usefulness of lead in caustic is limited to concentrations of not more than 10% up to about 90°C (195°F). It suffers little attack in cold, strong amines but is attacked by dilute aqueous solutions.

Lead will resist most natural waters but is not suitable in soft aggressive waters. It must not be used to handle potable (i.e., drinking) water, because of the toxicity of lead salts.

Although lead is anodic initially to more highly alloyed materials, it may become cathodic in time due to the film of insoluble corrosion products formed on its surface. For example, Alloy 20Cb3 (N08020) or Alloy C276 (N10276) valves may suffer accelerated attack in lead piping systems in sulfuric acid services unless electrically isolated from the piping.

13.2 TIN

Tin is of somewhat limited availability in the United States, since all of it must be imported. It is a major alloying element in "phosphor" and other types of bronzes, but its major use as a material of construction is as tin plate and solder.

The use of tin as a packaging medium (toothpaste tubes, foil, etc.) has largely given way to other materials, such as plastics. However, tin plate (e.g., over steel) is produced both as a hot-dipped and as an electroplated coating. Attempts to replace "tin" cans for canned peaches and apricots have been unsuccessful from a marketing standpoint, because the organo-tin complex (which gives the characteristic taste) does not form in plastic or glass containers.

Tin is encountered to a limited extent in *terneplate* (a hot-dipped steel for roofing purposes). The most common solder is a 50–50 lead-tin alloy.

13.3 ZINC

Zinc is a major alloying element in brass. For materials of construction, the major engineering usage is in the hot-dipped galvanizing of steel and as a sacrificial pigment in certain types of paints. Electroplated zinc coatings are also encountered. The electrochemical protection is directly proportional to the thickness of the zinc, so the method of application to steel is selected on the basis of feasibility and economics.

Zinc die-castings are used for some artifacts not intended for exposure to corrosion. Zinc anodes are widely used for CP in saltwater services, such as to protect rudder irons from corrosion and propellers from cavitation.

CHAPTER 14

Copper and Its Alloys

Copper and its alloys have been known and utilized for more than 6000 years. The Bronze Age antedates the Iron Age by about 1500 years. The corrosion resistance of copper alloys was recognized almost from the beginning, as evidenced by their use in containers for food and drink and for long-lasting statuary. Apparently, initial workings of hammered copper were followed by crude castings of lean bronze from impure copper ores. Finally, true bronzes (e.g., tin, or phosphor, bronzes) appeared. In modern times, highly purified coppers, free of all but traces of other elements, as well as copper alloys compounded for specific properties, are widely used in industry. Table 14.1 lists the composition of some copper alloys.

14.1 COPPERS

There are basically two types of copper of interest in corrosion applications. Electrolytic tough-pitch copper (ETP; C11000) is used in sheet-metal work and process equipment. Phosphorus-deoxidized coppers [e.g., high-residual (DHP), C12200; low-residual (DLP), C12000)] have excellent response to hot-drawing (e.g., as for heat exchanger tubing), flaring, flanging, spinning, and welding. [Oxygen-free electronic (OFE), or high-conductivity copper (C10100) is used only for electrical services.]

The great majority of copper alloys cannot be hardened by heat treatment. They are hardened by cold-work, such as hammering, as in primitive times. (There is no "lost secret of the ancients" for hardening copper.) With subse-

Table 14.1 Composition of Some Copper Alloys

Name	UNS	Cu	Zn	Sn	Al	Ni	Other
Wrought							
Copper	C11000	99.9	—	—	—	—	—
Red brass	C23000	85	15	—	—	—	—
Yellow brass	C27000	69	31	—	—	—	—
Admiralty B	C44300	72	27	1	—	—	0.1 As
Phosphor bronze	C52400	90	—	10	—	—	0.3 P
Aluminum bronze D	C61400	90	0.2	—	7	—	3 Fe
High-silicon bronze	C65500	95	1.5	—	—	0.6	3 Si
90Cu−10Ni	C70600	86	1.0	—	—	10	1.5 Fe
70Cu−30Ni	C71500	68	1.0	—	—	30	1 Fe
Castings							
Ounce metal	C83600	85	5	5	—	—	5 Pb
Mn bronze	C86500	57	40	1	—	1	1 Mn
G bronze	C90500	87	2	10	—	1	—

quent reheating, there are several "tempers" available (e.g., quarter-hard, half-hard) with different capabilities for flaring or rolling. Modern technology has given us a few precipitation-hardening alloys (copper plus chromium or zirconium) and a grade which is dispersion-strengthened (e.g., C15710).

The corrosion-resistance and mechanical properties of the several types of copper (in the unhardened condition) are substantially the same. Copper will resist most natural waters within certain velocity limitations (except soft, aggressive waters), as well as both acids and alkalis (in the absence of dissolved oxygen or other oxidizing species). It should be noted that the ionic corrosion product (specifically the *cupric ion*) is itself an oxidant, so that acid solutions become more corrosive as corrosion products accumulate. As is evident from the electromotive series, copper will not displace hydrogen from acids. It is attacked only when the cathodic reaction is the reduction of dissolved oxygen, of metallic cations, or of the anion of the acid, as in oxidizing acids such as nitric acid. The copper alloys are corroded by ammonia and amines in the presence of oxygen or oxidizing agents because of the soluble copper-ammonium complex.

14.2 BRASSES

The term *brass* refers specifically to copper alloys in which the major alloying element is zinc. This is an exception to the use of the term *bronze* (see section

14.3), which includes almost any alloy of copper with a significant amount of alloying element (tin, silicon, aluminum, or nickel).

Modern brasses contain anywhere from 5 to 45% zinc. As the zinc content is increased, the characteristic red brass color is first observed, up to 10 to 15% zinc (C23000). The yellow brass next appears, commercially in the range 25 to 30% zinc (C26000). As the zinc concentration is further increased to about 38% (C46400, naval brass), the red color returns (due to the formation of a secondary beta phase in place of alpha brass) until, at about 42% zinc, the color is again a close match to 90−10 red brass. Small amounts of lead, which is insoluble in copper, may be added to brasses or bronzes to improve machinability and lubricity (as in bearing alloys).

A potential corrosion problem with brasses containing more than about 15% zinc is dezincification, a form of parting corrosion, in some environments. This is a problem in many waters, ranging from potable water to seawater. To combat this type of attack in seawater, the British developed Admiralty Metal by adding 1% tin to a 70−30 yellow brass. In modern practice, the beneficial effect of tin is increased synergistically by additions of about 0.2% arsenic, antimony, or phosphorus. These additions provide the three (roughly equivalent) alloys: Admiralty B (C44300), C (C44400), and D (C44500), respectively. Inhibiting additions of tin and arsenic are also made to other high-zinc alloys (e.g., aluminum brass, C68700; leaded Muntz Metal, C36600) intended for service in corrosive waters or other aggressive environments.

Another major weakness of brass and of other high-strength copper alloys is a susceptibility to environmental cracking, especially SCC and LMC (e.g., by mercury), as was described in Chapter 8.

14.3 BRONZE

There are four general categories of bronzes which are of interest from the corrosion engineering standpoint, although there are a great number of variants used in materials engineering of metal products. Bronzes and brasses (the nomenclature has always been rather loose until the advent of the UNS) have been widely used for naval and military applications, as well as architectural and machinery uses. Beryllium bronze is employed for improved hardness and wear resistance (e.g., as in nonsparking tools).

14.3.1 Phosphor Bronzes

These tin bronzes have taken their popular name from the use of phosphorus as a deoxidizer. The tin, usually used in concentrations up to about 10% (e.g., C52400), confers strength and increases corrosion resistance in some environments. Casting bronzes may be more complex, e.g., leaded phosphor bronze [ounce metal, C54400 (85Cu−5Sn−5Zn−5Pb)], because of the variety of properties desired, such as fluidity in casting, high strength, galling resistance, machinability, or corrosion resistance.

14.3.2 Silicon Bronze

Silicon bronzes are copper plus 1 to 3% silicon (e.g., C64900, C65500), noted particularly for strength and cryogenic suitability. However, these alloys are hot-short, because of the presence of a low-melting constituent at the grain boundaries. At 700 to 800°C (1290 to 1475°F), as from welding or hot-work, microfissuring occurs under stress. After welding, brazing, or hot-working, the microfissures may become apparent as macrocracks after only a few hours. On the other hand, they may take several years to become apparent. The IGC is difficult to distinguish from SCC under the optical microscope. (The alloys are susceptible to SCC in ammonia or even uncontaminated steam.) LMC, as by mercury or its salts, is also difficult to distinguish from hot-short cracking, although the scanning electron microscope should be enable one to do so.

14.3.3 Aluminum Bronze

Aluminum bronzes are alloys of copper and aluminum in the range from 5 to 10% (e.g., C61000). These are good corrosion-resistant alloys, with remarkable strength at moderately elevated temperatures when compared with other copper alloys. They are rated for service to about 260°C (500°F) by the ASME Boiler Code. A proprietary grade, C61900 or Ampco 8, has been developed, which is especially inhibited for resistance to SCC by steam or ammonia.

14.3.4 Cupronickels

The cupronickels, which are *not* commonly referred to as bronzes, are a series of alloys ranging from 90Cu−10Ni (C70600) and 80−20 (C71000) to 70−30 (C71500). These have superior resistance to seawater (e.g., as condenser tubes), and the resistance can be improved by the addition of small amounts of iron (1.0 to 1.8%). Cupronickels also have relatively good high-temperature properties, and better resistance to erosion and cavitation than do other copper alloys.

RECOMMENDED READING

Standards Handbooks Nos. 1−7, Copper Development Association, New York, 1978.

CHAPTER 15

Nickel and Its Alloys

The family of nickel alloys is among the most important because these alloys resist corrosion in a wide variety of environments. The alloys can be divided into two groups: those which depend primarily on the inherent characteristics of nickel itself (plus the influence of certain alloying additions), and those which employ chromium as a major element to develop a passive film analogous to the one that forms on iron-chromium alloys, such as stainless steels.

15.1 NICKEL ALLOYS

15.1.1 Nickel

Commercially pure nickel (e.g., Alloy 200, N02200) is a white *magnetic* metal very similar to copper in its other physical and mechanical properties. The *Curie point*, i.e., the temperature at which it loses its magnetism, fluctuates with the nature and extent of alloy additions, rising with increased iron and cobalt concentrations, falling with addition of copper, silicon, and most other elements. Nickel is also, of course, an important alloying element in other families of corrosion-resistant alloys (e.g., alloy cast irons, cupronickels, stainless steels).

Nickel is used alone as a material of construction, as a cladding on a steel substrate, and as a plating on steel or other less noble metals. The plating may be deposited either by electrochemical techniques or as *electroless* plating deposited by a chemical reduction process.

In addition to Alloy 200, there are a number of alloy modifications developed for increased strength, hardness, resistance to galling, and improved corrosion resistance. The several variants of nickel are substantially equivalent in corrosion resistance, but the low-carbon Alloy 201 (0.02% C maximum) is preferred for service above 300°C (570°F), as in caustic evaporators.

The major application of nickel is in the production of high-purity caustic in the 50 to 75% concentration range. The sodium hydroxide is produced in nickel or nickel-clad evaporators to meet the rigorous requirements of the rayon, soap, and other manufacturing industries for iron-free, copper-free caustic.

Nickel, like copper, is *not* resistant to ammonia or its derivatives in the simultaneous presence of air, oxygen, or other oxidants. This is due to the formation of soluble complex ions, similar to the copper-ammonium complex.

Nickel is moderately resistant to acids (since it does not displace hydrogen), except under oxidizing conditions. Oxidizing cations (e.g., ferric or cupric ions) or anions (e.g., nitrates, nitrites) cause rapid attack.

Nickel-plated steel, particularly of the electroless variety (actually a nickel–nickel phosphide alloy), is used for the shipment and storage of many chemicals which require protection against iron contamination.

15.1.2 Alloy 400 (Monel)

Monel or Alloy 400 (NO4400) is a well-known and widely used alloy containing about 30% copper and up to 2.5% iron. It is readily forged, worked, cast, and welded (or brazed). It has about the same machinability as steel. Its Curie point is very close to room temperature, hence it can lose its magnetism when merely warmed by the sun, only to recover it upon slight cooling. (Cast Monel has a higher Curie point because of increased silicon content.) There are a number of alloy variations (e.g., N05500, a precipitation-hardening variety) for improved strength, hardness, machinability, or resistance to galling.

Corrosion resistance is good in many (although not all) natural waters, including seawater. Both Alloy 200 and Alloy 400 can be attacked in *soft* waters (see Chapter 19) having critical ratios of oxygen to carbon dioxide. Alloy 400, however, is the standard material of construction for watermeter parts, pumps, valves, strainers, etc. A substantial amount is used in fabrication of hot-water tanks. It should be noted, however, that under hot-wall conditions (i.e., in coolers or condensers), some fresh waters will cause pitting, even though otherwise noncorrosive.

Alloy 400 and its variants will resist both acids and alkalis in the absence of oxidizing agents. As one would expect, these nickel-copper alloys are subject to corrosion by ammonia and its derivatives in the presence of oxygen or oxidants.

These alloys are subject to environmental cracking under some conditions (e.g., SCC by hydrofluoric acid vapors plus air and by *hot* concentrated caustic; HAC by atomic hydrogen, in the cold-worked condition; LMC by mercury or its salts).

15.1.3 Nickel-Molybdenum Alloys

Alloy B (e.g., Hastelloy B), N10001, is an alloy of nickel with about 30% molybdenum, developed to resist hydrochloric acid up to the atmospheric boiling point. This resistance is, however, severely impaired by the presence of oxidizing contaminants (e.g., ferric ions in muriatic acid). As one would expect, the alloy resists reducing acids quite well, and oxidizing acids not at all. Alkali resistance is also good, but use of such an expensive alloy is not warranted. Like other high-nickel alloys, it is susceptible to attack by amines because of the nickel-ammonium-type complex.

Because of a susceptibility to IGC in the HAZ after welding, in some environments, a low-carbon variant has been developed. Alloy B-2 (N10665) is gradually replacing Alloy B in most applications.

15.2 Chromium-Bearing Alloys

15.2.1 Nickel-Chromium Alloys

The prototype alloy in this category in Inconel or Alloy 600 (N06600), which contains about 77% nickel and 15% chromium, and the balance iron (sort of a reverse 18−8). The presence of chromium gives it a passive film and corrosion characteristics analogous to those of stainless steels. A variant is Alloy 601 (N06601), with a somewhat lower carbon content and a somewhat higher chromium content.

Alloy 600 is used as a heating coil in caustic evaporators unless traces of Cr(VI) ions are objectionable in the product. Nevertheless, at high stress levels, it is subject to SCC in strong caustic on prolonged exposure above about 300°C (570°F).

The alloy can replace austenitic stainless steel in some chloride environments, but can be pitted (although not cracked) under severe conditions. It is at least an order of magnitude better than 18−8 stainless steels in steam contaminated with *both* chloride and caustic, and is the first choice for corrugated expansion joints in such service.

Alloy 600 has excellent resistance to halogens and halogen acid anhydrides at elevated temperatures. However, as with all nickel alloys, it is subject to

LMC by sulfur contamination at elevated temperatures (e.g., in welding, where the materials must be scrupulously clean and free of any sulfur-bearing species).

A molybdenum-bearing variant is discussed further in Section 15.2.4 below.

15.2.2 Nickel-Iron-Chromium Alloys

The basic alloy in this group is Incoloy, now known as Alloy 800 (N08800). This is basically a superstainless steel with the composition $21Cr-32$ $Ni-$balance Fe. Strictly speaking, it is neither an iron-based nor a nickel-based alloy (since neither element is present at more than 50% concentration), so the N designation is arbitrary.

Alloy 800 has much better resistance to corrosion, oxidation, and chloride-induced attack than does S30403, for example. However, it is *not* better than the $18-8$s in resisting caustic cracking. Its place in the market for chloride-resistant grades is being taken over to a considerable extent by the super-stainless steel grades described in Chapter 12.

15.2.3 Nickel-Iron-Chromium-Molybdenum Alloys

A more corrosion-resistant alloy than N08800 was developed by the further addition of molybdenum (or molybdenum plus copper). Alloys 20 and 20Cb3 (N08020) have already been described in Chapter 12. The prototype higher alloy was Incoloy 825 (N08825), but two other proprietary alloys, Hastelloys F (N06001) and G (N06007) also belong in this category, as shown in Table 15.1. Alloy G-2 (N06975) is a low-carbon variant, designed to minimize IGC of weldments in severe services.

These alloys have higher chromium, nickel, and molybdenum content (plus copper in most instances) for increased corrosion resistance in sulfuric and phosphoric acid services. Resistance to organic acid corrosion is also enhanced. They are highly resistant to chloride pitting and SCC as well. The highest grade is also demonstrably superior in the cold-worked condition in chloride-bearing sour service (i.e., with hydrogen sulfide also present).

15.2.4 Nickel-Chromium-Molybdenum Alloys

The prototype alloy in this category was Hastelloy C (N10002), a nickel alloy containing about 15% each of chromium and molybdenum to enhance acid resistance under oxidizing conditions. An improved alloy of greater resistance

Table 15.1   Composition of Nickel-Iron-Chromium-Molybdenum Alloys

| UNS | Weight % | | | | | | |
	Cr	Ni	Mo	Cu	C	Fe	Other
N08020	19–21	32–38	2–3	3–4	0.07	32–44	Cb
N08825	20–24	38–46	3–4	2–3	0.05	24–40	Ti
N06001	21–23	44–47	5–8	—	0.05	22–30	Cb, W
N06007	21–24	46–54	4–8	2–3	0.05	18–21	Cb, W

to IGC is alloy C276 (N10276), and a superior variant is Alloy C-4 (N06455). An even newer alloy is Hastelloy C-22, whose higher chromium content extends its usefulness.

When Alloy 600 is improved by increasing the chromium content to about 23% plus 8% molybdenum, Alloy 625 (N06625) is obtained. Useful in seawater and other corrosive services, this material is usually somewhat less resistant than Alloy C276.

These types of alloys are outstanding in resistance to hot seawater, aggressive organic acids (e.g., boiling formic or acetic acid mixtures), and hot oxidizing acids (e.g., mixtures of nitric and hydrochloric, hydrofluoric, etc.). They are also sometimes employed for severe SCC environments (e.g., centrifuges for high-chloride resin or polymer mixtures, such as PVC) where the superstainless steels might be suspect or of too low a mechanical strength.

RECOMMENDED READING

Friend, W. Z.: *Corrosion of Nickel and Nickel-Base Alloys* (corrosion monographs), Wiley, New York, 1980.

CHAPTER 16

Reactive Metals and Noble Metals

The *reactive metals* are so named because of their affinity with hydrogen and oxygen, particularly at elevated temperatures, such as during welding. This is a misnomer, however, to the extent that these metals and their alloys are corrosion-resistant in many severe environments. The *noble metals* (as opposed to base metals) are those which are found free and unreacted in the natural environment. These terms are somewhat obsolete; the noble metals are now generally called *precious metals*, because of their monetary worth.

16.1 REACTIVE METALS

The reactive metals of practical interest are titanium, zirconium, and tantalum. Of these, the latter two are also classified as *refractory metals*, because of their high melting range and high-temperature strength. All three are refractory in the sense of being difficult to extract from their corresponding ores.

16.1.1 Titanium

Titanium is the ninth most abundant element on earth, but so reactive with the ordinary constituents of air at elevated temperatures that only in the 1950s did it become commercially practical as an engineering material. As we learned to extract, refine, alloy, and fabricate it, titanium became increasingly important. With a melting range of about 1670°C (3040°F), a low density (sp gr 4.5; about 60% that of steel), high strength [414 MPa (60,000 psi) minimum tensile strength], and good corrosion resistance, it showed great promise.

As discussed further below, it does have good corrosion resistance in strongly oxidizing environments, but *not* with reducing acids. The mechanical strength, furthermore, drops off rapidly with increasing temperature, and its reactivity with hydrogen, oxygen, water vapor, and nitrogen effectively limits applications to less than about 535°C (995°F), except perhaps in controlled inert atmospheres. All welding, for example, must be done with MIG, TIG, or similar inert-gas processes. Because of the absolute exclusion of atmospheric contaminants required, field fabrication is somewhat difficult.

The strength of titanium can be increased by alloying, some alloys reaching 1310 MPa (190,000 psi), although at some cost in corrosion resistance. Titanium has good impact strength at cryogenic temperatures. It can be readily shaped and formed and is available in conventional forms.

The commercial grades of titanium and its alloys are more commonly known by grade than by their UNS numbers. Some of the more important are given in Table 16.1.

The feature that moves titanium from its anodic position in the electromotive series to a noble position in the galvanic series is the development of an inert, passive surface film in oxidizing environments. It is widely used in such strongly oxidizing media as wet chlorine and strong nitric acid, although it can react catastrophically with *red fuming nitric acid* (see Chapter 21). Titanium makes heat exchanger tubing of superior resistance in seawater and other saline environments.

Titanium is generally not useful in nonoxidizing or reducing acids except in very dilute solutions (e.g., a few hundredths of a percent) or unless their redox potential is shifted by oxidizing contaminants (e.g., ferric ions, cupric ions,

Table 16.1 Grades and UNS Numbers of Titanium Alloys

Grade	UNS Number	Type
1	R50250	Unalloyed
2	R50400	"
3	R50550	"
4	R50700	"
5	R56400	Ti−6Al−4V
6	R54520	Ti−6Al−3Sn
7	R52400	Ti−Pd (0.2)
9	R56320	Ti−3Al−2V
10	R58030	Ti−12Mo−6Zr−5Sn

and nitrite. Titanium is treacherous in hot organic acids such as formic or acetic, in which it may suddenly lose its passivity and corrode at greatly accelerated rates. The addition of a small amount of platinum (grade 7) or substantial amounts of molybdenum (grade 10) greatly extends the tolerance for higher concentrations of reducing acids. It should be noted that titanium will not tolerate even trace amounts of *fluorides*, which cause severe hydriding and embrittlement with aggravated corrosion.

Environmental cracking has been observed in low-molecular-weight alcohols such as methanol and ethanol, the tendency to which is aggravated by traces of halides or halogen acids. Titanium can also suffer cracking in strong nitric acid and in *dry* sodium chloride above about 300°C (570°F).

There is also a problem in strong oxidants under some conditions. Although titanium is excellent in wet chlorine, it can *burn* in dry chlorine [a minimum water content of 2000 parts per million (ppm) is mandatory for successful use in chlorine service]. Crevice corrosion may be a problem even in wet chlorine, because of depletion of oxidizing species within the crevice. It can be *detonated* in liquid oxygen, where its good NDTT characteristics would otherwise make it very attractive.

In short, titanium is a marvelously useful material of construction with a number of severe limitations. It is also relatively expensive, except in the form of thin-walled heat exchanger tubing, which is produced in large quantities.

16.1.2 Zirconium

Zirconium is between titanium and steel in density (sp gr 6.5) and has a strength of about 345 MPa (50,000 psi) in the annealed condition. The strength can be increased to about 550 MPa (80,000 psi) by cold-work. The melting point is about 1850°C (3360°F).

Unless specifically removed, about 2% hafnium is present in zirconium (e.g., unalloyed zirconium R60701 and R60702). Although this does not impair corrosion resistance, it is objectionable in nuclear applications, for which an unalloyed reactor grade (R60001) is available. Other alloys, also reactor grade, are available (e.g., R60802, R60804, R60901). Zirconium is deliberately alloyed with aluminum, copper, molybdenum, niobium, tantalum, titanium, and tin to increase strength and corrosion resistance.

Zirconium and its alloys are easily fabricated, except for a hot-gas pick-up analogous to the one to which titanium is susceptible. Thoroughly shielded inert gas welding is required. Even nitrogen pick-up of as little as 500 ppm, while not affecting mechanical properties, will diminish corrosion resistance in supercritical waters in nuclear reactors. The materials are also notch-sensitive, and threaded parts such as tray support rods in distillation columns are susceptible to breakage if the column should be bumped in service.

Zirconium is quite acid-resistant, withstanding not only oxidizing acids like nitric acid but also concentrations of up to 60% phosphoric and up to 70% sulfuric acid, depending upon contaminants. It will also resist hydrochloric acid in the *liquid* phase, although not the hot vapors. In immersion service, arc-melted zirconium will resist HCL of all concentrations up to the atmospheric boiling point. However, if the material is not of high enough purity, corrosion of the weld HAZ may be a problem. This situation is exacerbated by the presence of oxidizing contaminants (e.g., ferric or cupric ions, nitrates, hypochlorites, and chlorine). Zirconium is *attacked* by hydrofluoric and hydrobromic acids.

Zirconium is caustic-resistant, but its use is rarely justified in such service. Hot molten metals like mercury, lead, and bismuth attack zirconium and its alloys.

Zirconium is several times more expensive than titanium, even in heat exchanger tubing, but finds application in intermediate-strength sulfuric acid services and in nuclear energy systems.

16.1.3 Tantalum

Tantalum is a very heavy metal with a density more than twice that of steel (sp gr 16.6). Its melting point is almost 3000°C (5430°F). The tensile strength is about 345 MPa (50,000 psi), which can be approximately doubled by cold-work. Like titanium and zirconium, it is easy to fabricate, contingent upon completely inert conditions during welding, but is even more susceptible to hydrogen pick-up. Even in a simple galvanic couple at room temperature (e.g., with carbon steel in an aqueous environment), it will be severely embrittled by absorption of over 700 times its own volume of nascent hydrogen.

The corrosion resistance of tantalum is very similar to that of glass, resisting most acids but being attacked by hydrofluoric acid and by caustic. Unlike glass, however, it is attacked by fuming sulfuric acid, chlorosulfonic acid, and sulfur dioxide.

Because of its very high cost, tantalum is usually used only in very thin sections, as a lining or thin cladding, or as a uniquely pore-free electroplated coating on a copper or steel substrate such as for orifice plates. Tantalum-plated copper can be immersed in nitric acid, or tantalum-plated steel in hot concentrated sulfuric acid, with no attack of the substrate (because of the absence of holidays in the plating).

Orifice plates, bayonet heaters, heat exchangers, valves, and tantalum-plated steel tubes are of interest in the process industries. Tantalum patches are used to repair holidays in glass-lined steel vessels, but *must* be electrically isolated from other metallic components in the vessel (to prevent embrittlement by hydrogen absorption as the cathode in a galvanic couple).

16.2 NOBLE METALS

The noble (or precious) metals are very expensive. Nevertheless, they do find some application in process equipment under special conditions. If fully resistant, their salvage value may easily offset the initial cost. If consumed in use, they may nevertheless pay for themselves on a cost-to-life basis, if they are truly needed for the service.

16.2.1 Silver

Silver was used for certain specific services before the development of modern nickel-base alloys and plastics. In everyday use (jewelry, silverware), the most common observation concerning silver is that it tends to tarnish. This brownish-black film is caused by traces of hydrogen sulfide in the atmosphere, but the film is fairly protective.

Silver is rapidly attacked by cyanides and by oxidizing acids such as nitric acid and strong sulfuric acid. It can form explosive compounds called *azides* with ammonia and its derivatives (whence the hazard from old ammoniacal silver nitrate solutions in the laboratory), but it has been used successfully in some urea plants.

Silver resists organic acids and, prior to the development of the nickel-chromium-molybdenum alloys (e.g., N10276), was used rather widely in such applications. Silver heating coils were used, for example, in S31603 acetic acid storage tanks, where stainless coils give excessive iron contamination. Silver has also been used in handling and storage of phenols, acidic foodstuffs, and pharmaceuticals. It has been used for dilute hydrochloric acid, although ingress of air impairs its service life. Good resistance to hydrofluoric acid has led to its use in some applications related to the manufacture of fluorinated solvents (e.g., refrigerants and propellants).

Silver is usefully resistant to high-temperature caustics and alkalis and has been used to handle molten alkaline salts.

16.2.2 Gold

Gold has been used for gaskets in certain severe services and, as the alloy of gold and platinum, for "spinnerettes" in the rayon industry. Gold is readily attacked by cyanides and by hologens. This is why, although it readily withstands nitric and hydrochloric acids separately, it is attacked by aqua regia (a 3:1 mixture of hydrochloric and nitric acids). It does, however, resist sulfuric acid.

Gold will resist alkalis well, although the cost is seldom justified, but is attacked by alkaline sulfides in a manner analogous to silver.

16.2.3 Platinum

Although platinum is even more expensive than gold, it is used for electrical contacts in oxidizing atmospheres. It is very resistant to acids and alkalis except for aqua regia, halogens in general, and halogen acids above 100°C (212°F).

All of the noble metals can be used as electroplated coatings, but this is quite dangerous for corrosive services because they are strongly cathodic to any substrate of baser metals, leading to localized corrosion at holidays in the plating.

CHAPTER 17

Nonmetallic Materials

There are a variety of organic and inorganic materials, in addition to metals and alloys, with which the working engineer should have at least a nodding acquaintance. Paints and coatings are materials, but are construed to be a corrosion control measure rather than materials of construction. They are considered separately in Chapter 35.

17.1 PLASTICS

Since the development of celluloid in 1869, engineers have been interested in potential industrial applications of plastic materials. There are hundreds of plastics available today, their use (or potential use) determined by particular chemical characteristics and physical and mechanical properties.

A *plastic* is a material that contains as an essential ingredient an organic compound of high molecular weight, is a solid in the finished state, and, at some stage in its manufacture or processing, can be shaped. In common parlance, a plastic is a *thermoplastic* if it can be softened and reshaped, without damage or degradation, under the influence of heat. If not, it is called a *thermosetting* material. However, most people refer rather loosely to both categories of resins as "plastics."

17.1.1 Thermoplastics

The thermoplastics are the most widely used organic materials of construction. When not modified or reinforced, their mechanical properties are the lowest of the several materials of interest, and rapid diminution of strength is encountered with only moderate temperature increases. However, the physical and mechanical properties are entirely adequate for many applications.

Properties

1. *Strength*.   The tensile and flexural strengths of the thermoplastic materials are rather poor, dropping off rapidly with increasing temperature. However, the use of organic or inorganic reinforcing agents can upgrade the strength, as can "alloying" with other resinous materials.

2. *Creep*.   Distension under constant strain at ambient temperature is roughly comparable to that of carbon steel at about 500°C (930°F). Consideration must be given to support of thermoplastic structures, particularly if exposed to direct sunlight or other heat sources.

3. *Modulus*.   This property, as well as thermal expansion (see below), deserves the greatest consideration in design of thermoplastic structures. The modulus is low and, in flexure, there really is no straight-line relationship between stress and strain.

4. *Thermal Expansion*.   Although the data are readily available in the literature, all too often the designer fails to provide adequate allowance for thermal expansion (which may be 15 times that of an austenitic stainless steel). There must be adequate room for the structure to expand and contract, while still providing adequate mechanical support.

5. *Impact*.   Thermoplastic materials, as a group, are tough. However, most of the materials are notch-sensitive, and impact values of notched materials can be low (a factor to consider before threading a product, for example).

6. *Conductivity*.   Unmodified resins are usually good insulators of both thermal and electrical conductivity. However, conductivity can be induced or enhanced by the addition of inorganic compounds, with significant variation in the final properties.

Environmental Resistance

Plastic materials do not corrode by electrochemical mechanisms, as do metals and alloys. The degradation of the material or its properties is related to the structural similarity between the material and the environment and/or to the permeability of the material. Permeability is controlled by the solubility of the material in the environment and by the rate of diffusion of the environment into the plastic (primarily under temperature control). When diffusion into the plastic matrix occurs and the environment is chemically incompatible, all mechanical properties of the plastic are downgraded. A simple hardness test will often give an indication of the rate and extent of degradation. Specific comments about chemical resistance of types of plastics are given in "Specific Materials," below.

Fabrication

Most of the thermoplastic materials can be hot-fusion-welded, or solvent-welded, at properly designed joints. Threaded couplings can be used for many materials, with careful attention to notch sensitivity. Solvent welding is usually preferred for joining all but the polyolefins, for which fusion welding is normally employed.

Specifications

There are a large number of ASTM specifications covering materials, qualification tests, test procedures, and properties. Commodity standards and military (MIL) specifications are also relevant.

Specific Materials

1. *Polyethylene.* This is the most widely used plastic today and is available in the form of gaskets, solid drums or containers, drum liners, piping, and small molded parts for process equipment. Polyethylene can be joined by thermal welding. *Ultra-high-density polyethylene* has improved mechanical properties, greater thermal stability, and improved solvent resistance compared with the older types of formulations. It is attacked by strong oxidants and is susceptible to environmental cracking by some chemicals (notably detergents, wetting agents, alcohols, ketones, aldehydes, and organic acids).

2. *Polypropylene.* Polypropylene is the next higher homologue of polyethylene. Stronger and somewhat more resistant chemically, it is used both as a plastic liner for steel pipe and as solid pipe or sheet material. Its strength and weldability make it a prime consideration for piping for corrosive waters, dilute acids, and many wastewaters (provided there are no incompatible organic species contained therein).

3. *ABS.* ABS (acrylonitrile-butadiene-styrene) is one of the older standbys, particularly for piping systems. This material can have considerable variation in properties, depending on the ratio of acrylonitrile to the other components. Higher strength, better toughness, greater dimensional stability, and other properties can be obtained, although sometimes at the expense of other characteristics. Although the ABS material has poor heat tolerance—about 90°C (195°F)—with relatively low strength and limited chemical resistance, its low price and ease of joining and fabrication make it attractive for distribution piping (for gas, water, and waste), vent lines, automotive parts, and other consumer items. The ABS plastic will withstand attack by only a few organic compounds, is attacked by oxidizing agents and strong acids, and will stress-crack in the presence of certain organic species. Problems with ultraviolet (UV) degradation have been largely overcome through the use of protective additives.

4. *CAB*.   CAB (cellulose acetate–butyrate) is one of a group comprising acetate, propionate, and butyrate plastics. These are used for piping and other industrial applications, although not in major quantities. They are found in a number of small items, such as nameplates, electrical component cases, high-impact lenses, and other applications requiring a transparent plastic with good impact properties. Overall chemical resistance is comparable to most of the other thermoplastics.

5. *PVC*.   PVC (polyvinyl chloride) piping is very popular for water service, particularly in the presence of chlorine or other oxidants. A variant, CPVC (chlorinated PVC), is used for *hot-water* services. PVC and CPVC have excellent resistance to both acids and alkalis, but their solvent resistance is very limited. Straight-chain hydrocarbons (i.e., aliphatics like kerosene or oil) do not affect them. Piping may be joined by hot-air welding or solvent welding. Sheet lining of vessels is a common application. PVC type I is an unplasticized form with good chemical resistance. Type II has been modified by the addition of styrene-butadiene rubber, improving notch toughness and impact strength at some sacrifice in chemical resistance.

6. *PVDC*.   PVDC (polyvinylidene chloride or Saran) is a variant of PVC, having both chlorine atoms on the same end of the monomer (instead of opposite ends, as with vinyl chloride). PVDC has improved strength, hardness, and chemical resistance, especially to organic solvents, mineral acids, and oxidants. Formerly, a major market was in Saran-lined steel pipe. Currently, it is more often found in valves, pumps, and piping.

7. *Fluorocarbons*.   These are the most versatile and important group of plastics for the process industries. Maximum chemical resistance and heat stability are provided by this class of materials as pipe liners, tank linings, impellers, mixers, spargers, tower packing, lined valves, etc. The original polytetrafluoroethylene (PTFE or Teflon) provides adequate heat stability to 290°C (555°F) for many applications, and resistance to essentially all chemicals except molten alkalis. Fabrication of PTFE is very difficult, as it cannot be welded or applied adhesively except by a special pretreatment, precluding its use as a liner. Note that, currently, the trade name Teflon no longer applies to the single type of polymer.

Modifications of the original PTFE developed rapidly. The modified variants have somewhat lower heat stability limits and slightly reduced chemical resistance, but are much more amenable to fabrication by welding, hot-forming, cold-working, and adhesion. Among these variants are FEP (fluorinated ethylene-propylene), CTFE (chlortrifluorethylene), PVF (polyvinyl fluoride), PVDF (polyvinylidene fluoride), ECTFE (ethylene chlortrifluorethylene), and PFA (perfluoralkoxy). Space does not permit a discussion of each of these materials. A proper understanding of the available products is necessary to assure selection of the optimum material for a specific application.

8. *Nylon.*   Nylon is a polyimide-type plastic used primarily for mechanical parts in appliances, but nylon coatings can be applied by fluidized-bed techniques. The material is heat-stable to about 175°C (345°F), but has very limited chemical resistance.

9. *Acetals.*   The acetal resins are competitive with nylon in mechanical properties and greatly superior in chemical resistance. Proprietary resins like Delrin and Calcon have three times the dimensional stability of nylon.

10. *Polycarbonates.*   The polycarbonate resins (e.g., Lexan) have mechanical properties equivalent to the acetals. Their usefulness in industrial applications, however, is limited by their susceptibility to environmental cracking in even mild atmospheric exposure.

11. *Others.*   Specific useful properties can be found in such other, less frequently used plastics such as polysulfones, acrylics, styrenes, and polyphenylene oxide or sulfide.

17.1.2 Thermosetting Resins

This group of plastics is hard, even brittle, at ambient temperatures. At higher temperatures, some loss in properties may occur, but in general the properties are retained until the materials degrade (usually by carbonization or oxidation). For engineering applications, all the thermosetting resins are reinforced by some means.

Reinforcement

Although silica, asbestos, paper, linen, and other plastics and materials are added as reinforcing materials, glass fiber and cloth are by far the most popular. Glass contents varying from 25 to 80% are used in the form of woven cloth and random veil, but the greatest strength is achieved by glass filaments overlaid at the proper angle. Other benefits are improved modulus and a much lower coefficient of thermal expansion than the unreinforced resin.

Fillers

Various other siliceous materials, as well as carbon and metal powders or fibers, can be added to produce even greater modulus values, greater strength, differing thermal and/or electrical properties, and desired colors in the composite products.

Physical and Mechanical Properties

With the almost infinite number of materials combinations possible, it is obvious that specific properties of almost any type can be designed into the product (even the strength of a carbon steel). Heat shields for reentry from space and graphite-fiber-reinforced golf clubs, tennis rackets, and fishing rods are examples of such specific applications.

Fabrication

The reinforced thermosetting materials are true structural components, which can be machined, threaded, bolted, and/or glued to fabricate equipment.

Materials

1. *Epoxy*. Epoxy laminates, reinforced with glass cloth for mechanical strength, have superior chemical resistance. They will withstand hot alkalis, mineral acids up to 20% (except nitric acid), and most organic solvents. The temperature limit is about 95°C (200°F). They have poor resistance to strong oxidants, amines, and chlorinated solvents.

2. *Phenolics*. Phenolics are heat-curing resins which offer a combination of excellent properties. Many forms of apparatus are available (e.g., pipe, fitting, pumps, valves, column sections, and heat exchanger components). Phenolics are resistant to many solvents and acids, being adversely affected primarily by alkalis, oxidants, and amines. Their temperature limit is about 110°C (230°F). Many types of process equipment use the phenolic resin for the inside, the exterior being "armored" with epoxy or polyester laminates.

3. *Polyester*. The most common designation for this type of construction is FRP (fiberglass-reinforced plastic) or GRTP (glass-reinforced thermosetting plastic). This terminology is very loose, as the polyesters comprise a family of materials which vary from vinyl esters to bisphenol polyesters. The different

resins have different chemical resistance to specific environments, but in general are better than epoxies or phenolics in oxidizing situations. A large amount of tankage, piping, ductwork, etc. is so constructed. Common applications include underground tanks for gasoline, storage tanks for mineral acids (e.g., hydrochloric, phosphoric), and piping for aggressive waters (e.g., seawater, raw water).

4. *Furanes.* The furanes, which are derived from furfuryl alcohol, have outstanding resistance, being chemically attacked only by certain nitrogenous or chlorinated organic compounds. Their application was limited previously by problems of aging and cracking, but modern formulations and supplemental reinforcement have extended their usefulness in industry.

17.2 RUBBER AND ELASTOMERS

The term *rubber* originally applied to the natural material. *Elastomer* is a term derived from the words "elastic" and "polymer," and is broadly used to embrace both natural and synthetic rubbers as well as plastics formulated to have rubberlike or elastomeric properties.

17.2.1 Specific Materials

Natural Rubber

Natural rubbers are made by processing the sap of the rubber tree, and compounding it with vulcanizing agents, antioxidants, fillers, pigments, etc. Red, black, and white rubbers are made with different pigments (e.g., iron oxide, carbon black, zinc oxide).

Natural rubbers have poor resistance to atmospheric oxygen, ozone, sunlight (UV rays), petroleum derivatives, and many organic chemicals. Resistance to nonoxidizing acids and alkalis is good. Rubber has been used for pumps, valves, piping, hoses, and machined products (when hardened by *vulcanization*). However, many of the historical applications have been taken over by the newer plastic materials.

Synthetic Rubbers

1. *Buna S.* This is a copolymer of butadiene and styrene used in tires, hoses, and miscellaneous goods. It offers no particular advantage in chemical service.

2. *Buna N.* The copolymer of butadiene and acrylonitrile, also called Hycar, is produced in ratios varying from 25:75 to 75:25. The manufacturer's designation should identify the percentage of acrylonitrile. Compared with natural rubber, it has good oil resistance and is used for hose, gaskets, and packing (e.g., O-rings). It has fair resistance to ozone and UV, but is severely embrittled at low temperatures.

3. *Butyl.* Butyl rubber is a polymer of isobutylene, with small additions of isoprene and butadiene. It is remarkably impermeable to gases and is used for tire innertubes and hoses. It resists aging and ozone and is more resistant to organic chemicals (except aromatic compounds) than are most synthetic rubbers.

4. *Neoprene.* Neoprene is a polymer of chloroprene and was developed for resistance to oil and solvents. It is resistant to aging, ozone, and moderately elevated temperatures, and has good abrasion and wear characteristics. It is widely used for hoses, gaskets, motor belts, tires, tank linings, etc.

5. *EPDM.* EPDM (ethylene-propylene diene monomer), or EPR (ethylene-propylene rubber), is a copolymer of ethylene and propylene. It has much of the chemical resistance of the related plastics and has good resistance to steam and hot water. It has become the standard lining material for steam hoses. EPDM is widely used in chemical services as well, having a broad spectrum of resistance.

6. *Specialty Elastomers.* There are basically three kinds of specialty synthetic rubbers.
  a. *Silicone rubbers* are based on silicon rather than carbon linkages. Although chemical resistance is relatively poor, silicone rubbers withstand aging and ozone as well as oil and can tolerate temperature extremes from minus 75°C (-103°F) to 200°C (390°F).
  b. *Chlorsulfonated polyethylene* (Hypalon) has outstanding resistance to oxidizing environments. Otherwise, its physical and chemical properties are similar to Neoprene.
  c. *Fluorinated elastomers* like Kel-F and Viton will withstand oxidants and have temperature capacities up to 300°C (570°F) for short periods of time. However, contrary to what one might hope for by analogy with the fluorinated plastics, they mostly have poor resistance in solvents or organic media. They do resist acids and alkalis. A new perfluorelastomer product, Kalrez, does have chemical resistance comparable to that of the fluorinated plastics.

17.3 OTHER NONMETALLIC MATERIALS

Besides the plastics and elastomers, there are a number of other nonmetallic materials of interest to the process industries. These materials are used both as materials of construction in their own right and as linings, barriers, or coatings of one kind or another.

17.3.1 Carbon and Graphite

Carbon products have a homogeneous structure, which is usually produced below 1230°C (2250°F). Graphite is a crystalline form of carbon produced by processing at temperatures in excess of 1980°C (3600°F). The main use of carbon and graphite per se is as brick for lining process vessels and as ring packing for fractionation columns.

There is an appreciable difference in corrosion resistance. Within certain limits, carbon will withstand more powerful oxidizing agents than graphite, such as hot concentrated sulfuric acid or halogens (which will attack graphite rapidly). Both forms will withstand mineral and organic acids, alkalis, salts, organic solvents, etc.

Where thermal conductivity is required (e.g., for heat exchanger tubes), impervious graphite or Karbate is manufactured by forming the desired shape from graphite, evacuating the pores, and impregnating with a resinous material (e.g., a phenolic resin). The impregnation seals the porosity but limits both the corrosion resistance and the maximum service temperature. In addition to heat exchangers, whose thermal conductivity is close to that of copper-tubed items, impervious graphite pumps and valves are available and find broad application in process services. They are, of course, susceptible to brittle failure by mechanical shock.

17.3.2 Glass

"Glass" equipment is of two types; solid glass and glass-coated steel. In glass-lined (or externally glass-coated) equipment, one may purchase a *crystallized glass* (e.g., Pyroceram) with outstanding resistance to thermal shock, which is a potential problem with conventional glass. Crystallized glass can be heated to at least 800°C (1470°F) and quenched in ice water without cracking. All glasses, however, are substantially equivalent in corrosion resistance and susceptibility to *mechanical* damage.

Soft glass was formerly used in laboratory apparatus but has been replaced with the tougher and stronger Pyrex glass. Pyrex glass is available also as pipe, distillation columns, and heat exchangers. Glass-lined equipment is available in the form of tanks, vessels, piping, valves, agitators, and pumps. The normal service temperature limitation is 175°C (345°F).

Glass will resist mineral and organic acids, except hydrofluoric and phosphoric acid containing fluoride contaminants, up to the atmospheric boiling point. Above those temperatures, measurable dissolution will occur. Strong alkalis (e.g., sodium or potassium), as opposed to ammonium (hydroxide), will attack glass, although some glass formulations will take a pH of 12.

Note that some "glass-lined" vessels such as *beer tanks* are only intended to prevent iron contamination; they are not capable of withstanding truly corrosive liquids.

17.3.3. Ceramics

Ceramics include not only the traditional silicate-base materials but also metallic oxides, borides, nitrides, carbides, etc. These are formed into useful shapes and given permanence and durability by heating to high temperatures.

In the process industries, the major applications are as chemical stoneware, porcelain, and acid-brick. Stoneware and porcelain differ in appearance and porosity. They are attacked by hydrofluoric acid, fluoride-bearing phosphoric acid, and alkalis, in a manner analogous to glass.

Ceramics are brittle materials, much stronger in compression than in tension, and must be protected against both thermal and mechanical shock. An important exception is a high-alumina (i.e., aluminum oxide) material, such as U.S. Stoneware's Alite, which can be used up to 1000°C (1830°F) and is more shock-resistant than other stoneware. In general, ceramics will tolerate more rapid cooling than heating, and start-up procedures can be very critical in this regard.

Acid-brick is used for lining vessels in many severely corrosive services. The brick is susceptible to penetration through its pores and at the joints. Its primary function is to reduce the temperature at which the environment encounters the substrate. With rare exceptions, it should *not* be used without a membrane (of rubber, plastic, or lead) to protect the metallic substrate, which is usually steel and low in resistance to the environment.

17.3.4 Refractories

The nonmetallic refractories (see also refractory metals) are highly heat-resistant. They are classified as acidic, basic, or neutral, the classification being indicative of their corrosion resistance. Acidic materials, like silica (silicon dioxide), are suitable when the environment is not alkaline (i.e., when it is neutral or acidic). Alkaline environments require alkaline refractories, such as alumina, zirconia, or magnesite.

One should always consider the possible presence of *sodium salts* in furnace applications, because these can be oxidized to sodium oxide, with attendant attack on an acid refractory.

17.3.5 Concrete

Conventional concrete is a mixture of portland cement with an inert aggregate, such as sand or gravel. The cement itself is a mixture of calcium salts (e.g., silicates, aluminates, carbonates), which tends to resist most natural environments, such as air or water.

There are two major problems. One is the corrosion of the steel reinforcing bars, commonly known as *rebar*; the second is corrosion of the concrete itself. Internal rusting of the rebar can occur within the concrete itself, due to ingress of moisture, salts, and oxygen through the pores of the material. Since rust occupies about seven times the volume of the corroded steel, great internal pressures are developed, which tend to crack or spall the concrete. Rebar corrosion may be minimized by coatings (epoxy or galvanizing), sealing the concrete against ingress of corrosive species, or (with suitable design) by CP of the steel rebar within the structure.

There are three basic mechanisms for the corrosion of concrete formulated with portland cement:

1. Corrosion I is the leaching of free lime (e.g., by soft waters or carbonic acid), or direct acid attack upon the calcium carbonate constituent.
2. Corrosion II is a base-exchange reaction between the readily soluble components of the acid and an aggressive solution. The reaction products may either be leached out or remain in place in a *nonbinding* form (e.g., magnesium ions will react to form insoluble salts, leaving a gelatinous mass in the voids).
3. Corrosion III is the formation of new internal salts, whose crystallization and expansion destroy the concrete by internal stresses. Sulfate ions, even from neutral salts, react with tricalcium aluminate to form calcium sulfoaluminate hydrate (the so-called sulfate bacillus) with a large crystallized water content (i.e., 31 mol of water per mole of salt).

Concrete is also attacked by certain organic solvents that react with calcium (e.g., ethyl acetoacetate and other esters).

Sulfate attack is more of a problem with flowing waters than under stagnant conditions or seeping water. Ammonium, magnesium, sodium, and calcium sulfates are particularly destructive. The first level of sulfate resistance is achieved by limiting the permissible concentration of tricalcium aluminate, but this effects only a nominal improvement. The suggested sulfate concentration limits for ASTM C150 portland cements under flowing conditions are 150, 500, and 1500 ppm for types I, II, and V, respectively.

The adverse effect of sulfates is ameliorated by increasing chloride concentration in the water. Although quantitative parameters have not been established, it is well known that type I cement is entirely adequate for seawater, despite the high sulfate content (about 4000 ppm) of that environment.

For more severe conditions, the cement can be pretreated with sulfite liquors or gypsum solutions to form the hydrated salts in situ while the cement is still in the plastic state (e.g., supersulfated cement). However, trass or pozzolanic cements (which give amorphous silicic hydrates in the structure) are more reliable (e.g., ASTM C595, types IP and P). In extreme cases, special alumina-based cements are used.

A special warning is in order regarding use of concrete in wastewaters, where sulfates may be present, yet unanticipated. Also, hydrogen sulfide (from bacterial action or other sources) can accumulate in the vapor zone of concrete sewage pipe, oxidizing to sulfurous or sulfuric acid and causing direct acid attack.

17.3.6 Wood

Wooden tanks and piping are often an economical substitute for alloy construction, particularly in aqueous solutions containing acid salts. The cellulose component in wood may be oxidized or hydrolyzed by acid conditions, while the lignin is subject to attack by alkalis. Wooden construction is generally not suitable for alkaline solutions, although a pH of up to 11 may be tolerated.

Strong acids like sulfuric, hydrochloric, and nitric will oxidize, hydrolyze, or dehydrate wood. Anhydrous hydrogen fluoride will char wood instantaneously. Oxidizing agents, such as nitric or chromic acid, permanganates, and hypochlorites, should not be used with wood. However, dilute acids and acid-salt solutions are handled well by wooden apparatus.

Several types of cedar, cypress, fir, redwood, and pine have been used. Douglas fir is preferred for the more severe services, for example, 95°C, (205°F), pH 2 to 11, while redwood is used to 80°C (175°F) in the pH range from 4 to 9. Heartwood is preferred for optimum resistance, while sapwood may be used where the process liquid itself actually preserves the wood (e.g., in brining or pickling foodstuffs).

Wood may be impregnated with preservatives to protect it from decay. It may also be married to plastics to make composite materials for special purposes. For corrosive and/or abrasive services particularly, professional assistance should be sought in selecting the particular wood and the applicable specifications.

RECOMMENDED READING

Biczonk, I.: *Concrete Corrosion and Concrete Protection*, 3d ed., Adler, New York, 1972.

Mallinson, J. H.: *Chemical Plant Design with Reinforced Plastics*, McGraw-Hill, New York, 1969.

"Plastics Annual," Society of the Plastics Industry, New York.

SECTION **4**

Corrosive Environments

CHAPTER **18**

Corrosion by Water and Steam

In the chapters concerning corrosion by specific environments, we will first discuss corrosion by water (and its contaminants) because its presence is a necessary condition for atmospheric corrosion and corrosion by soils and salts. Also, water is the most commonly encountered corrodent in both municipal and industrial applications.

Water is something that everybody utilizes without thinking very much about it; it is something that comes out of a tap or line to be used as needed. The professional water-treatment specialist understands the true complexity of the subject, but *anyone* involved in corrosion and materials work should learn at least the fundamentals, if only to know when to get professional help.

Pure water is not really corrosive, except to anodic metals at temperatures above at least 200°C (392°F). The corrosive action so often encountered is due to gases and minerals dissolved in the water.

18.1 WATER CHEMISTRY

In order to evaluate properly the characteristics of a water proposed for some specific use, a complete water analysis must be available. Table 18.1 is the basic minimum information which must be obtained, and the units in which it is expressed to facilitate evaluation.

Table 18.1   Characteristics Measured in Basic Water
Analysis

Variable Measured	Units
TDS (total dissolved solids)*	ppm (parts per million)
Ca (calcium hardness)*	ppm as Ca carbonate
Mg (magnesium hardness)	ppm as Ca carbonate
TH (total hardness, Ca + Mg)	ppm as Ca carbonate
PA (phenolphthalein alkalinity)	ppm as Ca carbonate
MOA (methyl orange alkalinity)*	ppm as Ca carbonate
pH*	pH
Cl (chlorides)	ppm Cl
SO_4 (sulfates)	ppm SO_4
SiO_2 (silica)	ppm SiO_2
Fe (iron)	ppm Fe
DO (dissolved oxygen)	ppm O_2

*Indicates use in scaling calculations; see 18.2.

For a water sample to be truly representative for analysis, the sample bottle
must be filled to the brim and tightly capped (to prevent loss of volatile
species, such as carbon dioxide, or ingress of gaseous contaminants, such as
air). The analytical data obtained can be used to diagnose the scaling characteristics and probable corrosivity of water.

18.2 SCALING INDEXES

Table 18.2 provides the data from which scaling characteristics can be estimated from the analytical data for pH, TDS, Ca, and MOA. Using these data,
one can calculate *either* the pH_s (pH of saturation of calcium carbonate) or the
temperature at which scaling will occur at the *observed* pH.

The scale usually comprises calcareous deposits (mixtures of calcium and
magnesium carbonates). The calculations are based on Ryznar's modification
of the *Langelier index*. In current terminology, the relationships are

$$LSI = pH - pH_s$$

where LSI stands for Langelier saturation index, and

$$RSI = 2pH_s - pH$$

where RSI stands for Ryznar stability index. The relationships, together with
the calculation of pH_s, are detailed in Table 18.2.

Table 18.2 Scaling by Water

$$LSI = pH - pH_s$$

where 0 indicates balanced conditions
  + indicates scale formation
  − indicates scale dissolution

$$RSI = 2pH_s - pH$$

where values > 7.5 indicate scale dissolution

$$pH_s = (9.3 + A + B) - (C + D)$$

Total Solids	A	Ca as CaCO₃	C	MO Alk.	D
50–400	0.1	10–11	0.6	10–11	1.0
400–1000	0.2	12–13	0.7	12–13	1.1
		14–17	0.8	14–17	1.2
Temp., °F*	B	18–22	0.9	18–22	1.3
		23–27	1.0	23–27	1.4
32–34	2.6	28–34	1.1	28–35	1.5
35–42	2.5	35–43	1.2	36–44	1.6
44–48	2.4	44–55	1.3	45–55	1.7
50–56	2.3	56–69	1.4	56–69	1.8
58–62	2.2	70–87	1.5	70–88	1.9
64–70	2.1	88–110	1.6	89–110	2.0
72–80	2.0	111–138	1.7	111–139	2.1
82–88	1.9	139–174	1.8	140–176	2.2
90–98	1.8	175–220	1.9	177–220	2.3
100–110	1.7	230–270	2.0	230–270	2.4
112–122	1.6	280–340	2.1	280–340	2.5
124–132	1.5	350–430	2.2	360–440	2.6
134–146	1.4	440–550	2.3	450–550	2.7
148–160	1.3	560–690	2.4	560–690	2.8
162–178	1.2	700–870	2.5	700–880	2.9
178–194	1.1	880–1000	2.6	890–1000	3.0
194–210	1.0	1000–1200	2.7	1000–1200	3.1

*To convert degrees Fahrenheit to degrees Celsius, the formula is: $\frac{5}{9}$ (°F−32) = °C.

Note: Use *actual* pH of water when calculating B, the temperature at which the water will scale.

Source: From *Corrosion Basics—An Introduction*, NACE, Houston, 1984. Reproduced with permission.

If the LSI is *positive*, it indicates the water is saturated with calcium carbonate at the observed temperature and pH and is therefore prone to scaling (because calcium carbonate has *decreasing* solubility with rising temperature). A *negative* LSI shows a tendency to *dissolve* scale (or corrode cement or concrete or other calcareous material). It should be noted that the LSI has little to do with corrosion of metals (although calcareous deposits may be protective), because of occluded salts and variations in permeability to dissolved oxygen(DO).

The RSI is simply a more meaningful refinement of the LSI. Values below 7.5 indicate increasing scaling tendencies. The LSI and RSI techniques are applicable to potable waters (see further below) and other fresh waters.

Two other indexes of interest are the Stiff-Davis index, or SDI, which extends the usefulness of this type of calculation to oilfield brines and other high-salinity waters, and the aggressiveness index (AI), which predicts corrosivity to cement. The formula for the latter is $AI = pH + \log (Ca \times MOA)$, with values below 12 becoming increasingly aggressive to cement.

Note again that, at the measured pH, one can calculate the temperature at which the water begins to scale, by solving for B in the equation provided in Table 18.2 for calculation of pH_s.

18.3 CORROSION OF STEEL BY WATER

In a general way, corrosion of iron and steel is proportional to the chloride content when DO is constant, and vice versa.

Corrosion of steel (cast iron is slightly more resistant in most instances) increases with chloride content of the water to reach a maximum at about 6000 ppm (Figure 18.1). Above that level, the chloride effect is offset by diminishing solubility of DO, as in seawater or brines.

On the other hand, with fresh waters particularly, the corrosion of steel is governed by DO over a broad pH range (e.g., pH 4.5 to 9.5) at relatively low temperatures (Figure 18.2). Note that corrosion rate in this figure is actually

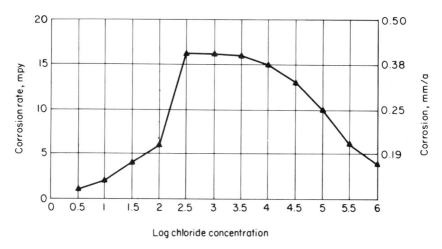

Figure 18.1   Steel vs. Chloride, pH 6–9.

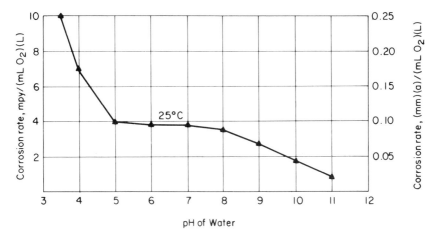

Figure 18.2 Steel: pH vs. corrosion.

expressed as mils per year (millimeters per annum) *per milliliter of DO per liter.* Below pH 4.5, the corrosion is controlled by hydrogen evolution under acid conditions; above 9.5, corrosion is suppressed by an insoluble film of ferric hydroxide.

In an *open* container, corrosion reaches a maximum at about 80°C (175°F) because of decreasing solubility of DO (Figure 18.3). However, in a *closed* container, corrosion will increase with temperature more or less indefinitely

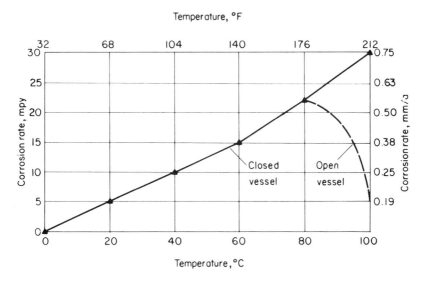

Figure 18.3 Steel: corrosion vs. temperature.

because of retention of small amounts of DO under pressure. As we will discuss further below, this is the main basis for removal of DO from boiler feedwater.

18.4 TYPES OF WATERS

Waters may be classified in terms of origin, nature, and/or utilization. Many corrosion and materials problems arise from a basic misunderstanding of nomenclature and characteristics.

18.4.1 Origin

Waters may be classified as of surface or subsurface origin. *Surface waters* comprise the rivers, lakes, and seas, which are the major sources of water for common industrial usage. *Subsurface waters* consist of waters from springs or wells and "produced water." Spring water comes to the surface from an aquifer, lifted by hydrostatic pressure. Well waters are brought forth by digging to a source. Artesian wells are those in which impermeable geological strata are perforated, allowing the water to surface by its own pressure. Other wells simply pump the water to the surface, usually using submerged pumps. Produced water is peculiar to oil- and gas-well-drilling operations, being coproduced with the hydrocarbons. It may be fossil water, entrapped for eons in the geological strata before being released by the drilling operation (as distinct from an aquifer which is replenished by drainage from surface sources or rainfall).

18.4.2 Natural Waters

Natural waters particularly are classified as *fresh, brackish,* or *salt*. Fresh water is also classified as hard or soft, although these are relative terms on a sliding scale and should be quantified according to the LSI or RSI.

1. Fresh water typically contains less than 1000 ppm of chloride ion.
   a. Soft water is low in calcium and magnesium salts, sudses easily with soap, and is difficult to rinse.
   b. Hard water is relatively high in calcium and magnesium and tends to form insoluble curds when used with conventional sodium-based soaps. Originally, water hardness was actually determined by titration with standardized soap solutions, but these have been replaced with more modern analytical techniques (e.g., titration with "versenates").

2. Brackish waters typically contain more chlorides than fresh water but less than seawater (e.g., 1000 to 10,000 ppm). Such waters are found as surface waters due to salt deposits in the ground, as tidal waters (mixed from river and seawater), and as subsurface geological brines or saline wells.

3. Seawater typically contains from 2.5 to 3.5% sodium chloride, depending on its geographical location. The salt content may increase due to surface evaporation, as in the Arabian Gulf or the Dead Sea. *Brines* are still-more-concentrated salt solutions, either natural (as in oilfield brines) or artificial (i.e., formulated for refrigeration purposes to take advantage of their low freezing point).

18.4.3 Use

From an industrial standpoint, waters are more often classified by their particular use. There are really three categories. The first (category I) involves nomenclature which clearly tells one something about the chemistry or nature of the water. In category II, there is an *implicit* (but not wholly reliable) statement about the nature of the water. In category III, the common name says really nothing about the nature or properties of the water despite the popular jargon.

Category I

Distilled water has been boiled and the vapors condensed specifically to separate it from its mineral salts. It is supposed to be pure, and its major use is in the laboratory. Even so, the actual purity depends on the efficiency of the distillation system. Triple-distilled water has the highest purity and is used in scientific work, where required.

Demineralized (DM) water has had both cations and anions removed by the action of specific ion exchange resins, substituting hydrogen ions for the cations and hydroxyl ions for the anions. The resulting water is free of almost all its mineral content except perhaps a little silica. It will contain a trace of organic species from the synthetic resin contact. In industrial use, DM water is considered to be equivalent to distilled water in quality (e.g., in nuclear reactor applications and as boiler feedwater makeup for high-pressure boilers). In fact, it can be contaminated with traces of material from the various operations involved, such as resin regeneration. The conductivity of both distilled and demineralized water is a measure of purity and can be correlated with total dissolved solids (TDS).

Potable water is fresh water of restricted mineral content (less than 250 ppm chlorides by U.S. standards; less than 350 ppm by World Health Organization standards), which has been specifically sanitized for drinking purposes

by treatment with chlorine, chlorine dioxide, ozone, or other oxidizing biocides. It is therefore free of coliform and other potentially harmful bacteria,
within the control limits of the treating system.

Raw water is a term used in some parts of the world to indicate a water
which has been disinfected by chlorination but exceeds the mineral content
stipulated for truly potable water.

Category II

Softened water is water from which all or most of the total hardness has been
deliberately removed to prevent scaling in service. There are several processes which involve either precipitation of calcium and magnesium salts or
replacing those cations with sodium ions. Hot or cold lime softening diminishes the calcium and magnesium concentrations, while Zeolite softening
replaces all cations with sodium ions (by ion exchange), raising the pH
simultaneously. Softened (and naturally soft) waters are *extremely* corrosive
unless completely deaerated, attacking even copper-base alloys.

Boiler feedwater makeup (BFWMU) is the *new* water added to a boiler. It
has been softened to some desired quality but is not yet deaerated. It may
range from partially softened to fully demineralized water, depending on the
pressure rating of the boiler.

Boiler feedwater (BFW) may be the same as the makeup water or it may be
largely returned steam condensate (or some mixture of makeup and condensate), depending on how a steam plant is operated and how much of the steam
is condensed and recovered for recirculation. In many plants, a good figure
might be 95% returned condensate and 5% makeup comprising the BFW.

Condensate, in steam plant terminology, is condensed steam. It differs
from distilled water in degree of contamination, as by dissolved iron, oxygen,
or carbon dioxide and/or entrained caustic, sodium carbonates, chlorides, and
silica. *Good-quality* condensate should have a conductivity of not more than
50 μmhos.

Desalinated water is water produced from a seawater or other saline source
after certain regimens of treatment. It is not *necessarily* a high-quality water
or even of condensate quality.

Utility water is a term sometimes used to describe a water of too high a
salinity to be potable but otherwise sanitized to a degree which permits its use
in eyebaths, safety showers, etc. However, in some cases, it might even be
seawater.

Sanitary waste implies that it is the discarded water from kitchen and
lavatory facilities only, and was probably originally a potable water (but
possibly raw or utility water).

Category III

Process water is any kind of water applied to or recovered from a chemical or other process. It may thereby contain strange contaminants.

Chilled water is a water specifically cooled for temperature control of a reaction.

Tempered water is held at some specific elevated temperature for the same purpose.

Produced water, or *formation water*, is the water phase from an oil or gas well, usually containing variable amounts of chloride ions, carbon dioxide, hydrogen sulfide, etc.

Fire water, or *fire-control water*, is any kind of water used for that purpose. It varies from potable water to seawater.

Cooling water is used to remove sensible heat from plant processes. It may be from any source and of any quality.

Wastewater may be either municipal (which may combine sanitary waste with some industrial waste) or purely industrial. Industrial wastewater may contain any and all types of organic and/or inorganic species. However, antipollution requirements are encouraging increasingly specific waste-treatment facilities to protect the environment and encourage reuse of wastewater for cooling or for BFWMU purposes.

18.5 BOILERS, STEAM, AND CONDENSATE

A boiler is a device for generating steam by heating water to the boiling point at a particular pressure. The steam generated may be used for heating (e.g., as in reboilers or calandrias) or to run engines or turbines (e.g., for generation of electricity). Fossil fuel boilers use coal or oil as fuel for combustion, while nuclear boilers utilize the sensible heat from atomic reactors to heat the water.

18.5.1 Boiler Water

In order to be nonscaling, the BFW must be softened or demineralized. In order to be noncorrosive to the steel and low-alloy-steel components from which boilers are usually constructed (nuclear plants also use steel in the secondary loops for steam), the water must be thoroughly deaerated.

The makeup water is rendered nonscaling by a means appropriate to the design and operating pressure of the boiler (e.g., Zeolite softening up to perhaps 600 psi; demineralizing at 900 psi and above). It is then partially deaerated by thermomechanical means and the last vestiges of DO removed by chemical agents (e.g., sodium sulfite or hydrazine). The chemical scavengers may be catalyzed to increase the speed of reaction with DO.

Returned condensate, which is combined with BFWMU to constitute the BFW, may be treated (e.g., polished by filtration and ion exchange) to prevent accumulation of iron or other salts in the system.

In addition to these *external* treatments, the boiler water chemistry is further controlled by internal treatments to adjust the pH and control solids precipitated in the "mud drum." An alkaline pH of the order of 9 to 10 is usually desired, and specific ratios of sodium diphosphate to trisodium phosphate are often employed to this purpose, minimizing the possibility of exposure to free caustic. Chelating agents may also be added to tie up specific cations in a harmless form.

Regardless of the degree of external softening or demineralization, enough solids will eventually accumulate in the mud drum to pose operating problems unless it is subjected to *blowdown* [or has been subjected to *all volatile treatment (AVT)*, as in nuclear applications]. This continuous or intermittent blowdown controls the residual solids. (*Note*: the terms makeup and blowdown will also be encountered in our discussion of recirculated water systems of other kinds.)

A simplified diagram of a two-drum boiler is shown in Figure 18.4.

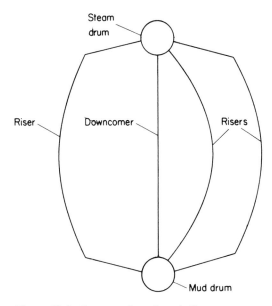

Figure 18.4 Diagram of two-drum boiler.

18.5.2 Steam

Dry steam is noncorrosive to steel. Wet steam, or mixtures of steam and water as with the watertube of a boiler, is likewise noncorrosive in the absence of contaminants. However, it is not uncommon to experience entrainment of water salts or boiler-treatment chemicals. Sodium salts may react with oxide films or with the metal itself to liberate atomic hydrogen under certain conditions. More often, they simply cause *caustic gouging* or *caustic embrittlement*.

Silica (i.e., silicon dioxide) is quite volatile and may be carried over in high-pressure steam (unless properly controlled) to form deposits on steam-driven turbines, for example, adversely affecting their mechanical balance.

18.5.3 Condensate

The steam condensate from a properly controlled boiler should likewise be noncorrosive. Unfortunately, it may be contaminated by carbon dioxide (e.g., from a high-bicarbonate makeup) or DO (e.g., by ingress to the condensate return or by improper deaeration of BFW). Corrosion in steam condensate systems is usually controlled, if required, through additions of either neutralizing or filming amines (e.g., morpholine or octadecylamine).

18.6 COOLING-WATER SYSTEMS

There are basically two kinds of cooling-water systems, once-through and recirculated. The former is employed where there is an abundant source of surface water, but is falling into disfavor as the effects of thermal pollution are recognized. (Thermal pollution is the potentially adverse effect of relatively high-temperature discharged cooling water on aquatic life.)

18.6.1 Once-Through Systems

Where there is an adequate supply of inexpensive raw water, industries may elect simply to pump water through the plant heat exchangers and return it to the source. This is permissible if thermal pollution is not a problem and if there is adequate pollution control from the chemical standpoint.

Usually, the water source must be presumed to be corrosive, since the surface waters are open to the atmosphere. In the past, some rivers had no DO (because of municipal or industrial pollution), but this condition does not usually now apply. It must be remembered that both fresh and saline waters are sufficiently corrosive to steel so that more corrosion-resistant materials must be employed. The *volume* of water circulated through such a system effectively precludes chemical inhibition (from a cost-effective standpoint).

In fresh water, galvanized steel is often adequate, but brackish or salt water requires more resistant materials (e.g., copper alloys, superstainless steels, plastic, FRP or plastic-lined steel, or concrete). Table 18.3 suggests recommended materials of construction for a variety of equipment in both fresh- and seawater once-through systems.

In once-through systems, chlorination is usually necessary to control biological growth such as bacteria, slime, marine organisms.

Table 18.3   Materials of Construction for Once-Through Systems

Equipment	Fresh Water	Seawater
Screens	Steel (bare or coated) Alloy 400	FRP or coated cast iron body, Alloy 400 screens
Filters	FRP or coated steel; Cu or Alloy 400 elements	Same
Pumps	Stainless, bronze, cast iron; SS impeller	Ni-resist with Alloy 400 impeller
Chlorinators	PVC- or Saran-lined steel	Same
Piping	Cement-lined cast iron or concrete underground; FRP, Cu or galvanized steel above	Concrete underground; FRP or 90–10 Cu-Ni
Valves	Bronze or stainless	Alloy 400 or bronze
Exchangers		
		Seawater in Tubes Only
Tubes	Cu, Admiralty, SS	Ti, Cu-Ni, 625, C276
Tubesheets	Bronze, SS	Ti, Ti-clad, Bronze
Baffles	Steel*, bronze, SS	Same metal as shell
Tie-rods	Steel*, bronze, SS	"
Shell	Steel*, Cu, SS, FRP	Metal† or FRP
Heads	FRP, bronze, lined steel	FRP or 90–10 Cu-Ni

*Only with water in tubes and steel compatible with process side.
†Any metal and alloy compatible with process.

18.6.2 Recirculated Systems

When water is in short supply or when its chemistry must be rigorously controlled, recirculated systems are employed. These may be considered in two categories, closed and open.

Closed Recirculated Systems

In a closed recirculated system, there is no makeup after the initial charge (except to replace accidental leakage) and no blowdown. Since there is no opportunity for evaporation either, the water chemistry can be established and easily maintained at the initial charge. These systems are exemplified by the automobile radiator and by engine jacket cooling systems.

These systems may be treated either by rendering them anaerobic (if free of bacterial contamination) or by use of either oxidizing or nonoxidizing inhibitors. The cost of treatment, including softening and pH control if required or desirable, is minimal.

The sensible heat which would otherwise accumulate in the closed loop is removed either in air-cooled heat exchangers or in water-to-water exchangers cooled by an external cooling-water system.

Bactericidal treatment may be required, using a *nonoxidizing* biocide such as hexamethylene biguanide, if sulfate-reducing bacteria would otherwise be a potential problem.

Open Recirculated Systems

Open recirculated systems use ponds, fountains, or cooling towers to dissipate sensible heat by evaporative cooling. All of these types involve constant air saturation as well as some concentration of water-borne solids in the circulating water. Such systems are inevitably corrosive to steel (unless suitably inhibited) and potentially scaling unless the hardness, pH, and alkalinity are also controlled. Fortunately, as discussed below, they are usually amenable to economical treatment, unlike the once-through system with its higher water usage, especially if cooling towers are employed.

In a cooling tower system, the process equipment is cooled by the recirculated water, and the warmed water is then cooled by being sprayed over the tower packing while air is blown or drawn through the cycle water (Figure 18.5). The total amount of water actually *used* is limited to that lost by evaporation *plus* the blowdown established to limit the buildup of salts and solids in the system. The extent of the soluble salt concentration is expressed as *cycles of concentration*, which is the ratio of chlorides in the blowdown to those in the makeup (or the ratio of makeup to blowdown in liters per minute

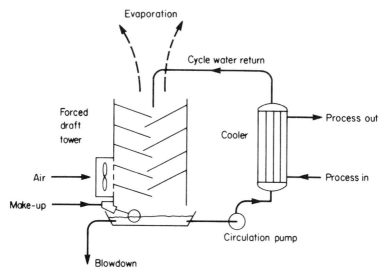

Figure 18.5 Diagram of cooling tower.

(gallons per minute). For example, if three volumes of water were to be boiled away in a pan until only one volume of water remained, the residual water would contain three times the soluble salts of the original charge, analogous to three cycles of concentration.

The amount of water evaporated in a cycle water system is determined by the circulation rate (CR) and the heat load on the system (which is indicated by the temperature difference (ΔT) in degrees Fahrenheit* between the cool water from the basin or sump and the warm water returning to the tower from the plant). The evaporation rate (ER) is then

$$\text{ER} = \text{CR} \times \Delta T/1000$$

while the cycles of concentration C, makeup (MU), and blowdown (BD) are related as follows:

$$\text{MU} = \text{ER} + \text{BD}$$

$$C = \frac{\text{MU}}{\text{BD}} = \frac{\text{ER} + \text{BD}}{\text{BD}}$$

$$\text{BD} = \frac{\text{ER}}{C - 1}$$

---

*To obtain SI equivalents, measure CR in liters per minute, ΔT in degrees Celsius, and divide ΔT by 555.5; 1 gpm $\approx$ 3.8 L/min.

Thus, for a cycle water system requiring 5000 gallons per minute (gpm) circulation and a ΔT of 15°F, the ER would be 75 gpm. To maintain four cycles of concentration (which is a good working value), the BD = 75/3 or 25 gpm, and MU would be 100 gpm. Note that this system only *uses* 100 gpm, while a once-through system would use the entire circulation rate of 5000 gpm. Actually, water-treatment chemicals need only be replaced in accordance with the *blowdown* rate. This feature is what makes open recirculated systems preferable when chemical treatment is required and closed systems are impractical.

In most such systems (water chemistry permitting), the optimum savings are effected at four to six cycles (Figure 18.6). The additional savings from a higher number of cycles is usually offset by the increasing difficulty of coping with higher dissolved salt and hardness concentrations.

Note that because of the warm temperatures and constant air scrubbing in the tower, the water is not only corrosive but also a breeding ground for slime and algae introduced from air-borne spores. There is also a tendency to pick up particulate matter from the air.

Open recirculated systems must usually be corrosion-inhibited (if steel-tubed condensers are to be successfully employed; see Chapter 34), treated with biocides to control biological growths, and chemically treated to control scale and deposits. The cost of such treatment must be balanced against the obvious savings in water consumption. Such water treatment is an area in which even the competent corrosion engineer may need help from a specialized consultant or from a professional water-treating company.

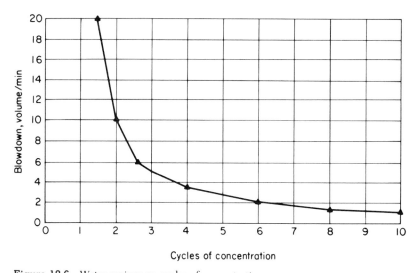

Figure 18.6 Water savings vs. cycles of concentration.

Table 18.4   Materials of Construction for Cooling Tower Systems

Equipment	Inhibited Water*
Filters	FRP or cast iron
Pumps	Steel or cast iron volutes, bronze or SS impellers
Chlorinators	PVC- or Saran-lined steel
Piping	Carbon steel
Valves	Cast iron or steel, SS trim

	Exchangers	
	Water on Shell	Water in Tubes
Tubes	Steel (if process-compatible), CU, Admiralty, SS, or nickel alloys	Same
Tubesheets	Steel (if process is compatible), Cu, SS, or Ni (solid or clad)	Same
Baffles	Steel; other	Metal compatible with process
Tie-rods	Steel; other	Metal compatible with process
Shell	Carbon steel	Metal compatible with process
Heads	Metal compatible with process	FRP, lined or coated steel

*Uninhibited aerated water is handled the same as once-through (see Table 18.3).

Modern pollution control requirements are limiting some previously useful chemicals, such as chromate-based inhibitors, or requiring that they be removed from the blowdown. Fortunately, new treatments are being constantly studied and commercialized, although they may be of limited applicability in the more aggressive saline waters. The choice between corrosion inhibition vs. resistant materials of construction is simply one of economics and pollution abatement considerations.

Table 18.4 suggests suitable materials of construction for freshwater-type open recirculated systems.

18.7 BEHAVIOR OF MATERIALS

Some generalizations are given below which characterize the behavior of engineering materials in water service.

18.7.1 Carbon and Low-Alloy Steels

With the exception of steam condensate (in which an A-242 weathering steel may show some advantage), carbon and low-alloy steels show approximately equivalent corrosion in water. Corrosion is primarily under the control of DO (or other oxidizing agents, such as chlorine or dissolved sulfur) over a broad pH range, as shown in Figure 18.2. Corrosion reaches a maximum at about 6000 ppm chloride ion. Generally speaking, steel should *not* be used in uninhibited water systems. However, a useful life is obtained if the water is naturally anaerobic (with no bacterial action) as from artesian wells, *or* in essentially closed systems (e.g., fire-control water storage, hot-water heating). In closed systems, the water becomes self-deaerated by superficial corrosion and noncorrosive until or unless fresh DO effects entry to the system, or unless sulfate-reducing bacteria (SRBs) provide dissolved sulfur as an alternative corrosive agent.

18.7.2 Cast Iron

Cast iron has an inherently better resistance than steel in most natural waters because the graphite flakes tend to aid in the adherence of a more protective rust film. The resistance is still frequently inadequate for long-term service, and modern usage usually calls for internal cementitious coatings or organic films. Soft aggressive waters cause graphitic corrosion of cast iron, as do acidic waters (e.g., coal-mine runoff).

18.7.3 Zinc

Zinc has good resistance in its own right to many natural waters. However, because of its anodic nature, it corrodes preferentially in contact with steel. Galvanized steel resists freshwater attack *until* the substrate is exposed, after which the zinc coating corrodes preferentially to protect the steel. The corrosion rate of zinc is linear with time, so protection is a function of the thickness of the zinc, whether galvanized or electroplated.

Galvanized steel lacks adequate resistance in high-chloride waters or seawater. Further, in some fresh waters of specific chemistry (e.g., a high bicarbonate-to-chloride ratio), the potential of zinc becomes cathodic to steel and accelerates corrosion of the substrate. Accelerated pitting of some hot-water systems has been ascribed to this reversal of potential, and an unproven water should be tested at about 80°C (175°F) to determine the possible occurrence of this phenomenon.

18.7.4 Aluminum

Aluminum and many of its alloys have good resistance in many natural waters. However, resistance is affected by water chemistry and flow conditions. High-chloride waters will pit aluminum under stagnant conditions. Aluminum is also subject to attack under deposits by oxygen cell effects and under organic matter *(poultice corrosion)*. It is corroded by heavy-metal salts from other equipment upstream (cementation). It has, however, good resistance to steam condensate, in the absence of appreciable iron or caustic contamination.

18.7.5 Copper Alloys

Except for dezincification of brasses containing more than 15% zinc (unless specifically inhibited), copper and its alloys are the most reliable and cost-effective alloys for many water services. Copper, red brass, Admiralty brasses, aluminum brass, aluminum bronze, and cupronickels, in that order, are used for waters of increasing salinity and/or velocity. In seawater, 90−10 cupronickel with iron should be specified for condenser tubing in most cases where a copper alloy is desired.

Note that *soft* waters can be highly corrosive to copper alloys in the presence of DO, and superstainless steels or plastic construction is recommended.

18.7.6 Stainless Steels

Stainless steel will resist water. It is the dissolved salt that causes problems. Any 12% chromium stainless steel will resist condensate or even BFWMU if the water is totally deaerated. The 18−8 grades are prone to pitting (and SCC at moderately elevated temperatures), even in potable water under stagnant conditions, although aerated high-velocity seawater can be handled in S31600 (provided it is kept flowing!). The 18−8 grades can be used for water-cooled condensers if the tubewall temperature does not exceed 50°C (125°F).

Optimum reliability in water service is provided by some of the superferritic grades and by the superstainless grades of the 20Cr−25Ni−4Mo variety previously described.

18.7.7 Nickel Alloys

Alloy NO4400 is widely used for long-term freshwater and many seawater applications. NO6625 or N10276 are used for seawater-cooled condensers where the process-side conditions are incompatible with copper or titanium alloys.

18.7.8 Titanium and Zirconium

Titanium is one of the most cost-effective materials for seawater applications, especially as condenser tubing. Zirconium is equally good, although more expensive and used only where process-side conditions require. Zircalloys find application in water-cooled nuclear reactors.

18.7.9 Plastics and Elastomers

Within their inherent temperature and pressure limitations, the plastic materials in general are excellent for water service. PVC, CPVC, PE, PP, and others are useful in all kinds of natural waters. FRP systems based on many resin systems (e.g., epoxy, phenolic, polyester, vinyl ester) are used where still greater mechanical strength is required. Plastic-lined steel is useful where still higher strength and temperature limits are required. Elastomers are useful to about 80°C (175°F), with EPDM withstanding even low-pressure steam.

These comments refer to natural waters. In wastewaters, both plastics and elastomers can suffer degradation by continually absorbing trace amounts of incompatible organic species (e.g., sorbic acid vs. polypropylene, aromatic hydrocarbons or chlorinated solvents vs. rubber).

18.7.10 Concrete

Portland cement–type concrete structures are suitable for water immersion if a type appropriate to the sulfate concentration, chlorides, and other chemical variants is selected. Even type I cement is suitable in seawater, as previously described.

18.8 SPECIAL INFORMATION SOURCES

In addition to the scientific and engineering publications which deal specifically with water, several water-treating companies (Betz, Nalco, and others) publish handbooks which discuss water treatment for corrosion and scale control in great detail. The technology of water treatment for industrial usage is a complex and evolutionary subject in which professional help is extremely useful.

RECOMMENDED READING

The Betz Handbook, Betz Laboratories, Inc. Philadelphia, Pa., n.d.

Nalco Chemical Company: *The Nalco Water Handbook*, McGraw-Hill, New York, 1979.

CHAPTER **19**

Corrosion by Soil

Dry soil is not corrosive. It becomes so by virtue of the water content and related water-soluble salts which allow it to function as an electrolyte. In that event, we are dealing with an immersion condition similar to that encountered in corrosion by water. Just how corrosive a soil may be to a specific material (and we are primarily concerned with steel and cast iron) depends upon the specific constituents in the soil, its degree of aeration, and its bacterial content.

19.1 TYPES OF CORROSION

Moisture transferred to the soil from the atmosphere contains specific contaminants (as discussed further in Chapter 20) and picks up specific water-soluble materials from the soil (e.g., salts of aluminum, calcium, magnesium, and sodium; sulfates, chlorides, carbonates, phosphates, silicates). For this reason, all of the types of corrosion to which construction materials are susceptible can be encountered.

Besides conventional phenomena and localized corrosion cells, however, buried structures of significant length (e.g., pipelines) are subject to *macrocell* action. Whole sections of line may become anodic to other long sections because of differences in soil chemistry, soil compaction, bacterial action, and thermal effects, as by gas compression heating effects or downhole temperature gradients.

In addition, fluctuations in the earth's magnetic field can induce *telluric currents*, and ac power lines can induce stray currents, both of which can cause corrosion of buried structures.

19.2 FACTORS IN SOIL CORROSION

There are three factors which influence the corrosivity of soil: resistivity, chemistry, and physical characteristics.

19.2.1 Resistivity

Resistivity is the property of a material, as opposed to *resistance*, which is the resultant property of a physical entity. For example, copper has a certain resistivity, but a piece of copper wire has resistance.

Soil resistivity is the net result of many chemical and physical aspects of the soil. It is determined by passing a known current I through a known volume of soil (volume = depth $\times$ width $\times$ length) and measuring the difference in voltage E due to current flow. By Ohms' law,

$$R = \frac{E}{I}$$

and resistivity (ρ) is

$$\rho = R \times \frac{w \times d}{l}$$

If R is expressed in ohms, area in square centimeters, and length in centimeters, it will be observed that resistivity must be expressed in ohm-centimeters. For example, seawater has a resistivity of 25 to 75 ohm-cm; only a specific *volume* of seawater has so many ohms of resistance.

This concept is useful in categorizing soils because of the interaction of chemical and physical effects cited. Generally, soil is considered highly corrosive if its resistivity is 2000 ohm-cm or less. Between 2000 and 10,000 ohm-cm, soil is moderately corrosive, while at 10,000 to 20,000 ohm-cm it is normally considered only slightly corrosive. In everyday life, CP is recommended for buried steel pipelines if the soil is below 25,000 ohm-cm. Rare instances have been cited of corrosion in 100,000 ohm-cm soil.

19.2.2 Soil Chemistry

As mentioned above, different types of soil can contain a wide variety of chemical species. Some of these will not only influence the electrolytic nature of the soil but will also have specific ion effects (e.g., chlorides for pitting or SCC, sulfides for SSC). Varying amounts of water may be available from water-table or atmospheric ingress. DO will vary with physical condition and with effects of decaying organic material and bacterial action.

Some investigators indicate that the overall redox potential (i.e., the potential which is the net result of all the possible oxidation and reduction reactions in the soil) is very important. So, of course, is the pH.

19.2.3 Composition and Condition

Soil may consist of different components, perhaps even in different strata. Sand, clay, loam, and rock are four major categories. Any of these, with the exception of nonporous rock, can have varying degrees of moisture and chemical contaminants. Wet salty sand is a totally different environment than dry desert sand.

Table 19.1 Assessment of Overall Soil Corrosivity to Steel

Parameter	Points	Parameter	Points
1. pH		4. Soil Type	
0–2	5	Clay (blue-gray)	10
2–4	3	Clay and stone	5
4–8.5	0	Clay	3
8.5+	3	Silt	2
		Clean sand	0
2. Chloride		5. Soil Resistivity	
1000+	10	<1000	10
500–1000	6	1000–1500	8
200–500	4	1500–2500	6
50–200	2	2500–5000	4
0–50	0	5000–10,000	2
		10,000+	0
3. Redox ($Cu:CuSO_4$)		6. Overall Rating	
Negative	5	Severe	15+
0–50	4	Appreciable	10–15
50–100	3.5	Moderate	5–10
100+	0	Mild	0–5

Ordinary earth will also have different degrees of compaction. Freshly excavated and filled trenches will have far more accessibility to moisture and oxygen than undisturbed soil.

19.2.4 Overall Corrosivity

Rather than judging a soil solely by its resistivity, several authorities have devised tables for overall rating of soil according to the several parameters described above (Table 19.1). This table gives different arithmetical point values for the several parameters, which can be totaled for an overall appraisal of the soil corrosivity. The parameters usually considered include pH, chloride content, redox potential, type of soil, and soil resistivity. Point allocations are higher with the more corrosive conditions, with high cumulative scores indicating greater corrosivity (e.g., 15+ indicating severe conditions, 0 to 5 mild corrosion only).

19.3 BEHAVIOR OF SPECIFIC MATERIALS

The behavior of different materials of construction in soil will vary with the basic chemistry of the soil. We can, however, make certain generalizations and point out specific problems.

19.3.1 Steels

Basically, steel items should not be exposed to soil without corrosion control measures as described below. This is because steel can be rapidly attacked under even temporarily aggravated conditions and because corrosion control is a very small part of the installed cost. Also, a buried structure or a tank bottom is going to be pretty inaccessible for a long time, if a useful life is planned. Steels are also susceptible to corrosion by external influences (stray currents, telluric currents, galvanic effects, etc.). As described further in Chapter 37, steels are best protected underground by a combination of coatings and CP.

19.3.2 Cast Iron

Historical records indicate that cast iron pipe in the soil may last as little as 5 or as much as 75 years, depending upon specific conditions. Cast iron is inherently more resistant than steel, because of the more adherent nature of the rust formed under normal conditions. Nevertheless, it can suffer graphitic corrosion in soils of low pH or saturated with soft aggressive waters. In modern usage, underground cast iron is conventionally protected by barrier coatings. CP is somewhat difficult because of the problem of establishing electrical continuity across the mechanical joints of cast iron pipe.

19.3.3 Zinc

Zinc may be quite resistant or poorly so, depending upon specific soil chemistry. From a practical standpoint, galvanized steel is not a good selection for underground service because the zinc coating is very thin and anodically active to everything else around it. This does not preclude the use of galvanized steel structural legs for powerlines and the like, which can be further protected by coatings.

19.3.4 Aluminum

Aluminum gives useful service underground provided it is protected from galvanic demands and specific ion effects (e.g., chlorides). Great care must be taken in the use of CP, because of the possibility of generating high alkali concentrations on this amphoteric material.

19.3.5 Stainless Steels

All of the stainless steels are subject to pitting by high chlorides and/or oxygen concentration cells. Stray current effects are inherent in the use of dc reverse-polarity welding of 18−8 lines in the ground. Austenitic stainless steel piping should be coated and cathodically protected for underground installations. One never knows when corrosive conditions will arise, and the localized attack characteristic of 18−8 can lead to rapid penetration.

19.3.6 Lead

Lead sheathing has been successfully used in underground telephone cable for many years. It is generally resistant except for stray current effects, but can be corroded by specific chemical contaminants.

19.3.7 Copper Alloys

The behavior of copper alloys in soil follows along the lines discussed for water. Soft, acidic waters arise in soil from organic matter deteriorating in marshlands. Sulfate-reducing bacteria (SRB) can cause sulfide attack. If ammonia is formed by rotting of nitrogenous compounds, corrosion or SCC can ensue. Nevertheless, copper is usually satisfactory even in saline soils because of the static nature of the exposure, unless local cell action develops.

19.3.8 Concrete

The corrosion behavior of concrete in soil follows the principles described for water, especially as regards pH and sulfate effects. However, even sulfate-bearing soils are less aggressive than the corresponding waters under flowing conditions. Concrete cylinder pipe and cement-asbestos pipe have a long history of successful application in soil. It should be remembered, however, that the so-called cement bacillus (i.e., sulfate ion effects) was reported first in high-sulfate soils.

19.3.9 Plastics

Where conditions of temperature and pressure otherwise permit, plastic pipe and tanks (e.g., PE, PP, FRP) are ideal for service in soil. The major problem is mechanical damage from rock fill and other foreign objects, due to ground subsidence or surface traffic imposing a loading force against the pipe or vessel wall.

19.4 CORROSION CONTROL

All five of the standard corrosion control procedures apply, although some are more useful and prevalent than others.

19.4.1 Materials Selection

Most often, the engineer is faced with an established material such as a steel pipeline, a stainless transfer line, or a copper water or gas line. Opportunities for materials selection are limited in soil-type applications.

19.4.2 Environmental Control

Usually, the soil conditions are relatively fixed. Occasionally, the corrosivity of the soil can be lessened by mixing extraneous materials in the backfill, such as sand, lime, or water repellents.

19.4.3 Barrier Coatings

Various types of barrier coatings, usually those with a high dielectric constant and good alkali resistance, are employed in soil service. These, conjointly with CP (see below), are the major practical means of corrosion control. Their primary function is to decrease the current demand of the buried structure, facilitating CP, but they also serve to exclude specific corrosive species.

19.4.4 Electrochemical Techniques

CP, specifically, is the major means of corrosion control for underground structures, using either sacrificial anodes or an impressed current system (see Chapter 37).

19.4.5 Design

There is good and bad design of underground installations, as in other engineering works. Major aspects of good design, from the corrosion standpoint, include electrical grounding practices, allowance for thermal expansion and contraction, soil control and compaction, and the design elements inherent in the CP systems.

CHAPTER **20**

Atmospheric Corrosion

Atmospheric corrosion is the third area in which water plays a significant role, although the corrosion is also largely due to the 20% oxygen in air. The combined action of water and oxygen can be severe on the less-resistant metals and is acerbated by certain contaminants. Atmospheric corrosion is a very large part of the overall cost of corrosion, affecting consumer items such as automobiles as well as industrial plants.

20.1 TYPES OF CORROSION

All types of corrosion phenomena may be encountered, depending upon the particular materials and specific atmospheric contaminants involved. Because of the large amount of steel potentially subject to atmospheric corrosion, general corrosion is the rule. However, localized forms such as pitting, IGC, and SCC may be encountered with susceptible alloys.

The possibility of galvanic corrosion is somewhat minimized because the electrolyte available consists only of a thin film of condensed or adsorbed moisture, instead of the freely conductive volume available under immersion conditions. There is also a possibility that the accumulation of corrosion products between the mating surfaces of dissimilar metals may spread them apart and break the electrical contact. This cannot be relied on, however, and galvanic corrosion must always be considered in design for atmospheric exposures.

20.2 CONTROLLING FACTORS

Both chemical and physical factors affect behavior of materials in atmospheric exposure.

20.2.1 Chemical Factors

Oxygen

Oxygen is always available in atmospheric exposures, playing a dual role. As in immersion conditions, it functions as a cathodic depolarizer, aggravating the corrosion of iron and steel. On the positive side, it polarizes the anodic reaction of metals which form passive films, providing the good atmospheric corrosion resistance of aluminium, titanium, and the stainless steels. It can also influence the nature of complex salts, aiding in the protective nature of corrosion products on other nonferrous metals.

Water

Water (moisture) is the other overriding factor in the atmosphere. *Relative humidity* (the fraction of water contained in the air relative to the saturation value, expressed as percent) is the significant parameter. For carbon steel, there is a lower critical relative humidity of about 65%, and a second at about 88%. A marked increase in corrosion rate occurs at these values. Corrosion of steel is quite low below 50% humidity.

Although dry air is substantially noncorrosive, one should be aware that the metal surface can see *high* humidities in its vicinity (e.g., due to hygroscopic salts or adsorption in films), even though the humidity in the bulk atmosphere is low. This is a perennial problem in ballast compartments of barges or tanker ships, and also in large atmospheric storage tanks. Even in the open desert, there can be condensation of moisture on a metal surface cooled by thermal radiation. Relative humidity may be high *locally*, as in the lee of a cooling tower, despite a dry prevailing wind.

Contaminants

Contaminants are inherent in atmospheric exposure. They may consist of volatile species or particulate matter and may be either of natural origin or synthetic. Those which are most commonly encountered are as listed in Table 20.1.

Humans contaminate the atmosphere by their very presence. Our flocks and herds contribute to the ammonia content and our fires to the oxides

Table 20.1 Atmospheric Contaminants

Type	Volatile	Particles
Natural	Carbon dioxide	Sea salts (NaCl)
	Sulfur dioxide	Ashes
	Hydrogen sulfide	Dust
	Ammonia	
	Oxides of nitrogen	
Synthetic	Carbon dioxide	Coal dust
	Sulfur dioxide	Fly ash
	Sulfur trioxide	Smoke
	Chlorine	Fumes
	Hydrogen chloride	
	Oxides of nitrogen	

of carbon, sulfur, and nitrogen. Industry adds the more aggressive acidic species. Particulate matter such as elemental sulfur, coal dust, and fly ash (from combustion of coal) can *catalyze* certain corrosion reactions to promote atmospheric corrosion.

20.2.2 Physical Conditions

The degree of shelter from particulate fallout; orientation relative to sunshine, rainfall, and prevailing wind; even the time of year of initial exposure can affect initial and ultimate corrosion rates.

20.3 TYPES OF ATMOSPHERES

Although meteorologists classify air systems as to temperature and moisture (e.g., polar, temperate, tropical; desert, marine), corrosion specialists have traditionally classified exposure conditions as *rural, marine, industrial,* and *indoor.*

A rural atmosphere traditionally was that of the inland farm. Marine atmospheres are associated with coastal areas of up to several miles inland, at least. Industrial atmospheres originally meant the coal-polluted atmospheres of commercial cities. An indoor exposure suggested the temperature, humidity, and freedom from contamination of an office or warehouse. Even in the original context, it is evident that there is no clear line of demarcation between these categories.

Thanks to increasing concern over the environment, the atmosphere is generally less polluted today. Nevertheless, there can be industrial pollution of rural atmospheres, which may also have routinely high humidities. Mixtures of marine and industrial effects are common in many areas, each type of contaminant aggravating the other. Whether marine atmospheres effectively cease 100 m from the shore or 10 km inland depends upon the prevailing winds, their *fetch* (the distance traversed over water at speed), and the height of the local surf.

Indoor atmospheres may be as pristine as a controlled-atmosphere room for precision watchmaking or as severe as those around a pickling bath in a steel mill. Really, any atmospheric condition should be defined in terms of temperature, humidity, and contaminants *or* its corrosivity quantified in relation to the materials of interest (e.g., steel, zinc, aluminum). One should always consider special circumstances such as cooling-tower drift or spray, or spills or releases of water or chemicals.

20.4 CORROSION CONTROL

20.4.1 Materials Selection

This approach is used fairly often, although the materials of construction are often dictated by the end use of the artifact.

20.4.2 Environmental Control

Such an approach is used only in the case of air-conditioned buildings or special installations for finished machining operations.

20.4.3 Barrier Coatings

Paints and coatings are the major corrosion control technique employed against atmospheric corrosion.

20.4.4 Electrochemical Techniques

CP in the conventional sense is not applicable to atmospheric corrosion because there is no bulk electrolyte to convey current. However, metallic coatings of an anodic nature relative to the substrate (e.g., zinc or cadmium on steel), as well as zinc-pigmented paint systems, will confer CP to the underlying metal at scratches, faults, or holidays in the coating.

20.4.5 Design

While certain metals and alloys have their own characteristic behavior in the atmosphere, proper design is important in many cases. For example, stainless steel or anodized aluminum in architectural applications can behave in a very disappointing manner unless the design permits regular washing or cleaning. Dirt or other films can cause pitting as well as unsightly stains. Weathering steels must be boldly exposed (i.e., with no crevices) to develop their characteristic protective oxide film.

20.5 SPECIFIC MATERIALS

Following is a brief résumé of the important properties of specific metals and alloys in atmospheric exposure.

20.5.1 Magnesium

Despite its very anodic nature, magnesium will resist mild atmospheric exposure. It is used for ladders and other lightweight structural assemblies (e.g., in lighter-than-air craft).

20.5.2 Aluminum

Aluminum may often be freely exposed to the atmosphere, as with vessels, tank trucks, aircraft, etc. Performance will vary with the alloy and heat treatment (IGC and SCC may be problems in industrial or marine atmospheres) and with specific contaminants. Even in apparently similar marine atmospheres, there may be as much as a tenfold difference in susceptibility to pitting between different alloy and location combinations. Aluminum is amphoteric, being attacked under both acidic and alkaline conditions. However, it is useful in hydrogen sulfide– and sulfur dioxide–type atmospheres. Chlorides are conducive to pitting and SCC, and aluminum alloys are very subject to under-deposit or poultice attack. Anodizing, by chemical or electrochemical means, will reinforce the surface oxide film and improve performance in atmospheric exposure. Aluminum is also successfully used as a hot-dipped coating and as metallic pigment for paints and coatings, as well as a metallized surface for some marine applications.

20.5.3 Iron and Steel

Except in the most innocuous atmospheres, iron and steel must be protected from corrosion by one of several means. Temporary rust preventatives, painting, galvanizing, and other protective coatings may be employed, depending upon the severity of the atmosphere and the required performance or life.

There is a group of low-alloy steels of relatively high strength, known as *weathering steels* (ASTM A-242), which form self-protective rust films when *boldly* exposed to uncontaminated atmospheres. An example is U.S. Steel's Corten. Such steels are used for structural purposes and rolling stock, unpainted, where advantage can be taken both of their higher strength and improved corrosion resistance, as compared with carbon steel. They will not resist contaminated industrial or industrial-marine atmospheres. Crevices, as in riveted lapped joints, must be sealed with some sort of mastic against ingress of atmospheric moisture.

20.5.4 Zinc

Zinc has useful resistance in mild atmospheric exposures. It is used primarily as hot-dipped galvanizing and as a paint pigment, but electroplated zinc is also employed. In ordinary atmospheres, corrosion is linear with time and the degree of protection of the steel substrate is a function of thickness of zinc, regardless of the method of application. The corrosion rate is quite low until the steel is exposed, when galvanic effects take over, but corrosion will be exacerbated by acidic or alkaline species (zinc also being amphoteric). Galvanizing is inadequate for long-term marine atmospheric exposure.

20.5.5 Cadmium

Cadmium is actually better than zinc, both in inherent resistance and as a sacrificial plating. However, it is only available as an electroplate in thin films and is therefore inadequate except for mild indoor service.

20.5.6 Lead

The only practical application is as terneplate, a 4:1 lead-tin alloy used for roofing applications.

20.5.7 Copper

Copper and its alloys in mild atmospheres take on a protective patina, known as *verdigris* (French for "green-gray"). High-strength copper or copper alloys are susceptible to SCC due to trace amounts of ammonia. All acid fumes are corrosive to copper because of the synergistic effect of atmospheric oxygen and moisture. Hydrogen sulfide in the air will cause severe corrosion of copper under heavy black deposits, but yellow brasses may form a protective film.

20.5.8 Stainless Steels

Stainless steels will remain bright in uncontaminated atmospheres. Even the austenitic grades, however, can rust and pit if chloride contamination is prevalent or if dirt or deposits are allowed to accumulate on the surface. Continued cleanliness is the key to successful performance.

20.5.9 Higher Alloys

The high-nickel alloys (e.g., N06625, N10276) and titanium and its alloys should remain bright, retaining even a mirror finish, in atmospheric exposure.

20.6 SPECIAL PROBLEMS

There are three special problems, arising from or akin to atmospheric corrosion, which should be mentioned.

20.6.1 Threaded Fasteners

Because of the stresses and crevices inherent in a nut-and-bolt assembly, corrosion of steel is greatly aggravated in aggressive atmospheres. Cadmium-plated steel is useful only for indoor and noncorrosive service. Galvanized steel bolts perform well in mild to moderate atmospheric service, but even cooling-tower spray (let alone marine situations) quickly causes corrosion. In such fasteners, "freezing" of the nut causes problems, perhaps long before metal wastage itself is significant. Hot-dip aluminized bolts (e.g., Bethalume) are superior in severe industrial-marine atmospheres. *Properly* coated bolts (e.g., polyimide and PTFE over cadmium-plated steel, Xylan) are an acceptable and economical alternate in most cases.

20.6.2 Wet Insulation

Wet insulation holds a reservoir of available moisture on the metal surface which, together with the permeability of air, causes severe attack [up to several *tenths* of an inch per year (200 to 300 mpy)] on steel. With other specific contaminants, it can cause SCC of high-strength copper alloys and ESCC of 18−8 stainless steels. Aluminum is rapidly attacked in the presence of chlorides or alkaline contaminants.

20.6.3 Cryogenic Plants

Cryogenics relates to very low temperature operations, in which two types of problems are encountered. First of all, any structural members which are fastened to the vessels and extend out through the insulation are chilled by the service temperatures. Moisture tends to condense and freeze on the chilled surfaces. The immediately adjacent areas, as well as the frozen areas which thaw during shutdown, are subject to high rates of attack. High-quality coating systems are required to withstand corrosion in near-freezing zones.

In some vessels, the top may be at subzero temperatures but the bottom at 40 to 80°C (105 to 175°F). In such cases, atmospheric moisture is drawn in through the insulation to freeze on the colder parts. Some of it melts (all of it during shutdown) and runs down behind the insulation to cause severe corrosion of steel. Steel and low-alloy-steel vessels in low-temperature service should be coated with a good quality, heavy-duty paint system (e.g., a heavy-duty catalyzed epoxy) before the insulation is applied.

CHAPTER **21**

Oxidizing Acids

Because the corrosion of metals to their ions necessarily entails oxidation (i.e., the loss of electrons), there is some confusion over what constitutes corrosion under "oxidizing" conditions. Acids, after water, are the most common corrosives, and it is customary to classify them as either oxidizing or reducing acids.

With a reducing acid, while the anodic oxidation of the metal is occurring, the cathodic reaction is primarily the reduction of hydrogen ions to atomic, then molecular, hydrogen. This is exemplified by the evolution of hydrogen by zinc in dilute hydrochloric acid.

In an oxidizing acid, the cathodic reaction is the reduction of the acidic anion rather than hydrogen evolution. For example, brown oxides of nitrogen are liberated by the reaction of dilute to moderate concentrations of nitric acid on steel.

It is important to note, however, that the characteristics of a metal-acid reaction are also influenced by the nature of the metal component. For example, boiling 55% sulfuric acid is a reducing acid to steel or 18−8, liberating hydrogen, while it is oxidizing to the cast silicon-nickel alloy, the sulfate ion being reduced to sulfur dioxide and hydrogen sulfide (with elemental sulfur being formed as a consequence of their interaction). This is in accord with the generality that any oxidizing agent can be a reducing agent in the presence of a stronger oxidant.

In some combinations (e.g., 18−8 vs. dilute sulfuric acid), oxidizing cations like ferric or cupric ions move the redox potential in an oxidizing direction by providing an alternative cathodic reaction to hydrogen evolution. We then have oxidizing conditions although not, strictly speaking, an oxidizing acid.

Solutions of oxidizing acid salts (e.g., ammonium nitrate) act like dilute solutions of the parent acid.

In general, oxidizing acids tend to corrode nonpassivating metals (e.g., copper) rather than those which form a passive oxide film (e.g., titanium, aluminum). Reducing acids are sometimes *more* aggressive to the normally passive metals than to active metals, because of the reaction of nascent hydrogen with the oxide film or direct hybriding of the metals itself, as with titanium, zirconium, and tantalum. Some of the more important oxidizing acids are discussed in detail below.

21.1 NITRIC ACID

Nitric acid is not only a strong mineral acid but a powerful oxidizing agent, even in dilute solutions. Most nitric acid is manufactured by a process involving oxidation of ammonia to give a product of about 60% concentration. This is purified and concentrated to give reagent grade, chemically pure acid of 70% concentration. Very strong acid in the 90 to 100% range can be made by dehydrating weaker solutions with concentrated sulfuric acid. Acid above about 85% concentration is known as *fuming nitric acid* because it gives off red or white oxides of nitrogen (e.g., nitrogen tetroxide). The corrosion characteristics of very strong nitric acid are somewhat different from those of more dilute concentrations because of an excess of nitronium ions (NO_2^+) over hydronium ions (H_3O^+).

The following discussion relates to the corrosivity of pure nitric acid to the common materials of construction, except where otherwise noted. Contaminants such as halogens, halides, or oxidizing cations can profoundly alter the expected corrosion behavior.

21.1.1 Materials of Construction

Aluminum

Aluminum and its alloys have good resistance to the fuming acids above 95% concentration. The alloys most frequently used are A91100, A93003, and A95052. It is important not to permit localized dilution, as by leakage or by ingress of moist air, as this will cause very rapid attack.

Iron and Steel

Iron and steel, even when "passivated" by cold concentrated nitric acid with no evolution of brown fumes, show corrosion rates too high for practical consideration, in most instances. Very strong "mixed acid," containing less than 2% water and about 15% sulfuric acid, has been handled in steel equipment. Dilute acid attacks cast iron and steel very rapidly. The relative activity of intermediate concentrations of acid can be used to differentiate low-alloy chromium steels (1 to 9%) by spot test; freshly abraded 12% chromium stainless steel is unaffected by 20% acid, being passivated rather than corroded.

Silicon Cast Irons

Silicon cast irons (e.g., 14% silicon; UNS F47003) have outstanding resistance to acids above 45% concentration to the atmospheric boiling point. The resistance *increases* with acid concentration, the rate being nearly nonexistent in strong acid at high temperatures. The corrosion resistance is due to formation of an adherent siliceous film.

Stainless Steels

Stainless steels of the ferritic type (e.g., 17% chromium stainless steels; UNS S43000) were among the first used in nitric acid service. Welding problems and the brittleness of the cast forms ultimately led to their replacement with the austenitic grades.

The austenitic stainless steels of the 18−8 variety are outstanding for their resistance to nitric acid in the annealed condition. However, the potential for IGC is high, and the low-carbon S30403 or stabilized grades (e.g., S34700) are required for welded equipment if it is not amenable to solution-annealing with a water quench. IGC can also occur, regardless of composition or heat treatment, if hexavalent chromium ions [$Cr(VI)$] accumulate in the acid to some critical concentration level.

Stainless steel tanks have been severely attacked in the *vapor* phase of strong nitric acid (e.g., 93 to 99%), apparently due to an autocatalytic effect of the nitric oxides.

Titanium

Titanium is highly resistant to dilute acid up to 60% concentration at the atmospheric boiling point. In 65 to 70% boiling acid, rates are less than 0.25 mm/yr (10 mpy). Titanium also resists fuming acid, but there is danger of violent phyrophoric reactions if the water content is less than 1% or the nitrogen dioxide more than 6%. SCC can also occur in red fuming nitric acid. Only a professional corrosion engineer should select materials for this type of service.

Other Metals

Copper and nickel alloys (except for the chromium-bearing varieties such as N06600, N06625, N10276) are rapidly attacked by even dilute nitric acid. The chromium-nickel alloys are not usually economically attractive compared with stainless steels.

Lead is nonresistant in nitric acid.

Of the noble metals, gold and platinum are resistant, but silver is rapidly attacked. However, a 3:1 mixture of hydrochloric and nitric acid (aqua regia) is the classical solution for dissolving gold, due to oxidation of the HCl to nascent chlorine.

Of the other reactive metals, tantalum has excellent resistance. Zirconium is less resistant than tantalum, except in strong acid.

Nonmetallic Materials

PTFE, plain or glass-filled, is routinely employed in nitric acid service. Carbon is a useful material, provided it is free of oxidizable binders. Other organic materials are limited by the temperature and concentration of the acid, which control its oxidizing capacity. Some suggested limitations are given in Table 21.1.

21.1.2 Handling and Storage

Following is a listing of materials of construction which are thought to constitute good engineering practice for a variety of items in concentrated nitric acid:

Tanks.   S30403; aluminum (over 90%)

Piping.   S30403

Table 21.1 Concentration and Temperature Limitations on Nonmetallic Materials in Nitric Acid Service

Material	Concentration at Ambient Temperatures 25°C (77 °F), %	Concentration at Elevated Temperature, %
PTFE	100	100 @ 260°C (500°F)
FEP	100	100 @ 200°C (392°F)
PVC (unplast.)	50	40 @ 60°C (140°F)
PE or PP	60	20 @ 40°C (104°F)
Butyl rubber	50	30 @ 60°C (140°F)
Karbate	30	10 @ 85°C (185°F)

Valves. CF3 (CF3M acceptable alternate)

Pumps. CF3; titanium

Gaskets. Spiral-wound stainless steel and PTFE

21.2 CHROMIC ACID

Chromic acid requires highly resistant metals, such as titanium, zirconium, or tantalum. Platinum is also resistant, although not economical except for special applications. Fluorinated plastics and glass, or the nonmetallic materials, are useful. The stainless steels and Ni-Cr-Mo alloys are nonresistant, and even the high-silicon cast irons (F47003) are inadequate.

21.3 CONCENTRATED SULFURIC ACID

One cannot set the limits for oxidizing characteristics of sulfuric acid independently of the materials to which it is exposed. However, it *starts* to have a definite oxidizing nature at about 5 N (25%), being reduced by N02200 or N04400. By 60%, at about 80°C (175°F), it will carbonize polyvinylidene chloride over a prolonged exposure period. At 95% and 25°C (77°F), it carbonizes FRP instantaneously.

For purposes of this discussion, we can consider concentrated sulfuric acid to be 70% or more. Dilute acid (e.g., below 25%) and the intermediate strengths between 25 and 70% will be considered in the next chapter as reducing acids, even though specific oxidizing ions or other contaminants can radically alter the corrosion characteristics.

21.3.1 Materials of Construction

Aluminum

Aluminum and other light metals are, for all practical purposes, nonresistant to concentrated acid.

Cast Iron and Steel

Cast iron and steel are just beginning to be useful at 70% concentration; 80% is a better minimum value and concentrations above 90% are routinely handled in iron and steel, *provided* velocities are below about 0.7 m/s (2 fps) for steel and below 1.5 m/s (5 fps) for cast iron, whose protective iron sulfate film is more tenacious. The *ductile* cast iron is much to be preferred for safety reasons.

Ductile cast iron, rather than ordinary gray iron, *must* be used with fuming sulfuric acid (i.e., more than 100% concentration, containing free sulfur trioxide). Otherwise, internal corrosion will occur along the graphite flakes. The gaseous products, plus iron sulfates and silica (from oxidation of silicon), can cause explosions of cast iron vessels.

In storage of concentrated acid, localized dilution by ingress of atmospheric moisture can cause attack in the vapor space, unless a desiccating vent is provided.

Silicon Iron

Silicon iron (F47003) is resistant up to the boiling point of sulfuric acid and would replace ordinary iron or steel at temperatures above about 50°C (122°F).

Lead

Lead has been a longtime favorite in the sulfuric acid industry, only recently falling somewhat into disfavor because of toxicity during joining ("lead-burning"). Depending on a sulfate film for resistance, like steel, lead is very susceptible to velocity effects [limit about 1 m/s (3.3 fps)]. Also, solubility of lead sulfate increases sharply at 95% concentration and, at lower concentrations (e.g., 80%), at about 120°C (250°F).

Austenitic 18−8 Stainless Steels

Austenitic 18−8 stainless steels are resistant to cold concentrated sulfuric acid. S30403 is routinely used for piping in sizes below 75 mm (3 in), where cast iron is not available. With increasing velocity and turbulence, higher alloys are employed (e.g., CF3M for valves, CN7M for pumps).

Copper and Nickel

Copper and nickel alloys are not used in concentrated acid. The lower alloys are nonresistant to oxidizing acids; the chromium-bearing nickel alloys are not economical in conventional applications.

Reactive Metals

Tantalum will withstand 95% acid to 175°C (350°F) and lower concentrations to the atmospheric boiling point. It is attacked by sulfur trioxide, and suffers hydrogen attack in galvanic couples. Titanium and zirconium are not resistant in concentrated acid, as defined.

Noble Metals

Gold (P00010) and platinum (P04980) have been widely used in sulfuric acid concentrators, but silver is not resistant.

Nonmetallic Materials

Pure carbon is resistant to boiling 100% acid and resists 115% acid to about 70°C (160°F). Impervious graphite (e.g., Karbate) will perform up to about 150°C (300°F) *unless* it has cemented joints, which imposes a temperature limit of 60°C (140°F).

   Glass, porcelain, stoneware, and acid-brick are useful in many applications involving hot concentrated acid.

   Fluorinated plastic (e.g., PTFE, FEP, Kynar) are restricted only by their inherent temperature limitations. Other plastics (PE, PP, PVDC, PVC) will withstand 75% acid to 50°C (120°F) and 90% acid at 30°C (85°F); above these limits, carbonization will occur. FRP, with a suitable resin, will withstand 75% acid and 25°C (77°F) maximum.

   Elastomers, other than the fluorinated variety, are limited to a maximum of 75% acid and not more than 80°C (175°F) even at 70%.

21.3.2 Handling and Storage

Following is a list of materials of construction for various items of equipment. Use of these materials is considered good engineering practice for the handling and storage of concentrated acid at ambient temperatures.

   Tanks.   Carbon steel (with drying vent); coat with baked phenolic or anodically protect if iron contamination is objectionable.

   Piping.   Ductile cast iron (S30403 in small diameter). *Note:* electric or hot-water tracing only.

   Valves.   CF3M (or CN7M for "throttling")

   Pumps.   CN7M

Gaskets.   Spiral-wound stainless steel and PTFE

Dilution tees.   PTFE- or Kynar-lined; N10276 check-valves.

RECOMMENDED READING

"Process Industries Corrosion," NACE, Houston, 1975.

CHAPTER 22

Reducing Acids

The nonoxidizing or reducing acids are the inorganic and organic acids which characteristically evolve gaseous hydrogen during the corrosion of active metals. They are corrosive to metals above hydrogen in the electromotive series only in the presence of oxygen or oxidizing agents, whose reduction substitutes for hydrogen evolution. The behavior of passive metals and alloys may be fairly unpredictable, depending on acid concentration, temperature, DO, and specific contaminants. (*Note:* The acid *gases*, carbon dioxide and hydrogen sulfide, are covered in separate chapters, although their water solutions fall into this category of reducing acids.)

22.1 INORGANIC ACIDS

This group includes the mineral acids (i.e., low concentrations of sulfuric acid, phosphoric acid) and hydrochloric acid. Other reducing acids will have similar corrosive properties.

22.1.1 Hydrochloric Acid

Hydrochloric acid is an aqueous solution of hydrogen chloride. As the concentrated acid (36%), it is a pungent liquid. The "constant boiling mixture" (CBM) is 22% at atmospheric pressure; concentrations above 22% give off hydrogen chloride to reach the CBM. Dilute solutions tend to evaporate water to reach the same value.

A highly corrosive acid in its own right, the corrosion behavior can be drastically altered by contaminants. Muriatic acid is a commercial 30% acid, heavily contaminated with dissolved ferric iron, Fe(III), salts. Many "by-product" acids are heavily contaminated. Trace amounts of chlorinated solvents or aromatic solvents profoundly influence the resistance of plastics and elastomers to hydrochloric acid. The discussion below refers specifically to pure hydrochloric acid, except where otherwise noted.

Specific Materials

1. *Aluminum and Magnesium.* The alloys of these metals are severely attacked by hydrochloric acid.

2. *Iron and Steel.* These metals are inherently nonresistant to hydrochloric acid. However, steel piping and vessels can be chemically cleaned with *inhibited* acid for a few hours at a time up to 65°C (150°F) under controlled conditions (e.g., controlled velocity, no cast iron or stainless components in the system).

3. *Stainless Steels.* Stainless steels of all kinds are incompatible with hydrochloric acid.

4. *Copper.* Copper and its alloys are attacked by hydrochloric acid in the presence of DO or oxidizing cations. Since the cupric ion is itself an oxidant, few practical applications will be found. Dealloying is also a potential problem (e.g., dezincification, dealuminumification, destannification).

5. *Lead.* Lead shows reasonable resistance in laboratory tests up to about 30% acid at 25°C (77°F) and to 20% at 100°C (212°F), but field experience has not been good. Corrosion products are quite soluble and easily washed away by flow.

6. *Nickel.* Nickel and its alloys are superior to copper but not really useful until the 30% molybdenum alloy (N10001) is employed (although Alloy N06600 may replace 18–8 stainless steels where only trace amounts of acid are encountered). Alloy B (N10001) and its derivatives will resist boiling hydrochloric acid, but *not* if traces of oxidizing agents [e.g., Fe(III)] are present. The chromium-bearing grades (e.g., N10276, N06455) will resist dilute acid plus ferric chloride, but only to intermediate temperatures.

7. *Noble Metals.* Platinum will resist concentrated acid to 300°C (570°F). However, silver and gold will withstand only room-temperature service.

8. *Reactive Metals.* Titanium is nonresistant, but zirconium will withstand concentrated acid to 107°C (225°F), provided there are no more than 50

ppm oxidizing species [e.g., Fe(III), Cu(II)] present. In the absence of oxidants, zirconium will withstand 37% acid to 120°C (250°F), 25% to 160°C (320°F), and 15% acid to 200°C (390°F), although, if not high-purity material, a sort of "weld decay" may be encountered in the HAZ. Tantalum offers useful resistance to about 175°C (345°F), but is attacked by HCl *vapors* as low as 130°C (265°F).

9. *Nonmetallic Materials.*

a. Glass and other ceramic materials are very resistant. *External* spillage or vapors corroding glass-lined steel equipment will generate nascent hydrogen, which penetrates the steel and dimerizes at the internal interface to cause internal spalling of the glass coating.

b. Rubber-lined equipment is traditional for handling HCl up to 80°C (175°F). However, organic solvent contaminants (e.g., chlorinated hydrocarbons or aromatic solvents such as benzene or toluene) can be preferentially absorbed and concentrated to cause failure either of the rubber or its adhesive.

c. Plastics (e.g., PVC, PE, PP) are resistant, and FRP tanks and piping are routinely employed to handle concentrated HCl.

Handling and Storage

Following is a listing of materials of construction for various items, which are thought to constitute good engineering applications for pure concentrated HCl with minimum risk:

Tanks.   FRP; rubber-lined steel

Piping.   FRP; polypropylene-lined steel

Valves.   Alloy B (N10001); PTFE-lined or FEP-lined

Pumps.   Alloy B: impervious graphite; PTFE-lined

Gaskets.   Rubber-asbestos

21.1.2 Hydrofluoric Acid

Both anhydrous hydrogen fluoride and its 70% water solution are commercially available. The largest usage has been as an alkylation catalyst for gasoline and in the manufacture of fluorocarbon refrigerants (e.g., Freon) and propellants. (*Note:* Hydrofluoric acid and hydrogen fluoride are extremely toxic and very dangerous to personnel, producing painful and slow-healing burns.)

Specific Materials

1. *Magnesium.* Despite its anodic nature as a general rule, magnesium will resist hydrofluoric acid up to about 2% concentration, due to a film of insoluble corrosion products. This is of academic interest only.

2. *Aluminum.* Aluminum and its alloys should not be exposed even to dilute concentrations of hydrofluoric acid.

3. *Cast Iron and Alloy Iron.* These materials should not be used in hydrofluoric acid service because of both corrosion and safety considerations.

4. *Steels.* Steels are resistant to concentrated acid (e.g., 70% minimum) up to about 65°C (150°F). This is due to a protective film of corrosion products, so velocity conditions cannot be tolerated. Hydrogen blistering may occur and welds may be preferentially attacked. *Hardened* steels are susceptible to environmental cracking (HAC).

5. *Lead.* For many years lead was the conventional material for handling HF, resisting concentrations up to 60% at 25°C (77°F). Corrosion rates are acceptable up to 25% acid and 80°C (175°F). Attack increases with acid strength, temperature, and velocity. Anhydrous hydrogen fluoride rapidly attacks lead.

6. *Copper.* Copper and its alloys are corroded to the extent that oxygen or oxidants are contained in the acid. Although not usually considered for this type of service, protective surface films may permit their use in certain processes containing HF as a reactant.

7. *Stainless Steels.* Stainless steels of all types are unreliable, being subject to pitting and/or SCC as well as general corrosion.

8. *Nickel.* Nickel 200 will resist anyhydrous HF up to about 150°C (300°F), but its usefulness in aqueous solutions is limited to nonoxidizing conditions below about 80°C (175°F).

Monel 400 has long been used for all concentrations to temperatures up to 120°C (250°F), although it is subject to SCC in the *vapors* in the presence of air.

Inconel 600 resists dilute aqueous solutions and anhydrous HF but is unreliable in intermediate concentrations due to its pitting propensities. Although used commercially in hot gaseous HF, it is not otherwise an economical choice.

The high-nickel molybdenum-bearing alloys (e.g., N10001, N10276, N06625) are not economically competitive with the lower nickel-base alloys.

9. *Precious Metals.* Silver, gold, and platinum have been used traditionally to handle hydrofluoric acid. "Fine silver" is recommended for pure HF, rather than sterling silver with its small amounts of copper, but the reverse is true in some process mixtures.

10. *Reactive Metals.*   Titanium, zirconium, and tantalum are all severely attacked by even traces of fluorides, with hydriding and embrittlement.

11. *Plastics.*   Plastics *without hydroxyl groups* are very resistant and polyethylene has replaced the traditional wax-lined glass as the laboratory container for concentrated HF. Polystyrene, methacrylates, and vinyls can be used for up to 60% acid to 50°C (120°F). Phenolformaldehyde plastics may be used to 130°C (265°F), while fluorinated plastics are resistant up to their temperature limits. Because HF has a tremendous appetite for water, it rapidly attacks hydroxylated materials like polyesters.

12. *Rubber.*   Natural rubber is limited to about 3% acid and 25°C (77°F), but the synthetic soft rubbers (e.g., Butyl, Neoprene) will withstand 60% acid to 70°C (160°F). The *compounding* is critical. For example, despite its fluorinated structure, Viton is severely attacked by anhydrous HF at room temperature.

13. *Glass.*   Glass and other siliceous ceramics are rapidly attacked by HF, as well as by fluoride contaminants in other acids.

14. *Carbon and Graphite.*   Carbon and graphite are resistant, but the *impregnated* impervious graphite (e.g., Karbate) is limited to boiling 48% acid or to 60% acid at 85°C (185°F).

15. *Wood.*   Wood is charred almost instantaneously by anhydrous HF.

Storage and Handling

Following is a listing of materials of construction for various types of equipment for storage of concentrated hydrofluoric acid at ambient temperatures, which are considered to be good engineering practice with minimum risk:

Tanks.   Steel or Alloy 400

Piping.   Alloy 400 or PTFE-lined steel

Valves.   PTFE-lined, Alloy 400, or steel with resistant trim (Alloy 400 or N08020)

Pumps.   Alloy 400

Gaskets.   Graphoil or spiral-wound Alloy 400 and PTFE

22.1.3 Phosphoric Acid

Phosphoric acid is a syrupy liquid whose process of manufacture profoundly affects its corrosion characteristics. Acid made by the old "wet" process of digestion of phosphate rock with sulfuric acid is heavily contaminated with impurities such as fluorides, chlorides, sulfates, and metal ions. Used mostly in the fertilizer industry, its corrosion characteristics are unpredictable. Acid made directly from combustion of phosphorus is much more predictable, although it too can at times be a problem.

Specific Materials

1. *Aluminum and Magnesium.* These metals are of no practical interest in phosphoric acid services.

2. *Steel and Cast Iron.* Steel and cast iron are not used for phosphoric acid service. However, a 1% solution is sometimes used as a "washcoat" to prepare a steel surface for painting, and cold syrupy phosphoric acid (e.g., 85%) will *phosphatize* a steel or iron surface against rusting (if subsequently oiled) in indoor atmospheres for a period of time.

3. *Stainless Steel.* Of the stainless steels, the 12 and 17% chromium grades have poor resistance to phosphoric acid. Despite optimistic data from laboratory tests, field experience with the S30400 or S30403 has been poor. The molybdenum-bearing S31603 is usually reliable for tanks, piping, valves, and pumps handling *uncontaminated* acid up to 85% at 95°C (200°F) maximum. S31703 or a super grade (e.g., N08020) may be substituted for an extra margin of resistance (see also "Nickel" below). The molybdenum-bearing high-alloy grades (e.g., N08825, N08020) will resist up to 85% acid at the atmospheric boiling point (in the absence of aggressive contaminants).

4. *Lead.* Lead is a traditional material for handling phosphoric acid (particularly prior to the development of modern high-nickel alloys) and will withstand 80% pure (or 85% impure) acid up to about 200°C (390°F). However, the resistance is due to films of insoluble lead phosphates, so erosion or impingement effects will cause problems.

5. *Copper.* Copper and its alloys are governed in their corrosion behavior entirely by the influence of DO or other oxidants. Alloys immune to dealloying phenomena are useful in all strengths of acid to about 80°C (175°F) in the absence of oxidizing species.

6. *Nickel.* Nickel (i.e., N02200) has very limited application in phosphoric acid, but Monel (N04400) will withstand all concentrations to about 90°C (200°F) *if* there are no stronger oxidants present than DO and the cupric ion corrosion products do not accumulate. Alloys B (N10002) and B-4 (N10665) are resistant only in the absence of strong oxidants [e.g., Fe (III), Cu (II)].

N06600 is not very useful, but its molybdenum-bearing variant (N06625) has been successfully used in wet-process evaporators. Alloy G (N06007) is the most economical alloy among the nickel-chromium-molybdenum alloys. N10276 is seldom needed.

7. *Noble Metals.* Silver, gold, and platinum will resist all concentrations at least up to the atmospheric boiling point.

8. *Reactive Metals.* Titanium is nonresistant (unless protected by oxidizing contaminants). Zirconium is useful up to about 60% concentration. Tantalum will withstand any concentration up to about 175°C (345°F), but *only* if the fluoride concentration (a common contaminant) is less than 10 ppm. Otherwise, hydrogen embrittlement and pitting will occur.

9. *Glass.* Glass in its several applications (e.g., Pyrex, glass-lined steel) may be used to handle *fluoride-free* acid up to 60% and 100°C (212°F). At higher concentrations or temperatures, increasing rates of attack will occur.

10. *Plastics and Elastomers.* Plastics and elastomers (as well as carbon and graphite) are useful within certain temperature and pressure limits. Some recommended temperature limits are as follows:

Material	Temp., °C (°F)
PTFE	260 (500)
FEP	205 (401)
Polyesters	95 (203)
PE, PP, PVC	60 (140)
Elastomers	60 (140)

FRP tanks and piping are widely used for atmospheric storage.

Handling and Storage

Following is a listing of suggested materials of construction for concentrated phosphoric acid which are thought to constitute good engineering practice for a variety of items, with minimum risk:

Tanks. FRP or S30403

Piping. FRP or S31603

Valves. CF3M

Pumps. CF3M

Gaskets. Elastomeric or graphite fiber

22.1.4 Sulfuric Acid

Dilute (i.e., less than perhaps 85%) sulfuric acid is entirely different from the oxidizing concentrated acids discussed in the previous chapter. The most important thing to recognize is that its corrosive nature is affected *both* by straightforward dilution (and temperature) and by contaminants. The latter profoundly affect the redox potential of the solution, and we will discuss in this section both oxidizing and reducing contaminants, while maintaining that dilute sulfuric acid is per se a reducing acid.

It should first be understood that there is a relationship between specific materials and various concentrations of sulfuric acid as to whether hydrogen gas is evolved (as from a reducing acid) or whether the sulfate ion is reduced. (The behavior of specific metals and alloys is discussed under "Specific Materials" below.) For example, some authorities indicate that sulfuric acid *starts* to become an oxidizing acid at and above 5 N concentration (about 25%). This may be based on measured redox potential or on some thermodynamic calculation. Certainly, a broad range of concentrations evolve hydrogen during the corrosion of ferrous alloys. It is evident, however, that finely divided *nickel* (e.g., Raney nickel) will react with 25% acid at room temperature, liberating hydrogen sulfide by reduction of the sulfate ion. *Boiling* 53 to 57% acid is similarly reduced during corrosion of high-silicon cast nickel alloys (e.g., Hastelloy D).

Over the entire range of dilution from about pH 2 (about 0.05%) to 90% concentration, specific oxidizing species [e.g., cations like Cu (II) or Fe (III)]; anions like chromates, nitrates, nitrites; or reducing species like hydrogen sulfide and stannous salts can *control* the redox potential of the sulfuric acid solution. This profoundly influences its corrosive action. Of course, chloride ion contamination also influences specific phenomena, such as pitting or environmental cracking, while fluoride contamination adversely affects the resistance of the reactive metals (i.e., Ti, Zr, and Ta).

Specific Materials

1. *Aluminum.*   Aluminum and its alloys are totally unsuitable for dilute sulfuric acid.

2. *Cast Iron and Steel.*   Cast iron and steel are unsuitable for other than cold concentrated acid. However, nickel cast irons will find some applications in intermediate-strength acid, while the high-silicon cast irons (e.g., UNS F47003) are very resistant. Even the silicon cast iron will corrode at about 20 mpy (0.5 mm/yr) in 5 to 55% acid at the atmospheric boiling point.

3. *Stainless Steel.*   The stainless steels must be considered by category. The martensitic and ferritic grades are generally inapplicable in dilute sulfuric, but the 18−8 austenitic grades may sometimes be employed, depending upon the conditions of exposure.

A question that frequently arises is what temperature and concentration limits are relevant in *very* dilute sulfuric acid (e.g., in pH control of water systems). The following data in *aerated* acid may be helpful for such decisions:

% Acid	Temp., °C (°F)	Corrosion Rate, mm/yr	
		S30400	S31600
0.05	95 (203)	Nil	Nil
0.25	60 (140)	36	Nil
0.50	90 (194)	800	5
1.00	100 (212)	300	50

In these very dilute solutions, both dissolved oxygen (a weak passivator) and molybdenum content are significant. No doubt, chloride contamination would adversely influence these rates, which therefore relate to distilled water or demineralized water only. Also, severe corrosion has been observed in the rolled joints of tube-shell heat exchangers, where the dilute acid concentrated locally to some intolerable level due to process-side heat.

In laboratory investigations, 50 to 65% acid at 80 to 90°C (176 to 194°F) (which would otherwise *dissolve* either S30400 or S31600) has been rendered totally noncorrosive by the addition of as little as 500 ppm Cu (II). Note that this would be potentially dangerous in the field, where the inhibitor might not access crevices or joints.

Of the superaustenitic grades, the Alloy 20Cb3 (UNS N08020) was specifically developed for dilute and intermediate concentrations of sulfuric acid. The literature contains "isocorrosion charts" which define the ordinary limitations of concentration and temperature. It must be remembered that these parameters are profoundly affected by specific oxidizing, reducing, or halide contaminants. Note also that the newer grades of lower alloy content (UNS S31254, etc.) will have less resistance than Alloy 20Cb3 but more than S31600.

4. *Lead.* Lead and its alloys have resistance to a relatively wide range of sulfuric acid concentrations below the atmospheric boiling point (see isocorrosion charts in *Corrosion Resistance of Metals and Alloys*). However, not only is erosion a problem, but the protective sulfate film may be removed by some organic contaminants (e.g., alkyl sulfates, organic acids). On the other hand, an intact sulfate film can render the lead *cathodic* to high-alloy valves (the reverse of the initial situation), with attendant galvanic corrosion of the valve unless electrically isolated.

5. *Copper.* The *zinc-free* copper alloys (e.g., coppers and bronzes) are profoundly influenced by oxidizing and reducing species. They will in fact resist dilute sulfuric acid, but are corroded by as weak an oxidant as DO. Worse still, the stable corrosion products are the Cu (II) ions, themselves oxidizing species, as opposed to Cu (I) ions, so the attack is autocatalytic, accelerating with the accumulation of dissolved corrosion products. Copper alloys should only be employed under nonoxidizing or reducing conditions.

6. *Nickel.* Of the nickel alloys, the nonchromium grades like N02200 (nickel), N04400 (Monel) and N10001 (Alloy B) resist nonaerated acids free of oxidants. Monel is similar to copper because of its high copper content, but is used as auxiliary hardware in acid pickling operations where the hydrogen evolved from steel products keeps the iron and copper salts in a reduced state.

UNS N06600 is of little interest in dilute sulfuric, but the molybdenum-bearing grades like N06625, N08825, and N10276 are useful (see appropriate trade literature for isocorrosion charts).

7. *Noble Metals.* Platinum and gold are quite resistant but see very few industrial applications. The corrosion rate for gold is adversely affected by oxidants. Silver is resistant in very dilute acid, but the rate increases significantly as the concentration *or* temperature is increased.

8. *Reactive Metals.* Titanium is *not* useful in dilute sulfuric acid unless oxidizing contaminants [e.g., Cu (II), Fe (III)] are present to maintain passivitiy.

Zirconium resists up to 70% sulfuric acid at the boiling point. Above this concentration, rapid "breakaway" corrosion occurs. In some plant operations, it was found that the entire curve derived from laboratory tests in chemically pure acid was displaced to the left (i.e., to about 60% limiting concentration) by unknown contaminants. Furthermore, *pyrophoric* corrosion products were encountered when a zirconium valve was disassembled. This is a real hazard where ignition sources are a danger.

Tantalum will resist dilute sulfuric acids to the atmospheric boiling point. Only fluoride contamination poses a serious threat, as it does also with zirconium.

9. *Nonmetallic Materials.* These are routinely used in dilute sulfuric services, with the caveats mentioned below.

   a. Glass and other ceramics resist dilute sulfuric acid (in the absence of fluorides). Acid-proof brick construction is commonly employed for hot intermediate-strength acid vessels, with a suitable membrane.

   b. Rubber and elastomers resist dilute sulfuric acid, within their normal temperature limitations. Organic contaminants might cause problems, as previously discussed.

   c. Of the family of plastics, the fluorinated variety are completely resistant, within their temperature limitations. This is true also of the nonfluorinated types (PE, PP, PVDC, etc.), *except* that prolonged exposure to, for example, 65% acid at 85°C (185°F) or so will carbonize the plastic due to the oxidizing action of the hot acid. FRP is useful within its temperature limitations, but could also be carbonized in prolonged service at elevated temperatures.

d. Carbon and graphite are useful materials. Carbon-lined, lead-lined steel pipe has been used for hot intermediate strengths of acid. Carbon brick−lined vessels have been employed. Impervious graphite heat exchangers, although subject to mechanical damage, have many decades of successful applications as calandrias (reboilers) in this type of service.

Handling and Storage

Dilute and intermediate strengths of sulfuric acid are not routinely stored or transported. However, the occasion may arise (e.g., for process day tanks, for regeneration of ion-exchange beds), so some suggestions can be made, subject to the caveats about contamination effects. The recommendations below are intended to resist up to intermediate strengths of sulfuric acid, within their normal temperature limitations, and without undue concern over oxidizing or reducing species in the acid.

Tanks.   Brick-lined, glass-lined, plastic-lined, rubber-lined, FRP

Piping.   Plastic-lined, glass-lined, rubber-lined, Pyrex, FRP, Alloy 20Cb3, Alloy 625, Alloy C276, zirconium

Valves.   Plastic, rubber or glass-lined; tantalum-plated, high-silicon cast iron; alloys as for piping above

Pumps.   Same as valve materials; impervious graphite

Gaskets.   Graphoil, felted PTFE, rubber, and elastomers

22.2 ORGANIC ACIDS

The major organic acids of interest are formic acid (HCOOH), acetic acid (CH$_3$COOH), and the higher homologues of the general formula RCOOH (where R indicates ethyl, propyl, butyl, and other aliphatic radicals).

22.2.1 Formic Acid

Formic acid is a strong acid, approaching the dilute mineral acids in its activity (i.e., its tendency to release hydrogen ions). It can be particularly aggressive when hot and anaerobic.

22.2.2 Acetic Acid

Acetic acid is probably the most commercially important of this group. The specifics of the manufacturing process have a lot to do with the corrosivity in the crude state (although refined or chemically pure acid is quite predictable). When produced by oxidation processes, peracids or peroxides are formed which, although unstable, can profoundly affect the behavior of many metals and alloys.

Specific Materials

1. *Aluminum.* Aluminum is widely used for shipment and storage of refined concentrated acids, free of chlorides or heavy-metal ions. (Dilute solutions are more corrosive because of increased ionization and can be severely corrosive.) Even in cold concentrated products, a fine haze of aluminum salts may develop, which may be incompatible with product specifications.

2. *Iron and Steel.* Iron and steel are subject to attack at several hundredths of an inch per year in all concentrations of organic acids and cannot be used for shipment and storage. However, the high-silicon iron (UNS F47003) will resist all concentrations at least to the atmospheric boiling point.

3. *Stainless Steel.* Stainless steels of conventional martensitic and ferritic groups are of no practical importance in this application, but the superferritics (e.g., S44626) can be employed.

Austenitic grades, on the other hand, are very important. S30400 is used for handling and storage of refined acids up to about 70°C (160°F), although hot-wall effects can be dangerous. Above that temperature range (or for steam-traced piping), S31603 must be used. IGC is a chronic phenomenon in all hot organic acids. To ensure continued passivity of even austenitic grades, at least trace amounts of oxygen or oxidants must be present. Selective corrosion of welds may be encountered, independently of carbon or sensitization effects.

The superstainless steels (e.g., N08825, N08020) handle some very tough, borderline conditions. They are sometimes used for welding S31603 vessels or weld-overlaying flange faces and other areas subject to crevice corrosion.

4. *Lead.* Lead is not commercially useful in organic acids, although it has sometimes been successfully employed in very dilute acetic acid streams. Oxidizing agents severely aggravate attack.

5. *Copper.* Copper and its alloys are resistant or not, depending entirely upon the presence or absence of oxidizing agents. Copper and its high-strength, zinc-free alloys are used in all concentrations of organic acids up to the atmospheric boiling point, but *only* under anaerobic and otherwise nonoxidizing conditions.

6. *Nickel.*   Nickel Alloy 200 is rarely employed in this type of service, although Alloy 400 is occasionally used in place of copper. N06600 is not usually of any interest in such applications. Alloy B (N10001) or its variants are used only for special process conditions. However, N06625 and N10276 are used for the toughest services (acetic acid vaporizers, seawater-cooled heat exchangers, etc.).

7. *Reactive Metals.*   Titanium is the most commonly employed of the reactive metals. It has performed well under oxidizing conditions, but can corrode catastrophically otherwise (e.g., condensing pure formic acid). Zirconium is an acceptable but more expensive material, while tantalum is resistant but rarely required.

8. *Silver.*   Silver was a traditional material for handling hot organic acids and for heating coils in stainless tanks. Currently, it has been replaced to a great extent by modern nickel-base alloys.

9. *Plastics.*   Plastics are suspect because of the solvent effects of organic acids, but fluorinated grades are fully resistant and polyethylene drums are ideal for ambient temperature storage of chemically pure acetic acid. The bisphenol polyesters have been successful in some applications.

10. *Rubber.*   Rubber is a traditional material in *dilute* acetic acid storage. Above 5% concentration, only a few synthetic elastomers (e.g., Butyl, EPR) are resistant, and only Butyl will resist glacial acetic up to 80°C (175°F).

11. *Other Nonmetallics.*   These include wood (traditionally used for dilute acetic acid and vinegar), glass or ceramics, and carbon or graphite. Impervious graphite heat exchangers have been used in the most demanding services for heating or cooling organic acids.

Handling and Storage

The ambient storage of organic acids presupposes aerobic conditions, because of the high solubility of DO. Following is a listing of materials of construction for a variety of equipment for storage of refined acetic acid. The selection is thought to constitute good engineering practice with minimum risk.

Tanks.   Aluminum or S30403

Piping.   S31603 (traced) or S30403

Valves.   CF3M or CF8M

Pumps.   CF3M

Gaskets.   Spiral-wound stainless steel and PTFE

RECOMMENDED READING

LaQue, F. L., and H. R. Copson (eds.): *Corrosion Resistance of Metals and Alloys*, 2d ed., ACS Monograph Series. Reinhold, New York, 1963, p. 333.

CHAPTER **23**

Carbon Dioxide

Carbon dioxide is an acid gas which forms a weak reducing acid (carbonic acid) upon dissolution in water. It is a naturally occurring constituent in air (several hundred parts per million), from which it dissolves in condensed moisture or water, with a buffered pH of about 5.7, corresponding to about 12 to 15 ppm in the solution. At higher partial pressures of carbon dioxide, as when it is in a natural gas or process stream, a pH as low as 3.5 may be encountered in accompanying water. *Dry* carbon dioxide is noncorrosive.

The weak water solution (carbonic acid) is sometimes thought of as only mildly corrosive. This is because many of the studies have been conducted with natural waters, in which bicarbonates and other ions may buffer the acidity and otherwise influence corrosion.

In distilled water and in process streams containing water, carbonic acid can be severely corrosive to iron and steel, because of its low pH of 3.5 to 4. In fact, in carbonic acid, hydrogen evolution begins at about pH 5, and *total acidity* is a better indication of corrosivity than pH.

Low-pH solutions will lose carbon dioxide by volatilization at ordinary temperatures and pressures (like a carbonated beverage going flat). Great care must be taken in sampling water solutions for analysis (i.e., containers full to the brim and tightly sealed), to be sure that the samples are truly representative of the original dissolved gases.

23.1 SPECIFIC MATERIALS

23.1.1 Light Metals

Magnesium is corroded by mildly acidic carbonic acid solutions, but aluminum and its alloys are resistant (in the absence of heavy-metal ions like iron, copper, or lead, and in the absence of chlorides).

23.1.2 Zinc

Zinc, as galvanizing for example, is rapidly corroded by carbonic acid, both because of the acidity and because the corrosion products are quite soluble.

23.1.3 Ferrous Metals

Carbon dioxide alone (i.e., in the absence of DO) is often reported to be only slightly corrosive (e.g., in natural waters). However, if the carbon dioxide in the form of carbonic acid is constantly replenished, as either by flow or by a high partial pressure of carbon dioxide in the vapor space, corrosion of iron or steel will occur at rates of several tenths of an inch per year. In the presence of oxygen, there is a synergistic effect, the total corrosion being greater than would be caused by the same amount of DO and carbon dioxide acting separately. Also, cast iron suffers graphitic corrosion in such weak acid environments.

The ASTM A242 "self-painting" steels are somewhat better than carbon steel in steam condensate contaminated with carbon dioxide.

23.1.4 Stainless Steels

All grades of stainless steels are satisfactorily resistant to carbonic acid. Corrosion, when it does occur, is the result of contaminants such as chlorides or the conjoint or independent action of other species such as hydrogen sulfide.

23.1.5 Lead

Lead and its alloys are usually only slightly attacked by carbonic acid solutions, except under velocity conditions. However, corrosion is severe in the presence of oxygen or, particularly, peroxides or other strong oxidants.

23.1.6 Copper Alloys

Except for the problem of dezincification of yellow brass, corrosion of copper by carbonic acid is controlled solely by DO or other oxidants. In practice, copper alloys are rarely employed, because of the ever-present danger of oxygen ingress and the economic superiority and reliability of other materials such as stainless steels.

23.1.7 Nickel Alloys

With the exception of N04400 (and it is only attacked at certain critical ratios of oxygen to carbon dioxide in water), all nickel alloys resist attack by carbonic acid. However, they are not usually an economical choice unless there are other corrosive species such as chlorides present simultaneously.

23.1.8 Reactive and Noble Metals

With the possible exception of titanium under low-pH, chloride-contaminated, and anaerobic conditions, such materials (while resistant) would be uneconomical for this service.

23.1.9 Plastics and Elastomers

All plastics and elastomers of industrial interest are resistant to carbonic acid corrosion within their normal temperature and pressure limitations.

23.1.10 Inorganic Materials

Cement and concrete are subject to severe attack by carbonic acid because of the solubilization of calcium compounds. However, glass, ceramics, carbon, and graphite are inert.

CHAPTER **24**

Hydrogen Sulfide

Hydrogen sulfide is a colorless, flammable gas which has a "rotten-egg" odor at low concentrations. It is *lethal* (more so even than hydrogen cyanide). It is even more dangerous because it paralyzes the olfactory nerves at a relatively low concentration. Persons are generally unaware of their exposure to dangerous concentrations.

As a corrosive species, hydrogen sulfide is of concern in many oil, gas, and petrochemical operations. Hydrogen sulfide is a by-product of many sulfur-bearing compounds and a decomposition product of certain natural organic nutrients. While it is often an undesirable constituent to be removed from a product (e.g., natural gas), it may also be a desired reactant (as a feedstock for the production of sulfur or as an extractant for deuterium oxide from water in the production of heavy water, for example).

24.1 CORROSIVITY

24.1.1 General Corrosion

A weak acid in water solution (e.g., 0.3%; about three times as soluble as CO_2), hydrogen sulfide is only moderately corrosive to steel when acting as the sole corrosive species, unless the protective iron sulfide film is solubilized or swept away by velocity effects. If fresh metal is continuously exposed to attack, high corrosion rates are experienced.

In conjoint action with DO, hydrogen sulfide can be highly corrosive, both of itself and by reason of complex reaction products such as polythionic acids. There is also some reason to suspect a conjoint action with carbon dioxide, although this may be due simply to the higher total acidity experienced from the combined acid gases.

24.1.2 Localized Corrosion

In oil and gas services, a variable degree of protection from oil-saturated corrosion products will lead to the formation of corrosion lakes, which are shallow areas of localized corrosion. If imperfections exist in the iron sulfide film, a severe pitting type of attack may be experienced.

24.1.3 Hydrogen Effects

A most unfortunate characteristic of hydrogen sulfide is its ability to inhibit the formation of molecular hydrogen by the dimerization of nascent atomic hydrogen formed at the cathodes by corrosion (see also Chapter 29). The atomic hydrogen readily penetrates the metal lattice, as previously described, and this effect may be aggravated by iron sulfides.

Steel may suffer slow-strain-rate embrittlement, rendering it suscept-ible to brittle rupture, or may develop hydrogen blisters. Lastly, SSC may develop.

24.1.4 Environmental Cracking

Anodic Cracking

SCC of austenitic stainless steels such as UNS S30403 or S31603 can occur in the simultaneous presence of sulfide and chloride ions, and at lower chloride concentrations and much lower temperatures than when sulfide is absent. This effect is most prevalent in heavy water manufacturing processes. The sulfides apparently compete with oxygen at adsorption sites, locally weaken-ing the passive film. A sulfide-chloride transcrystalline cracking is then en-countered, even at room temperature, in the presence of only a few hundred parts per million of chloride ion.

Cathodic Cracking

Hydrogen sulfide is specific for SCC of hardened steel and other alloys, as previously described.

24.2 SPECIFIC MATERIALS

The effects of wet hydrogen sulfide on the various categories of materials (*dry gas is noncorrosive*) are as follows.

24.2.1 Aluminum

Aluminum and its alloys will withstand wet hydrogen sulfide, even at elevated temperatures. However, oxidation of hydrogen sulfide will form sulfurous acid, and in some cases sulfuric acid, which *is* corrosive.

24.2.2 Zinc

Because of its poor resistance to acidic conditions, zinc (as galvanized steel) has little application in sour (hydrogen sulfide–bearing) environments. (*Note:* As a sidelight, zinc-pigmented primers contaminated by hydrogen sulfide–polluted atmospheres do not thereafter accept properly the application of a top-coat paint system.)

24.2.3 Iron and Steel

In the absence of oxygen, the sulfide films formed on iron and steel are quite protective at low to moderate temperatures, as long as the film is not mechanically disturbed. Typically, rates are less than 0.5 mm/yr (20 mpy). There is, however, a tendency toward pitting at weak points in the film, and the presence of DO can increase the pitting rate about thirtyfold. Slow-strain-rate embrittlement is a problem (e.g., in the vapor space of tanks holding sour petroleum products). Hydrogen blistering is combatted by using low-temperature-type steels (i.e., clean, killed steels of a fine grain size). Hardened, or otherwise highly stressed steels, are subject to environmental cracking (SSC).

24.2.4 Stainless Steels

The martensitic grades (e.g., S41000) are subject to SSC precisely because they tend to be used in the hardened condition. Ferritic grades (e.g., S43000) are more resistant, and the superferritics (e.g., S44626; ASTM A-176, grade XM-27) are totally so. (*Note:* The maximum allowable hardness for these and other alloys is defined in the NACE Standard MR-01-75.)

The austenitic grades (e.g., S30400, S31600) are immune to SSC (unless *severely* cold-worked to a hardness in excess of Rockwell C 22) but are subject to the sulfide-chloride transcrystalline cracking described above. Superstainless steels (e.g., N08800, N08020) are immune to the latter effect, however.

When 18–8-type stainless steels are *sensitized*, they are subject to the intergranular SCC known as *polythionic cracking*. Polythionic acids (the tetrathionic acid and its salts are thought to be the worst) are formed by the interaction of wet hydrogen sulfide with sulfur dioxide. To combat this type of attack during downtime, refinery operations usually specify a stabilized grade (e.g., S34700), which is substantially immune to sensitization and weld decay.

Precipitation-hardening grades (e.g., S17400, S17700) require specific heat-treatment control of hardness levels for sour service, per MR-01-75.

24.2.5 Copper Alloys

Copper and the various bronzes have poor resistance to wet hydrogen sulfide, because of the voluminous nonprotective black sulfide corrosion products. However, yellow brasses (e.g., Admiralty B, C44300; aluminum brass, C68700) can be quite resistant, simply because their black tarnish is dense and adherent. Normally, their use is not recommended in sour service, although they have been successfully used in specific applications. Cupronickels suffer localized pitting in saline waters contaminated with hydrogen sulfide (e.g., as from bacterial action by SRBs).

24.2.6 Nickel Alloys

Although chromium-free nickel alloys are more resistant than copper alloys, only the chromium-bearing alloys such as N06600, N06625, and N10276 are highly resistant. Even these can suffer SSC *if* highly cold-worked and the cathodic member of a galvanic couple, where nascent hydrogen is generated.

On all nickel alloys, sulfur contamination may lead to LMC if heated or welded. This is due to the low-melting nickel sulfide eutectic previously described.

24.2.7 Lead

Lead and its alloys are moderately resistant to hydrogen sulfide, in the absence of velocity or abrasive effects.

24.2.8 Reactive Metals

Although titanium, zirconium, and tantalum are extremely sensitive to hydrogen pick-up, they seem to be inherently resistant to wet hydrogen sulfide *alone*. They could suffer hydrogen effects as cathodes in galvanic couples. However, titanium reportedly is an excellent material for instrumentation in certain specific sour services.

As a possible contaminant in more corrosive acids, hydrogen sulfide would act as a reducing agent, with possible adverse effects on the corrosion resistance of titanium.

24.2.9 Noble Metals

Gold is resistant, and platinum very much so, over a wide range of temperatures and concentrations. Silver, however, is moderately attacked. The commonly observed tarnishing of silver is due specifically to traces of hydrogen sulfide in the atmosphere.

24.2.10 Nonmetals

Of the nonmetals, only rubber and elastomers seem to pose any problem. They are subject to vulcanization and chemical deterioration in the presence of hydrogen sulfide at elevated temperatures and pressures (e.g., in downhole oilfield applications).

24.3 PYROPHORIC PRODUCTS

Certain metals can form pyrophoric corrosion products. The most common form is pyrophoric iron sulfide, probably ferric sulfide. It is not definitely known whether this forms directly on steel or indirectly from other corrosion products. It may require some oxygen present (to oxidize ferrous sulfide), or perhaps preexisting rust products [e.g., FeO(OH), or ordinary ferric oxide]. The specific problem is that these pyrophores get red-hot on exposure to air or oxygen (e.g., on opening equipment) and are a dangerous ignition source if flammable gases or liquids are about. Tires on vehicles have also caught on fire when parked on deposits scraped out of sour-service pipelines.

RECOMMENDED READING

NACE Standard MR-01-75: "Sulfide Stress Cracking—Resistant Metallic Materials for
  Oilfield Equipment" NACE, Houston, 1982.

CHAPTER **25**

Corrosion by Chlorine

The corrosion behavior of chlorine is profoundly affected by the presence or absence of water. Dry chlorine as either liquid or vapor is a powerful oxidant and chlorinating agent. Water solutions are aggressive oxidizing acids, containing both chloride and hypochlorite anions. While dry chlorine is not particularly corrosive at ambient temperatures (it is stored and handled in ordinary carbon steel), it becomes increasingly active with increasing temperature. Some metals like titanium will burn readily in dry chlorine.

25.1 SPECIFIC MATERIALS

25.1.1 Light Metals

Aluminum and magnesium will resist dry chlorine, theoretically. In practice, they are not considered for such service because they will react rapidly if even traces of moisture should become available.

25.1.2 Iron and Steel

Iron and steel will resist dry chlorine to temperatures of about 175°C (345°F) and 200°C (390°F), respectively. Liquid chlorine is routinely shipped, stored, and vaporized in steel equipment. Any ingress of water will result in rapid and severe corrosion. Traces of ferric chloride are inevitably present, which may clog fine orifices and interfere with valve seating.

25.1.3 Stainless Steels

The stainless steels will resist chlorine up to about 300°C (570°F). However, they are severely attacked if there is ingress of water. Also, being subject to chloride pitting and SCC with even parts per million of water, they are not usually employed in chlorine services.

25.1.4 Lead, Zinc, and Tin

Zinc and tin are not normally employed in chlorine service.

Lead will withstand both wet and dry chlorine up to about 110°C (230°F). It has been used successfully as a gasket material in such applications. Since it depends for its resistance on a film of insoluble corrosion products, it is not employed where significant flow or turbulence would be encountered.

25.1.5 Copper Alloys

Copper and its alloys will withstand dry chlorine up to about 200°C (390°F). However, there is little reason to select them for such service, and they would be severely attacked if any ingress of moisture should occur.

25.1.6 Nickel Alloys

Although all but the nickel-chromium-molybdenum alloys such as N10276 are attacked by wet chlorine, nickel and its alloys have excellent resistance to *dry* chlorine, even at elevated temperatures. The temperature limitations for some common nickel alloys are listed in Table 25.1.

25.1.7 Reactive Metals

Titanium will *not* resist dry chlorine. A minimum of 1500 ppm of water must be present or ignition will occur. Although titanium has outstanding resistance to wet chlorine, there is an inherent danger in crevices, in which the moisture may be consumed or the critical balance of hydrochloric to hypochlorous acid be disturbed. Serious crevice corrosion may ensue.

Table 25.1 Temperature
Limitations for Common
Nickel Alloys in Chlorine
Service

Alloy	Temp., °C (°F)
N02200	400 (752)
N02201	535 (995)
N04400	425 (797)
N06600	535 (995)
N10001	535 (995)
N10276	510 (950)

Zirconium offers no advantage in chlorine service. Tantalum is useful in both wet and dry chlorine up to about 150°C (300°F).

25.1.8 Plastics

Only the fluorinated plastics can be exposed to both wet and dry chlorine. In chemical processes, even PTFE may be unsuccessful because of chlorination of other organic materials absorbed within the interstices of the PTFE. This will cause mechanical damage (e.g., of valve diaphragms), even though the PTFE is itself unattacked.

PVC is widely used to handle wet chlorine (and dry chlorine well diluted with other gases). In concentrated chlorine, however, the PVC will continue to chlorinate and degrade.

Polyesters must not be exposed to dry chlorine but will withstand wet chlorine to about 90°C (195°F). Vinyl polyesters are preferred.

25.1.9 Rubber and Elastomers

Natural rubber has long been used in wet chlorine service. In general, rubber and elastomers must *not* be exposed to dry chlorine; even the fluorinated elastomers suffer attack of certain constituents.

25.1.10 Other Nonmetals

Glass and other ceramic materials are unaffected by either wet or dry chlorine.

Carbon and graphite will withstand dry chlorine to about 1650°C (3000°F) in the absence of oxygen. Otherwise, they can be used only to about 330°C (625°F) and 425°C (795°F), respectively. Impregnated impervious graphite will tolerate dry chlorine to about 120°C (250°F), but wet chlorine attacks the organic binders.

25.2 STORAGE AND HANDLING

There should be no occasion for storing wet chlorine, but glass-lined, titanium, or N10276 equipment would be resistant. Dry chlorine is stored, with minimum risk, as indicated below.

Tanks. Steel

Piping. Steel

Valves. Steel with N04400 trim and N10276 stems

Pumps. Ductile iron, Ni-Resist, Alloy 400

Gaskets. Spiral-wound Alloy 400 and PTFE

CHAPTER **26**

Corrosion in Alkaline Environments

Preeminent among the alkaline environments are sodium hydroxide and ammonia (the latter is covered, together with its organic derivatives, the amines, in the next chapter). Sodium hydroxide is commonly called caustic soda. The term *caustic* refers to materials capable of eating away (or burning, especially as to flesh); it is loosely used for the group of strong alkalis like sodium hydroxide, potassium hydroxide (caustic potash), and calcium hydroxide (caustic lime). Sodium carbonate is a relatively strong alkali, but its major problem is a tendency to hydrolyze to sodium hydroxide at elevated temperature.

26.1 SODIUM HYDROXIDE

26.1.1 Properties

Sodium hydroxide (NaOH) is a white hygroscopic solid with a melting point of 318°C (604°F) and a solubility in water at room temperature which yields a 78% concentration.

With amphoteric metals such as aluminum or zinc, the alkali reacts with the metal, liberating hydrogen (just as acids do). With other metals and alloys, reaction is characterized by the formation of relatively insoluble hydroxides on the surface, limiting the attack. For this reason, caustic or alkaline materials are not as universally corrosive as acids.

Corrosion, when it occurs, is due to special effects, such as the formation of complex compounds, double salts, basic salts, or double hydroxides. An example is the reaction of iron with caustic to form sodium ferroate. As the caustic solutions become hotter and more concentrated, there is a greater tendency for them to react directly with metal. In effect, iron and steel exhibit amphoteric characteristics in strong, hot sodium hydroxide.

26.1.2 Specific Materials

Light Metals

Aluminum and magnesium are nonresistant to caustic.

Iron and Steel

The corrosion resistance of iron and steel is usually acceptable up to concentrations of about 70% caustic at 80°C (175°F), except for the problem of SCC (i.e., caustic embrittlement), if iron contamination is not objectionable. However, the corrosion rate increases rapidly with temperature, reaching more than 12.5 mm/yr (500 mpy) at 100°C (212°F). This can cause high rates with steam-traced carbon steel piping, for example, when static rather than flowing conditions prevail.

Caustic embrittlement is a misnomer; the metal matrix retains its inherent ductility, although a brittle fracture typical of environmental cracking ensues. The parameters of temperature and concentration above which SCC is expected to occur are illustrated in Figure 26.1.

The time to failure can be greatly extended by thermal stress relief, which is mandatory for either *welded* or *cold-formed* steel equipment (e.g., flared pipe), within the SCC limits. Applied stresses are also to be avoided, as much as possible. It is generally believed that stresses must be at or above the yield point for caustic cracking to occur. Because of the relatively high freezing point of concentrated sodium hydroxide (which necessitates heating lines and vessels), SCC is a problem even under ordinary storage conditions.

Additions of *nickel* to iron and steel greatly increase corrosion resistance. The high-nickel cast irons (e.g., the several grades of Ni-Resist) are popular for caustic services.

Stainless Steels

The conventional straight chromium-grade martensitic and ferritic stainless

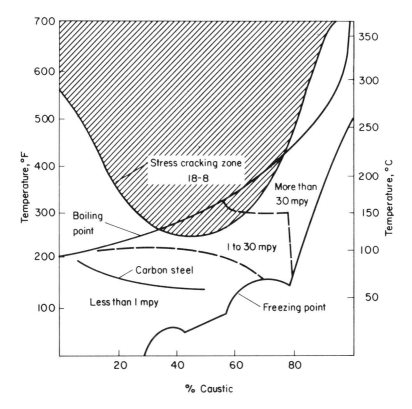

Figure 26.1 Caustic cracking curves for steel and 18−8 stainless steel.

steels are unreliable in caustic above ambient temperatures. They may become active and exhibit less resistance than ordinary steel.

The superferritics (e.g., S44626) have distinctly different properties and have been used successfully in caustic evaporators. (*Note:* This application may be profoundly influenced by the concentration of residual oxidizing species, such as chlorates, in the caustic.) Above about 300°C (570°F), SCC is a real problem.

The 18−8 grades are more resistant than ordinary 12 and 17% chromium grades, but can also lose passivity and suffer severe corrosion. The probable practical limits for S30403 and S31603 are 50% caustic at 70°C (160°F) and 40% at 80°C (175°F).

At and above 300°C (570°F), the austenitic stainless steels (including the superstainless grades) are easily cracked by caustic (or even by sodium carbonate, because of hydrolysis effects). Sodium hydroxide of 10% concentration has caused SCC in autoclave tests. Plant failures are encountered in environments ranging from caustic-contaminated steam to molten sodium contaminated with concentrations of water in parts per million. The temperature at which SCC of 18−8 stainless by caustic becomes a problem is not known with certainty, and probably varies with oxygen and/or oxidant content. A curve based on laboratory data in chemically pure sodium hydroxide is included in Figure 26.1 (the curve for steel is based on plant experience).

Copper Alloys

There is relatively little information about copper alloys in the literature, because copper contamination is objectionable in the rayon industry (color) and the soap industry (rancidity), both of which are major users of caustic. Nevertheless, in the absence of strong oxidants (e.g., chlorates, hypochlorites), copper alloys are very resistant. The cupronickels have been used in many applications in which copper contamination was not a problem. Low-zinc bronze valves and pumps are very economical for handling oxidant-free caustic, while copper pipe has sometimes been used when it was impractical to stress-relieve steel pipe in the field.

Nickel Alloys

Commercially pure nickel (N02200) will handle any and all caustic solutions and even molten 100% sodium hydroxide. Eventually, it may suffer SCC at temperatures of the order of 325°C (620°F) over a prolonged period of several years. It is widely used, in the form of nickel-clad steel vessels, to handle strong hot caustic. Above about 315°C (600°F), the low-carbon variety (N02201) is recommended.

Alloy 600 (N06600) is often preferred for piping because it is more easily welded in the field. It is also preferred for heating coils, because of its greater strength at steam temperatures, although this may introduce trace amounts of Cr(VI) ions (which may be detrimental to product quality). SCC will eventually occur above 300°C (757°F), but it takes months or years to develop (compared to hours in 18−8 stainless steels).

Alloy 400 (N04400) is somewhat less resistant than Alloy 600, and more susceptible to SCC by a factor of 3 or more. Furthermore, its iron and copper content make it objectionable for the more meticulous applications.

The higher-nickel alloys such as N10001 and N10276 are rarely needed or considered for this type of service, but should be highly resistant.

Reactive Metals

Titanium has good resistance up to concentrations of about 40% caustic at 80°C (175°F). Resistance is improved by anodizing the metal to reinforce the surface oxide film, and also by the presence of oxidizing species in the caustic. Galvanic couples may cause hydriding, and chloride contamination may lead to penetration of the protective oxide film at elevated temperature.

Zirconium has limits of about 15% caustic at 80°C (175°F) and 50% at 60°C (140°F). Tantalum is severely attacked by caustic.

Noble Metals

Silver has excellent resistance to even very hot, concentrated caustic. It was the traditional material of construction prior to the development of the nickel alloys. Gold and platinum are fully resistant, but have no common industrial application.

Nonmetals

Carbon and graphite are resistant per se up to the boiling point in all concentrations of caustic. However, commercial impervious graphite will suffer attack on the organic impregnant, and the use of cemented joints further limits its applicability. Phenolic resins are nonresistant and, even with epoxy resins, applications are limited to 10% caustic, maximum, and about 125°C (255°F).

Glass is readily attacked by hot caustic, the temperature being more limiting than concentration. Glass-lined equipment may be used for low temperatures and concentrations within the parameters shown in Figure 26.2, which has been used to set operating limits for such equipment. Assuming an 80-mil thickness, for example, and allowing a 100% margin of error, an 8-year life is limited by 0.1% caustic at 65°C (150°F) and a 13-year life by 0.5% caustic at about 50°C (120°F).

Unreinforced plastics (e.g., PVC, PE, and PP) are suitable for caustic solutions, within their normal limitations of temperature and pressure.

FRP piping based on epoxy resins has been used for up to 50% caustic, within its temperature limitations. An incremental advantage is gained by incorporating a Dynel veil below the surface of the gel coat, to protect the fibers of the glass reinforcement from direct contact with alkali.

26.1.3 Handling and Storage

Following is a listing of materials of construction for various items of equipment exposed to concentrated sodium hydroxide, which listing is thought to constitute good engineering practice with minimum risk:

Tanks.   Carbon steel, stress-relieved

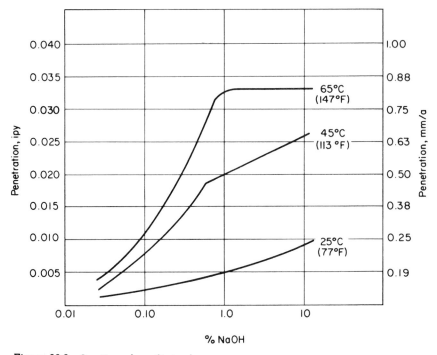

Figure 26.2   Caustic vs. borosilicate glass.

Piping.   Carbon steel, stress-relieved; cast iron; FRP (epoxy); plastic-lined steel; alloy UNS N06600

Valves.   Ductile iron; low-zinc bronze; steel (stainless trim)

Pumps.   Ductile iron; bronze; nickel cast iron; CF3M

Gaskets.   Elastomeric; Graphoil

26.2 POTASSIUM HYDROXIDE

In general, aqueous solutions of caustic potash are considered to have the same corrosion characteristics as caustic solutions of the same concentration.

26.3 CALCIUM HYDROXIDE

Despite its strong effect on flesh and other organic materials, lime solutions are not particularly corrosive to metals, other than the amphoteric varieties.

This is due to a low and inverse solubility (about 1500 ppm in water at room temperature, diminishing with increasing temperature). Lead has been attacked by lime-water freshly leached from cement.

26.4 ALKALINE SALTS

Alkaline salts are products of a strong base (e.g., sodium hydroxide) and a weak acid (e.g., carbonic acid, acetic acid, phosphoric acid). They act like a weak alkali. The alkaline salts are those of sodium, potassium, lithium, calcium, magnesium, and barium with weak acids. They are discussed in more detail in Chapter 28.

CHAPTER **27**

Ammonia and
Its Compounds

Ammonia is a pungent gas which dissolves in water to form the alkaline ammonium hydroxide. Ammonium salts are encountered particularly in the fertilizer industry. Organic derivatives are called *amines*, the bulk of which are encountered as alkyl amines, alkylene amines such as ethylene diamine, or alkanolamines such as monoethanolamine.

27.1 AMMONIA AND AMMONIUM HYDROXIDE

Anhydrous ammonia, as explained in Chapter 8, is specific for SCC of carbon steel unless inhibited with about 2000 ppm water. It is routinely handled in bulk storage in steel, however, and there is little to be said further concerning it. The presence of moisture or the formation of an aqueous solution changes the corrosion characteristics considerably.

27.1.1 Specific Materials

Light Metals

Aluminum and its alloys are mildly corroded [less than about 0.1 mm/yr (4 mpy)] in ammonium hydroxide up to about 50°C (120°F).

Iron and Steel

Iron and steel are suitable for wet ammonia and ammonium hydroxide, if iron contamination is not a problem. Rusting will occur, particularly in the vapor space of tanks, but the attack diminishes with time as the vessel becomes "seasoned."

Stainless Steels

All grades of stainless steel resist ammonia and ammonium hydroxide at ambient temperatures and moderately elevated temperatures [certainly up to 100°C (212°F)].

Copper and Its Alloys

Copper alloys are usually not employed in ammonia services, both because of the SCC problem and because of corrosion by formation of the copper-ammonia complex (the royal blue–colored compounds). The latter, however, requires the presence of oxygen or other oxidizing agents for its formation.

Nickel and Its Alloys

Nickel and its nonchromium alloys are more resistant than copper, and immune to SCC, but also form chromophoric compounds in the presence of oxidants. They are rarely employed in ammoniacal services. The chromium-bearing alloys (e.g., N06600) offer no advantage over 18–8 stainless steels in such applications.

Noble and Reactive Metals

Of these groups, silver can form very dangerous *explosive* complexes (azides) with ammonia and its derivatives. Gold and platinum, and the reactive metals, find no application in ammoniacal services. Tantalum (e.g., as patches for glass-lined equipment) would be suspect because of its low alkali resistance.

Nonmetals

Siliceous ceramics are attacked by ammonium hydroxide. Carbon and graphite are resistant per se, but phenolic binders are attacked. Plastics and elastomers resist ammonia solutions within their normal temperature and pressure limitations, but amines are powerful solvents.

27.1.2 Special Problems

A little-known problem arises from the reaction of ammonia with carbon dioxide. In the presence of large amounts of water, the noncorrosive ammonium carbonate or bicarbonate is formed. However, at slightly elevated temperatures [e.g., 60°C (140°F)] and atmospheric pressure or above, trace amounts of a corrosive species are formed (even in as dilute a medium as 20% ammonium carbonate, or in the vapors over ammonium hydroxide). This species is probably ammonium carbamate or a derivative, and can attack steel (and even stainless steel at higher temperatures and pressures) at rates of the order of 3 mm/yr (120 mpy) or more. This is the probable cause of a number of corrosion failures in vessels stripping ammonia from a process environment, when the potential problems due to carbon dioxide ingress were not recognized in advance.

27.2 AMINES

Certain characteristic problems arise from the handling of amines, either as the product itself or acid-gas scrubbing systems used to remove carbon dioxide and/or hydrogen sulfide from other gases. The problems arise from the dual nature of amines, which are at once strong solvents and, in water solution, alkalis.

27.2.1 Specific Materials

Light Metals

Aluminum is commonly used for the shipment and storage of refined amines. However, it must not be used as a *heating coil* in hydroxylated amines (e.g., monoethanolamine) because of severe exothermic corrosion after an indeterminate induction period.

Iron and Steel

Amines of all kinds readily form iron complexes with steel and may *not* be stored in steel when this is objectionable. Steel tanks are employed for monoethanolamine and other such products to be used in acid-gas scrubbing systems. Amines can be severely corrosive to steel under process conditions at elevated temperatures, particularly above 80°C (175°F). Amines are not specific for SCC. When encountered, cracking is usually due to contaminants.

Stainless Steels

Amines are successfully stored in S30400 tankage, but the molybdenum-bearing grades (e.g., S31600) are required above 100°C (212°F) in process vessels. IGC, requiring S31603, is not usually encountered unless there are specific contaminants present. Valves and pumps should be CF8M or equivalent, rather than CA6NM or other lower alloys.

Lead

Lead is subject to corrosion by aqueous amines. However, existing lead-lined tanks have been used for storage of monoethanolamine at ambient temperatures, when lead contamination was not objectionable.

Copper and Its Alloys

These can resist amines under anaerobic conditions. However, the ever-present danger of color formation, corrosion, and SCC due, for example, to ingress of air and moisture renders them generally unacceptable except for certain well-defined and controlled conditions.

Nickel and Its Alloys

With few exceptions, and because of cost considerations, nickel alloys are only rarely selected for amine-type services. Alloy C276 centrifuges have been used in some amine hydrochloride processes (where SCC of austenitic stainless steels has been a problem), separating salt from the amine products.

Noble and Reactive Metals

Silver must not be used for amine services, as previously noted, while gold and platinum have no known applications. Both titanium and zirconium have been used, but only to combat specific process problems such as in urea plants or in amine manufacture.

Nonmetals

Plastics and elastomers, other than some of the fluorine-based materials, are nonresistant to amines.

Glass and siliceous ceramics resist amines, but not their water solutions, in which alkalinity becomes excessive.

Carbon and graphite are resistant per se, but the solvent action will attack phenolic impregnants. Epoxy-cemented impervious graphite heat exchangers are successfully used in acid-gas scrubbing systems such as for monoethanolamine solution interchangers.

CHAPTER 28

Corrosion by Salts

Salts are the products of reaction between an acid and a base (e.g., sodium chloride from caustic and hydrochloric acid). In this case, the salt is a *neutral* salt, having neither acidic nor basic characteristics because it is the product of a strong acid and a strong base. Water solutions of neutral salts simply increase the electrical conductivity of the solution, although the effect of specific ions, such as chlorides causing pitting or SCC, must also be considered. In some cases, too, an oxidizing anion will have specific effects, as with sodium nitrate, for example.

Acid salts are formed by the interaction of a strong acid and a weak base and act very much like a weak solution of the parent acid. For example, ammonium sulfate solutions act like dilute sulfuric acid except for reactions specific to the ammonium ion, as with copper. Also, oxidizing cations such as cupric sulfate and ferric chloride will affect the redox potential and the corrosion characteristics of the solution.

Basic salts are the product of a strong base such as sodium hydroxide and a weak acid such as acetic acid. They act like a weak alkali. Any oxidizing capacity will derive from the acidic anion, as in sodium chromate, sodium nitrite, or sodium hypochlorite, as there are no strong oxidizing alkalis.

Oxidizing salts, whether acidic or basic, pose special problems and are discussed separately below.

28.1 NEUTRAL SALTS

These are usually sodium or potassium salts formed from the corresponding alkali. The sodium or potassium ion usually causes problems per se only in high-temperature corrosion (Chapter 30). The anions do have specific effects, as with chlorides causing pitting or SCC, and sulfates being reduced by bacterial action to sulfides and dissolved sulfur.

Increasing concentrations of salt lower the solubility of DO. Note that a solution with 6000 ppm of chloride ion has maximum corrosivity to steel, because of lower DO at higher concentrations.

The increased conductivity associated with any salt solution may aggravate galvanic corrosion by allowing greater cathode-to-anode ratios to come into play. Neutral sulfates are aggressively corrosive to portland cement mixtures, as previously discussed.

28.2 ACID SALTS

Although these act like weak solutions of the parent acid, corrosivity diminishes, with polybasic acids containing more than one hydrogen, as the hydrogen ions are successively replaced with less acidic cations. For example, monosodium phosphate is more corrosive than disodium phosphate.

Nonoxidizing acid chlorides such as magnesium chloride are not only corrosive to steel and other anodic materials by virtue of their acidic nature, but are highly specific for the SCC of 18−8 stainless steels, particularly.

Ammonium salts, in the presence of oxygen or oxidants, aggravate the corrosion of copper and nickel alloys (other than the chromium-bearing variety) by complexing and solubilizing the surface films which would otherwise limit corrosion.

28.3 ALKALINE SALTS

The alkaline salts are those resulting from the reaction of a strong base (e.g., sodium, potassium, lithium) with a weak acid. They act like a weak alkali. In most cases, the sodium salts are our primary concern.

Sodium carbonates and bicarbonates, particularly, may be thermally decomposed to yield free caustic, with its attendant problems. Otherwise, the sodium salts are a problem primarily with materials not resistant to alkalis. Trisodium phosphate, for example, is a mildly alkaline compound whose water solution is noncorrosive to copper and steel but has a mild etching effect on aluminum.

If the anion has oxidizing capacity, the corrosion characteristics can be drastically different, as described below.

28.4 OXIDIZING SALTS

Neutral or alkaline oxidizing salts, if they contain no halides as constituents or contaminants, are not very corrosive. Sodium chromate and sodium nitrite solutions can be handled in iron and steel and are in fact effective corrosion inhibitors for ferrous alloys in water (see Chapter 34). On the other hand, if sufficiently alkaline, solutions of oxidizing salts may attack amphoteric metals such as lead.

The hypochlorites are corrosive to copper, nickel, and lead but are easily handled by some plastics such as PVC. They will not corrode steel to a significant extent unless they also contain free chlorine, as with certain proprietary formulations such as HTH (high test hypochlorite).

With the acidic salts, oxidizing cations such as Fe(III) or Cu(II) convey oxidizing characteristics to solutions which would otherwise act simply like dilute acids. Ferric sulfate or cupric phosphate are more aggressive than the corresponding calcium or magnesium salts, because their cations (being capable of reduction) act as cathodic depolarizers.

Oxidizing halides, like ferric chloride or cupric chloride, are very corrosive, causing pitting and/or SCC in susceptible alloys, as well as general corrosion and IGC. At moderately elevated temperatures, even N10276 is of limited usefulness. For the more aggressive conditions, only tantalum, glass, fluorinated plastics, or carbonaceous materials will contain them.

It is interesting to note that ferric chloride hexahydrate, in the presence of an excess of acid to suppress internal hydrolysis, has a vapor pressure about equal to that of mercury. It can therefore travel about a process (where its presence may not be anticipated), leaving severe corrosion, pitting, or SCC in its wake, depending upon the material of construction. Steel may show localized corrosion of welds; copper and nickel alloys suffer general corrosion; and stainless steels suffer pitting and/or SCC.

CHAPTER 29

Hydrogen Phenomena

The little hydrogen atom is about one-third the size of the crystal cube in the metal lattice and can easily diffuse through the structure of the metal. When the crystal lattice is saturated by atomic hydrogen, an adverse effect is observed on the properties of many metals and alloys. In the absence of oxygen and in the presence of a clean metal surface, the hydrogen molecule dissociates (which it is otherwise reluctant to do) and the hydrogen *atoms* are occluded in the metal structure. This can cause a reduction in strength and ductility.

Four separate phenomena are observed

1. Slow-strain-rate embrittlement (SSRE)
2. Hydrogen blistering
3. HAC and hydrogen-induced blister cracking (HIBC)
4. High-temperature effects

The source of hydrogen may be corrosion (i.e., nascent hydrogen), electrochemical treatment (electroplating, CP) or high-pressure, high-temperature gaseous environments containing hydrogen (in which there is an equilibrium between molecular and atomic hydrogen).

29.1 SLOW-STRAIN-RATE EMBRITTLEMENT

SSRE is a *temporary* loss of ductility when steel becomes saturated with atomic hydrogen, as by pickling or electroplating (e.g., hydrogen plates out with cadmium during the operation). Ductility can be restored by heating for a short period of time at about 200°C (390°F), which drives out the hydrogen without permanent damage to the steel.

The outstanding feature of SSRE is that it is only detectable by *slow* strain, as in a tensile test. It does not show up in an impact test, for example. Field failures have occurred when storage tank roofs, saturated with hydrogen by corrosion in the presence of hydrogen sulfide, have been overpressured, resulting in a brittle fracture of the circumferential welds in the vapor space.

29.2 HYDROGEN BLISTERING

In relatively soft steels, hydrogen blistering may be observed under mildly corrosive conditions in the presence of specific species such as sulfides, selenides, arsenides, cyanides, or antimony compounds, which poison the dimerization of the nascent hydrogen formed. The nascent hydrogen is occluded in the lattice, where it dimerizes catalytically to molecular hydrogen at inclusions. Because the atomic hydrogen has weakened the lattice cohesion, the pressure generated by molecular hydrogen in the interstices of the metal causes blisters on the metal surface (sometimes also with splits or fissures). This tendency can be combatted to some extent by using steels of the same small grain size and cleanliness as are specified for improved NDTT in low-temperature service.

29.3 HYDROGEN-ASSISTED CRACKING

This subject has already been discussed in Chapter 8.

29.4 HIGH-TEMPERATURE EFFECTS

At elevated temperatures and partial pressures of hydrogen, the tendency for molecular hydrogen to dissociate is stronger and the mobile atomic hydrogen more active. Above about 400°C (750°F), for example, copper containing cuprous oxide inclusions will suffer localized reduction of the oxides in situ on exposure to hydrogen, generating high-pressure steam in the lattice, with attendant internal fissuring.

Of greater importance from the engineering standpoint is the *methanation* of steel. At temperatures above about 235°C (425°F), atomic hydrogen will react with iron carbides (i.e., cementite) in steel, forming methane within the lattice and causing localized decarburization and fissuring. Additions of alloying elements like molybdenum and chromium tie up the carbon in more stable forms, permitting exposure to higher pressures and temperatures of hydrogen before methanation occurs. Note that traces of hydrogen sulfide work in the opposite direction, permitting methanation to occur under less extreme conditions.

The parameters for successful use of ferrous alloys of increasing chromium content are defined by the "Nelson curves," which are based on practical experience and observation and periodically updated (API Publication No. 949, latest edition). A simplified curve, for illustrative purposes, is given in Figure 29.1.

It is *very* important to note that atomic hydrogen goes right through the common metals. In an alloy-clad steel vessel (e.g., copper-, nickel- or stainless-clad steel), the *backup* steel must be alloyed to withstand the temperatures and partial pressure of hydrogen contained by the alloy layer on the process side. Otherwise, the steel component of the alloy-clad pressure vessel is subject to methanation attack.

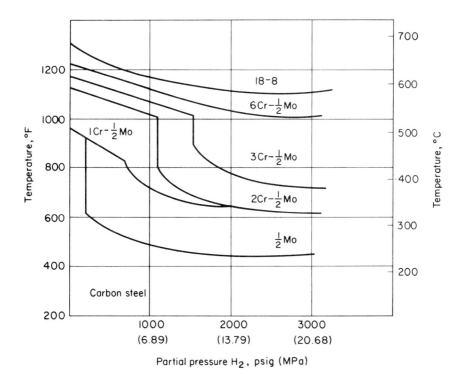

Figure 29.1   Simplified Nelson curves.

Only deoxidized copper, aluminum, zinc, cadmium, chromium, and silver (of the more common metals) are unaffected by exposure to hydrogen. They *are* permeable. Titanium, zirconium, tantalum, uranium, columbium, beryllium, and vanadium are all very reactive with hydrogen.

29.5 PRACTICAL GUIDELINES

In handling hydrogen at high pressures, the following precautions will help prevent equipment failures:

1. Maintain uniform hardness throughout the vessel.
2. Require the highest-quality welding, and check by thorough inspection.
3. Use materials of maximum 552 MPa (80,000 psi) yield strength (i.e., about Rockwell C 20 hardness maximum).
4. Reinspect frequently during the service life.
5. Always *vent* lined or multilayer vessels.

Note that, unlike other gases, hydrogen escaping under pressure gets *hotter* rather than colder. It can *autoignite*, forming an almost invisible flame which is very hazardous to nearby structures as well as to personnel.

CHAPTER **30**

High-Temperature Phenomena

It is somewhat difficult to define what is meant by "high temperature," because the different alloy systems go into specific modes of mechanical and corrosion behavior at different temperatures. Generally, a high temperature for any material is one at which it deforms under constant load and/or reacts with a low-humidity gaseous environment (although molten salts or liquid metals also comprise high-temperature environments).

The earliest demand for good high-temperature materials arose in the power-generating industry, whose temperature requirements for boilers have risen steadily.

Year	Temp, °C (°F)
1905	260 (500)
1926	400 (750)
1942	510 (950)
1956	620 (1150)

At the present time, demands are also made by the petrochemical and nuclear industries, as for gas cracking in the 1100°C (2000°F) range, and by aerospace requirements.

30.1 METAL BEHAVIOR

There is a fundamental change in a metal's behavior when the temperature exceeds about 35% of its absolute melting range (or 40 to 60% for some nickel-based and cobalt-based alloys). Below that value, application of mechanical loads below the yield strength results in no permanent deformation when the load is removed. After the load is released, the metal item resumes its original dimensions, for all practical purposes. (It should be noted, however, that metallurgical changes can and do occur at relatively low temperatures; e.g., tempering, recrystallization, and age-hardening).

Above some critical temperature, *creep* becomes a factor. Creep is time-dependent strain under constant load. The longer the load at some temperature is endured, the greater the permanent deformation (until rupture occurs). Creep is expressed as percent deformation per thousand hours. A typical creep curve is illustrated in Figure 30.1.

Design stresses for bolting and for unfired pressure vessels are 100% of the creep strength of 0.01% per 1000 h at temperature. ASME power boilers may also be designed at 60% of the 100,000-h rupture strength (Figure 30.2).

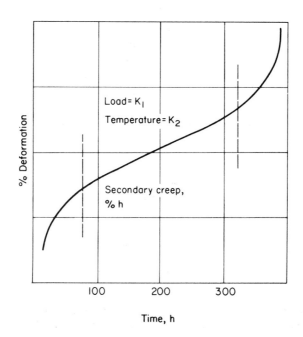

Figure 30.1 Time-deformation (creep) curve.

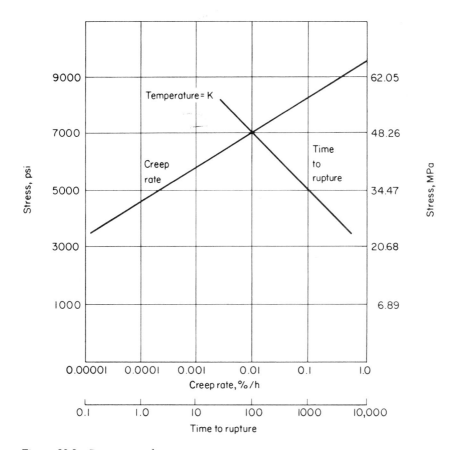

Figure 30.2 Creep rate and rupture time.

30.2 INTERNAL STABILITY

Temperature alone, without regard for the environment, can effect metallurgical changes in an alloy. In addition to the changes already mentioned, one
may encounter 468°C (875°F) *(temper)* embrittlement and/or graphitization of
steel, *sensitization* of austenitic stainless steels and certain other alloys, and
the formation of intermetallic compounds (e.g., sigma or chi phase) in specific
alloy systems. Such internal changes may affect mechanical properties or
corrosion resistance, or both.

30.3 SURFACE STABILITY

Depending on the nature and activity of the hot environment, an alloy may be subject to carburization, decarburization, or nitriding (sometimes severe, sometimes of a superficial nature).

30.4 HIGH-TEMPERATURE CORROSION

All forms of attack at elevated temperature in which the metal is converted to a corrosion product (solid, liquid, or vapor, depending on the metal and environment combination) are considered to be oxidation, in a manner analogous to aqueous corrosion. There is even electron transfer involved, and an "electrolyte" (i.e., the semiconductive layer of corrosion products). There is a definite migration of ions and electrons between the three phases (i.e., the metal, corrosion product layer, and environment). Unlike metals, electron transfer increases with temperature in a semiconductor.

There is an ordering of metals at high temperature, analogous to the electromotive series. Gold will remain bright and unoxidized up to its melting point, while less noble metals oxidize more easily. The important thing to note is the *reversibility* of the reaction of metals with oxygen to form the oxide, depending on the specific metal, the temperature, and the nature of the environment.

For example, mercuric oxide rapidly releases oxygen at atmospheric pressure at about 500°C (930°F). On the other hand, for nickel oxide to release oxygen at 1200°C (2200°F) requires that the partial pressure of oxygen be reduced to below 10^{-7} atmospheres. Otherwise, the nickel oxide will remain stable.

Just as the electromotive series does not apply when one departs from pure metals at standard conditions, diagrams relating the parameters for metal–metal oxide equilibria in different types of atmospheres (e.g., the Richardson diagram) do not apply to complex alloys. Also, the thermodynamics of a situation (which tell us what *can* happen) do not reveal the kinetics of what *will* happen.

The rate at which a metal will oxidize depends upon how protective the oxide layer is. If it is wholly nonprotective, the rate (i.e., usually a weight gain) will be *linear* with time. If it is protective (and remains in place), the rate will be *parabolic* or *logarithmic*, diminishing with time. The structure of the oxide film also determines how easily metal ions can diffuse out (and gaseous species in).

In practice, cycling temperatures may spall off the surface oxidation products, leading to a *paralinear* rate (which just means that oxidation proceeds in
a stepwise fashion). Changes in the nature of the environment, of course, can
also remove or modify the surface products, as can mechanical effects.

30.4.1 Oxidation-Reduction

In hot air, oxygen, steam, carbon dioxide, etc., the environment will tend to
oxidize a metal. With hydrogen, hydrogen-rich gases, or carbon monoxide,
the environment is reducing and tends to convert oxides back to the metallic
state.

In *mixtures*, the ratio of carbon monoxide to carbon dioxide determines the
carburization or decarburization conditions. The generalization extends to
other combinations of oxidizing and reducing species, such as hydrogen and
water vapor, nitric oxides and ammonia, and sulfurous oxides and hydrogen
sulfide. An atmosphere may be reducing to one component such as nickel and
oxidizing to another such as chromium or silicon, which further complicates
the picture. The most reliable data are those determined experimentally.

Catastrophic oxidation may also occur, as when silicon oxide dissolves in
nickel, or when molybdenum is vaporized as the oxide (e.g., from S31600
under insulation or deposits).

30.4.2 Sulfidation

Sulfidation is directly analogous to oxidation but is aggravated by the lower
melting points of many metallic sulfides and by the formation of low-melting
eutectics (as in welding of sulfur-contaminated nickel alloys). Also, sulfide
scales are less protective than oxide films.

30.4.3 Halogens and Hydrohalides

Because of the volatility of many metal halides, chlorine and hydrogen chloride are very aggressive at elevated temperatures. Fortunately, nickel alloys
tend to be resistant. However, gold and silver are readily attacked by hot
chlorine, while in hydrogen chloride silver is attacked at about 230°C (450°F),
although gold is good to about 870°C (1600°F).

30.4.4 Molten Salts

Many molten salts, whether alkaline or halide, attack metals at high temperature because they flux the surface films, continuously exposing fresh metal to attack. This is analogous to activation of passive metals, or solubilizing of films by complex metal ion formation, in aqueous corrosion.

30.4.5 Fuel Ash Corrosion

This is a special form of hot salt corrosion, in which the combination of sodium sulfate or chloride with vanadium compounds (as from certain types of crude oil fuels, for example) provides a very low melting eutectic compound. This aggravates the fluxing, causing it to occur at lower temperatures than one would otherwise expect.

30.4.6 Molten Metals

Certain molten metals (mercury, lead, bismuth, etc.) are used as coolants in nuclear reactors. A sodium-potassium alloy (NaK) is also used. Such metals may dissolve a metal in the hotter sections by solubilization and then deposit it in the cooler sections (where solubility is lower), causing physical blockage.

Contamination of molten metals by their own oxides, such as NaO in Na or NaK, can also cause specific corrosion phenomena.

30.5 EFFECTS OF ALLOYING ELEMENTS

Alloying additions, such as chromium, aluminum, and silicon, tend to form protective films which effectively limit the transport of reactive metals to the environment and of the environment inward to the metal. For practical purposes, these alloying elements enhance the formation of stable, low-volatility films, free of pores and adherent to the substrate. Nickel reinforces the effectiveness of chromium and also increases resistance to carburization, gas sulfidation, and (up to about 80% nickel) attack by hot ammonia.

Chromium is the major alloying element in iron-, nickel-, and cobalt-based alloys developed for high-temperature resistance. Aluminum additions, while effective against oxidation, yield alloys which cannot be readily fabricated. Silicon is used as a minor, supplementary addition to increase the effectiveness of chromium. Some rare earth metals also tend to improve the stability of the high-temperature scale.

30.6 HEAT-RESISTANT ALLOYS

This term usually refers to oxidation-resistant metals and alloys. However, it is desirable first to describe the temperature and oxidation limits for the carbon and low-alloy steels, which are in fact used to at least moderately elevated temperatures.

30.6.1 Carbon Steel

Steel is not truly useful at elevated temperature above about 450°C (850°F), except in comparison with some nonferrous alloys. Above this temperature, problems are encountered with high oxidation rates, "blue" or "temper" embrittlement at about 475°C (885°F), loss of mechanical strength, and graphitization. Graphitization involves the decomposition of iron carbides, liberating free graphite, and is particularly deleterious in the HAZ of welds.

30.6.2 Molybdenum Steel

The addition of about 0.5% molybdenum extends the usefulness of steel to about 565°C (1050°F) maximum. On exceeding this limit, however, the familiar problems with oxidation, loss of strength, and graphitization recur. Today, this type of steel, although long a favorite for steam piping, seems to be losing ground in favor of more highly alloyed, albeit still low-alloy, steels.

30.6.3 Alloy Steels

1.25Cr−0.5Mo and 2.5Cr−0.5Mo steels are used in refinery applications, particularly, because of their good high-temperature resistance to hydrogen and traces of hydrogen sulfide. They are also used in some high-temperature steam applications.

Higher-alloyed steels (total alloy content more than 5%) include the 5Cr−0.05Mo + Si steel, which is useful to about 815°C (1500°F), and the 7 and 9% chromium steels used for high-temperature, high-pressure hydrogen services.

30.6.4 Stainless Steels

1. The nickel-free, straight chromium grades are useful to about 650 to 760°C

(1200 to 1400°F), although there is a problem with sigma formation and attendant brittleness after extended service.

2. The 18−8 austenitic stainless steels, depending upon the specific grade such as S34700, S31600, are useful to temperatures as high as 870°C (1600°F). Above that temperature, declining strength and increasing oxidation limit their capabilities.

3. Higher-alloyed stainless steels, such as S30900 and S31000 (25−12 and 25−20), extend the usefulness of the austenitic grades in terms of improved resistance to oxidation and carburization, although adequate high-temperature strength is not obtained until the high-carbon cast variants are employed (see "Heat-Resistant Castings" below).

30.6.5 Specialty Wrought Alloys

These include a variety of complex iron-, nickel-, and cobalt-based alloys, such as

1. N08802 (Cr-Fe-Ni plus W, Cb, and Ti)
2. N06601 (Ni-Cr-Fe)
3. R30006 (Co-Cr-W)

30.6.6 Heat-Resistant Castings

The "workhorse" for high-temperature applications in the petrochemical industry is HK-40 (25Cr−20Ni; C 0.35 to 0.45%), used for ethylene pyrolysis furnace tubing. Other high-carbon, high-silicon castings (e.g., HT, 15Cr−35Ni) are used in heat-treating furnaces.

There is some evidence that internal porosity in centrifugally cast tubing aggravates the tendency for carburization of the internal surface of cracking sets. Much HK tubing purchased today is bored and honed to improve its resistance. A number of castings of proprietary composition are being marketed, based on allegedly superior resistance to carburization.

CHAPTER 31

Effects of Mercury

Mercury is a heavy metal (sp gr 13.6; about 1.7 times as heavy as steel), which is liquid above about −40°C. Everybody is familiar with its use in thermometers and barometers. It has also been used in manometers in plant for flow measurements by differential pressure across an orifice plate. Instruments containing mercury are always a potential source of process contamination.

Mercury has an appreciable vapor pressure even at room temperature; about 0.1 mm at 80°C (180°F). It will readily travel through piping and equipment as a vapor, contaminating the metal and causing specific effects.

The effects of mercury contamination on metals and alloys take three different forms:

Amalgamation

Environmental cracking (as LMC)

Increased general corrosion

The effect encountered depends on the materials involved.

Remember also that mercury is *poisonous* (specifically, it affects the nervous system—as in the old felt manufacturing process, whence the expression "mad as a hatter"). An open container of mercury will significantly contaminate the air in a room. Mercury may be purified and dried by boiling, but this should be done only under a suitable laboratory hood.

31.1 AMALGAMATION

Among the common materials of construction, lead, tin, copper, and aluminum are very susceptible to *amalgamation*, i.e., the formation of a low-melting eutectic.

Aluminum alloys are very susceptible once the mercury penetrates the oxide film on the surface. Of course, mercury *ions* have the same effect, due to cementation. The resulting alloy of aluminum and mercury is subject to rapid attack even in such otherwise innocuous media as moist air or distilled water (presumably because no protective oxide film can be formed). Catastrophic corrosion has been encountered in aluminum storage tanks for chemically pure acetic acid when contamination of the product was caused by mercury instrumentation.

Amalgamation of copper-nickel and nickel alloys is observed only at elevated temperatures, occurring rapidly at about 400°C (750°F) and only over an extended period of time at lower temperatures (but see "Environmental Cracking" below concerning LMC).

31.2 ENVIRONMENTAL CRACKING

The metals which are subject to environmental cracking by mercury (either by the metal itself or by solutions of mercury salts) are copper, nickel-copper (N04400, etc.), nickel (N02200, etc.). Ordinary iron and steel are unaffected. Both straight chromium and 18−8 stainless steels have been reportedly affected, but probably not by mercury alone. (Environmental cracking of austenitic grades is reported in mercuric chloride solutions, but it is not clear whether the phenomenon is influenced by the mercuric ion.)

The mechanism of cracking in nonferrous alloys appears to be a selective amalgamation at the grain boundaries, followed by mechanical damage to the weakened material by residual or applied stress. It is interesting to note that residual tensile stress is a prerequisite for attack by mercury salts. A standard mercuric nitrate test will differentiate degrees of cold-work from annealed material in yellow brass, for example.

Because of the very severe damage and the catastrophic rate of failure, this mode of attack is distinguished from the gross amalgamation described above.

31.3 ACCELERATED CORROSION

Although there is no amalgamation effect known, reliable investigators have reported definitely accelerated corrosion of S30400 in salt solutions to which as little as 0.5 ppm of mercury have been added.

SECTION **5**

Elements of Corrosion Control

CHAPTER **32**

Corrosion Control

As previously indicated, there are five basic approaches to corrosion control. These are

1. A change in the material of construction
2. A change in the nature of the environment
3. Placing a barrier film or coating between the material and the environment
4. Application of an electrochemical potential to the material
5. A change in the equipment design

Sometimes, these concepts overlap to a certain extent, as we will see in the following detailed discussions.

32.1 CHANGE OF MATERIAL

A change in material of construction is commonly required to meet changing conditions. The change may be total or partial.

32.1.1 Total Changes

A total change in materials of construction is a rather obvious step in many circumstances, as where the anticipated life for steel has not been obtained in atmospheric or water exposures. Copper, nickel, or stainless alloys might be substituted to obtain a more economical life.

It must be remembered that, from a standpoint of economics, it is usually necessary to accept some finite life for any specific material and that there is an equivalent uniform annual cost, as discussed in Chapter 33.

32.1.2 Partial Replacement

At other times, corrosion may be economically controlled by changing only the *surface* in contact with the environment, or perhaps only a part of the equipment. The former situation is exemplified by the use of a substantial heavy-duty surface (as distinct from thin coatings).

Surface Barriers

These would include metallic linings, claddings, and weld overlays as well as the organic and inorganic barriers, which are discussed in Chapter 36. The thinner platings and coatings are not considered in this category.

Vessel Parts

Sometimes, all that is required is to change a part of a vessel such as heat exchanger tubes, column trays, pump impellers, valve trim or install an additional component such as an impingement plate or an entrainment separator. Such changes should always be made with proper consideration of galvanic effects.

A classical example of partial replacement is the practice of *safe-ending* heat exchanger tubes. Where the inlet tube ends are subject to localized phenomena (e.g., SCC, inlet-end erosion), it is sometimes economical to weld a short length of corrosion-resistant tubing to the longer length of conventional material (e.g., a short length of N08800 to S30403, or N08825 to S31603). A 300 to 450 mm (12 to 18 in) length of resistant material in the hotter, more susceptible section of a heat exchanger bundle can obviate the need for a total retubing. However, the orbital (i.e., circumferential) welding of the individual short sections to the longer tubes is quite expensive, and the economics of safe-ending vs. total retubing must always be carefully evaluated.

32.2 CHANGE OF ENVIRONMENT

Within this category of corrosion control lie such measures as total change (e.g., from air to water cooling), neutralization of acidic or alkaline species, scavenging of corrosive species, inhibition, and even simple changes in temperature and/or pressure.

32.2.1 Total Changes

Total changes in environment, to be economically feasible, usually must be anticipated in the design stage. To change from water-cooled to air-cooled condensers, from seawater to freshwater systems, or from once-through to recirculated cooling water systems usually requires extensive redesign.

32.2.2 Partial Changes

Partial changes in the environment are often feasible. Indoors, relative humidity can be controlled and corrosive agents excluded by filtering and air-conditioning operations. For immersion conditions, the chemistry of the solution may be changed. Some common approaches are discussed below.

Acidity and Alkalinity Control

In aqueous media, pH is commonly controlled by minute additions of acid or alkali to establish conditions substantially noncorrosive to the materials of interest. In this manner, one may sometimes alleviate corrosion of steel and many nonferrous alloys or relieve the SCC propensity of austenitic stainless steels. As previously described, a high pH is conducive to the development of protective films for some alloy and solution combinations, such as calcareous deposits on steel in certain waters. Dilute acids, as in waste streams, may be brought into some degree of control by neutralizing to pH 6 to 8, in many cases.

In organic liquids, both acid and alkaline constituents may function only in their proportion to contained or dissolved water (as opposed to their nominal weight percent). In such cases, corrosion may be greater than anticipated from the percentage value and partial or complete neutralization of either contained caustic or contained acid may be necessary.

Scavenging

DO is frequently scavenged from water through treatment with sodium or ammonium sulfite, or hydrazine. As described in Chapter 18, catalyzed sulfite or hydrazine is available to hasten the speed of reaction.

Organic peroxides may be scavenged by reaction with sodium nitrite in some hydrocarbon applications, reducing the oxidizing capacity of the system.

Not so widely known is the capability of propylene oxide for scavenging traces of HCl from wet organic media, converting the HCl from the corrosive form to the noncorrosive propylene chlorhydrin.

Inhibitors

An inhibitor is a substance that reduces corrosion rates when relatively small amounts are added to the environment. Strictly speaking, an inhibitor should not be a major reactant, as in adjusting pH or scavenging oxygen. Inhibitors are discussed in detail in Chapter 34.

32.3 ANTICORROSION BARRIERS

These comprise some of the metallic and organic or inorganic barriers discussed in Chapter 36, as well as the paints and coatings covered in Chapter 35. Usually, these are less than 3 mm ($\frac{1}{8}$ in) thick, as distinct from heavy-duty applications discussed under "Change of Material."

32.4 ELECTROCHEMICAL TECHNIQUES

CP and AP have been mentioned in previous discussion. A fuller treatment is given in Chapter 37.

There are growing applications of techniques for holding process equipment at some predetermined potential for the alleviation of pitting, crevice corrosion, or environmental cracking. These are really field applications of the laboratory potentiostat, and are quite different from conventional CP or AP techniques.

Also in this category lies the use of galvanic couples for the detection of upset (corrosive) conditions, as described in Chapter 9.

32.5 DESIGN CONSIDERATIONS

Design considerations in corrosion control vary from the simple corrosion allowance against general attack to highly specific considerations for particular types of equipment.

32.5.1 Corrosion Allowance

In the happy circumstances that only general (i.e., uniform) corrosion is to be expected, at a constant or decelerating rate, a useful life can be achieved through the use of a corrosion allowance. This comprises an extra thickness of the wall of the vessel, pipe, or tubing which, when corroded away, will still leave sufficient wall thickness to meet the mechanical design requirements at temperature and pressure. Such an approach is practical if a reasonable corrosion allowance of 3 to 6 mm ($\frac{1}{8}$ to $\frac{1}{4}$ in) will suffice, and metallic contamination is not a consideration.

32.5.2 Velocity Control

Excessive velocity may result in erosion-corrosion or, in certain cases, cavitation.

Piping is traditionally limited to about 1.2 to 1.8 ms (4 to 6 fps) in process applications. Heat exchanger tubing limits vary from as low as 1 ms (3 fps) to 8 ms (25 fps), depending upon the material of construction and the specific service.

Special problems arise at areas of locally high volocity or impingement (e.g., opposite calandria return lines in columns, at ells and tees, in tube inlet areas, or where deposits or debris cause localized turbulence). For equipment inherently exposed to such effects, such as orifice plates, throttling valves, or pump impellers, erosion-resistant materials of construction are required.

32.5.3 Crevices and Drainage

Areas containing crevices or having inadequate drainage (e.g., flanges, threaded connections, internally protruding nozzles, or drain lines) are an invitation to pitting by oxygen concentration cells, localized accumulation of corrosive species, etc.

Crevices should be minimized, insofar as practical, and provision made for adequate drainage. Low "legs" in piping are to be avoided, as they may retain water or other corrosive or potentially corrosive materials, including sediment and deposits.

32.5.4 Stress Relief

There are two basic types of stress relief, thermal and mechanical. The former is more often employed against environmental cracking phenomena, the latter against mechanical fatigue. However, both are applicable as corrosion control measures against environmental cracking.

Thermal Stress Relief

Fabricated equipment is thermally stress relieved as a palliative measure against corrosion fatigue or environmental cracking. It is also used to minimize stress from the standpoint of mechanical considerations or NDTT problems.

Thermal stress relief consists of heating the item of equipment to a temperature appropriate for the alloy involved, holding it at that temperature for a specific period of time (usually for 1 h per inch (2.5 cm) of thickness and not less than 2 h, and then *slowly* cooling to room temperature (e.g., in the furnace, or in still air).

Mechanical Stress Relief

Mechanical stress relief consists of shot-peening the surface of an item of equipment with an appropriate type of shot (e.g., steel, stainless steel, or glass beads) to put that surface in a state of compressive stress. As previously explained, a surface in compressive (rather than tensile) stress is more resistant to mechanical fatigue, corrosion fatigue, or environmental cracking.

The shot-peening must be done under rigorously controlled conditions, using an *Almen strip*, which measures quantitatively the residual applied compressive stress (by the radius of curvature upward resulting from the peening operation).

It is evident that mechanical stress relief will be effective only as long as the surface under compressive stress is undisturbed by significant general corrosion.

32.6 SPECIAL FEATURES IN HEAT EXCHANGER DESIGN

Tube-and-shell heat exchangers present three problems related to their design and fabrication. These are roll leaks, tube defects (which can cause cross-contamination of one side of the exchanger or the other, possibly initiating corrosion problems which would not otherwise occur), and environmental cracking of tubes (which poses similar problems).

32.6.1 Tube-Tubesheet Joints

Roll Leaks

Roll leaks in the tube-tubesheet mechanical joint may arise from stresses imposed when the tube material has a higher coefficient of thermal expansion than the shell (e.g., austenitic stainless steel bundles in carbon steel shells). Unless adequate provision is made to take up the stress (usually by means of a suitable expansion joint in the shell for heat exchangers of double fixed-tubesheet design), the tube ends will eventually be forced out of their rolled joints by the forces developed by the differential thermal expansion.

However, the problem can also arise when hard tubes are rolled into tubesheets of softer material (e.g., titanium tubes in a bronze tubesheet or superferritic stainless tubes in an S30400 tubesheet). There may also be severe deformation of the tubesheet ligaments in such cases.

Roll leaks may also develop with soft tubes in harder tubesheets, but usually only under excessive thermal loads or cycles.

Welded Joints

Welding the ends of the tubes to the tubesheet is *not* a substitute for adequate design against differential thermal expansion. However, both seal welds and strength welds have their particular uses.

A seal weld, in which the tube end is merely fused to the face of the tubesheet, may constitute insurance against mixing of the two streams in case the mechanically rolled joint should loosen. It is also employed where tubes are rolled into a clad tubesheet (to prevent ingress of the tube-side environment to the nonresistant substrate material) or where conditions for crevice corrosion of the rolled joint from the tube side are severe. However, it is difficult to obtain a pore-free seal weld because of air trapped in the rolled joint (which tends to escape through the molten weldment during the operation).

A strength weld of proper design is a more reliable joint, is just as easy or easier to make, and permits subsequent thermal stress relief of the entire tube bundle, if required (see further below). A good strength weld requires following proper procedures in proper sequence. One good procedure is as follows (see Figure 32.1):

1. "Drift" the tube into position in the tubesheet, using a tapered pin. The tube end should protrude above the tubesheet for a distance equal to about 1 to $1\frac{1}{2}$ times the tubewall thickness. *Do not roll*.

2. Weld the tube end to the tubesheet face, either with an autogenous weld or with filler metal (at the discretion of the welder).

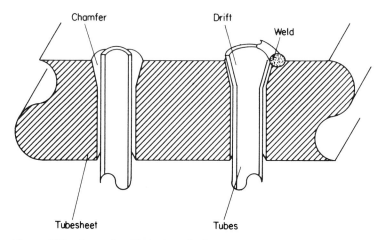

Figure 32.1   Strength-welded tube-tubesheet joint.

3. Apply an air test from the shell side; repair any leaking welds.

4. Complete the tube-rolling operation, starting about 6 mm ($\frac{1}{4}$ in) *behind*
the weld joint.

Since the strength now lies in the *welded* joint rather than the rolled joint, the
bundle can either be used in this condition *or* thermally stress-relieved, if
desired. A number of other strength-welding procedures may be found in the
literature.

32.6.2 Quality Control of Tubing

All tube-and-shell heat exchangers have a potential problem with the integrity
of the tubing. The quality of the tubing must be preestablished to ensure
against cross-contamination at through-wall defects. In a gas-to-gas exchanger, a minor tubewall leak may be of no consequence. However, in equipment
exchanging heat between steam or water and a process stream, the consequences of a minor leak vary from minor to disastrous. Even a minor leak in
either direction may have serious consequences in terms of either process
contamination or corrosion or of environmental pollution.

Both seamless and welded tubes may be good, bad or indifferent, depending on the care exercised during their manufacture and inspection. Although
the uninitiated tend to think of seamless tubes as a superior product, they can
and do contain flaws and defects. If the extrusion process is done at too high or
too low a temperature, the produce can contain "extrusion tears." Lubricant
or foreign matter may be retained on or in the tube wall. Stringers in the

original billet may be carried through to form "linecapping," or lap defects may be formed by "chatter" during the extrusion process. Such tears or cracklike laps can form either through-wall defects or areas capable of triggering localized corrosion or cracking.

Welded tubes are made from strip or skelp, which has already been inspected for flaws. When the skelp is hot-formed and the mating edges longitudinally welded by automatic inert-gas shielded arc welding (without filler metal), a tubular product of superior concentricity and dimensional control is produced. Unfortunately, there is always concern about the integrity of that continuous longitudinal weld in the as-welded condition.

However, when a welded tube is cold-drawn to about 15% reduction in wall or 35% in area, prior to the final solution-anneal, the energy introduced by the cold-work permits the weld to recrystallize, forming small grains with a wrought structure similar to that of the parent metal. This severe cold-work also stretches and tests every inch of the weld. Such a product is known as a *full-finished* tube and is very desirable for some critical corrosion services (e.g., hot organic acids).

For most services, aside from those highly conducive to localized corrosion (i.e., where minor defects might trigger cracking or pitting), it makes no difference whether the tubes are seamless, as-welded, beadworked (i.e., *locally* cold-worked only on and along the longitudinal weld) or full-finished. However, *if* full integrity is required, then adequate inspection is required.

For *maximum* quality assurance, tubing should be subjected to nondestructive electronic inspection (i.e., ultrasonic or eddy-current, as appropriate), hydrostatic testing to 150% of the highest working pressure (tube or shell side), and *also* tested by air under water at 125 psig internal pressure.

32.6.3 Stress Corrosion Cracking

Because SCC of heat exchangers is a perennial problem, it seems worthwhile to emphasize certain aspects of design and operation.

Venting

Concentration of water-borne salts under the top tubesheet is a problem peculiar to vertical condensers having water on the shell (a design often favored to optimize condensation and subcooling). SCC occurs most often in the rolled area immediately below the tubesheet, especially with 18−8 stainless steel tubes.

To alleviate this problem, the top tubesheet should be vented at three or four locations around its periphery, so that there is no vapor space, and the face of the tubesheet is continually flushed and cooled by flowing water. The vents must be kept open and operable at all times. Note that even nonferrous tubes such as copper can fail by pitting or corrosion in the vapor space of a vertical condenser unless tubesheet vents are provided.

Tubewall Temperature

It is desirable to design condensers so that the tubewall temperature does not exceed the temperature at which calcareous deposits are formed. Usually, a temperature of 60°C (140°F) maximum is suggested, although 50°C (122°F) may be preferable for some hard waters of high chloride content.

Safe Ending

Where the design is already fixed (as in retubing for maintenance purposes), or where the exchanger would be unduly large and expensive if designed for the suggested maximum tubewall temperatures, the tubes may be safe-ended, as previously described.

Stress Relief

Although stress-relieved *tubes* reportedly have been used, for example, for U-bundles in refinery exchangers, it must be remembered that additional stresses are imposed in assembly and operation (especially in the tube-rolling operation). To stress-relieve an entire strength-welded tube bundle is a more reliable approach, as described above.

RECOMMENDED READING

Pludek, V.R.: *Design for Corrosion Control*, Wiley, New York,

MTI Manual. No. 1: "Guidelines for Control of Stress Corrosion Cracking of Nickel-Bearing Stainless Steels and Nickel-Base Alloys," Materials Technology Institute of the Chemical Process Industries, Columbus, OH, 1979.

CHAPTER **33**

An Introduction to Economic Comparisons

Any recommendation for corrosion control involves asking management for money for cost-reduction purposes. Such requests must compete with requests for capital investment or operating funds for other purposes, and must stand on their own merits. The corrosion control recommendation(s) must be economically justified, and expressed in language that management can understand. To help the engineer do this, a simple calculation can be developed that includes a factor to correct for taxes and accounting procedures, which need not be understood in detail to be successfully applied. It is helpful, however, to understand the basic concepts described below.

33.1 RETURN ON INVESTMENT

The concept of *return on investment* (ROI), or its reciprocal concept of *payout period*, simply says that a proposed saving to be effected by diminished *annual cost* (i.e., investment amount divided by years of service or *life*) must yield at least a stipulated percentage return on the *increase* in capital investment. Payout, the reciprocal, requires that the increase be paid back within a specified number of years.

$$\text{ROI} = \frac{I/n - I'/n'}{I' - I} \text{ and Payout period} = \frac{1}{\text{ROI}}$$

where I and I' are the old and new (increased) investments and n and n' are the respective lives.

Because I/n is not a *true* annual cost (see below) and because this calculation does not permit comparison of capital outlays versus expense items, another concept must be established if we are to have an adequately sophisticated approach.

33.2 COMPOUND INTEREST

Compound interest has been called "the eighth wonder of the world" because, unlike simple interest, the *interest* earns interest. That is, interest is computed on the original *principal* together with its accrued interest. The principal is usually designated *present worth* (PW), and

$$\text{PW}(1 + i)^n = \text{FW}$$

where FW is *future worth*, i is the interest rate, and n is the number of periods the interest is compounded.

33.3 ANNUAL COST OR SAVINGS

Another way to arrive at some future worth is to put money aside at the end of each year, also at compound interest. It happens that end-of-the-year savings accrue according to the following formula:

$$\frac{A(1 + i)^n - 1}{i} = \text{FW}$$

where A is the annual cost.

33.4 PRESENT WORTH AND ANNUAL COST

Since things equal to the same thing are equal to each other, we have demonstrated that there is an *equivalent uniform annual cost (A)* for every present worth and future worth.

$$A = \frac{PW (1 + i)^n \times i}{(1 + i)^n - 1}$$

or

$$A = PW \times i \times F_n$$

where F is a variant from a "Sinking Fund" equation,

$$F = \frac{(1 + i)^n}{(1 + i)^n - 1}$$

Note that $1000 deposited in a savings account will draw interest over a period of years to attain some future worth. At 10% interest for 3 years,

$$\$1000 \,(1.10)^3 = \$1331$$

Another way to attain that FW is to set aside an annual saving, when

$$\$402 \,\frac{(1.10)^3 - 1}{0.10} = \$1331$$

and

$$\$402 = \$1000(0.10)F_3$$

where

$$F = \frac{(1.10)^3}{(1.10)^3 - 1} = 4.02$$

These relationships demonstrate that for the postulated conditions (i.e., money worth 10% over a 3-year period), $1000 of present worth, $1331 future worth, and $402 annual savings or cost are mathematically equal.

33.5 DISCOUNTING

So far, we have been concerned with *now*, the present worth and its equivalent uniform annual savings or cost. However, from the compound interest formula, it follows that if

$$PW(1 + i)^n = FW$$

then
$$PW = \frac{FW}{(1 + i)^n}$$

That is, any future worth can be *discounted* to its present worth. If money is worth 10% for a 3-year period, a *future* legacy of \$1331 has a present worth of \$1000.

This technique of discounting future worths is used to reduce them to equivalent present worths in order to sum them and then calculate the value of *A*. This permits us to compare all possible present or future income or expenditures on a directly comparable basis.

33.6 DEPRECIATION

The Internal Revenue Service permits one to "write off" or *depreciate* large capital expenditures over a period of time (either the actual life of the equipment or some earlier established duration, e.g., 11 years for process equipment).

Two of the most common depreciation schedules are *straight-line* and *sum-of-digit* (SOD). In straight-line depreciation, the cost of an item expected to last 3 years is written off in thirds (i.e., one-third for each year of the life, *n*). In SOD, the cost is written off in increments based on the fractions, the denominator of which is the SOD. For 3 years, the write-off fractions would be $\frac{3}{6}$, $\frac{2}{6}$, and $\frac{1}{6}$, since $1 + 2 + 3 = 6$. In general, the denominator is equal to $(n^2 + n)/2$ (i.e., for an 11-year write-off, the denominator would be $(122 + 11)/2$ or 66; the fractions 11/66, 10/66, . . . , 1/66).

The IRS permits a *tax credit* for each year's depreciation which is equal to the depreciation times the tax rate. If we depreciate \$1000 capital investment over a 3-year period by the straight-line method, with a 48% tax rate, the annual credit would be \$1000/3 × 0.48 or about \$160 per year.

33.7 DISCOUNTED CASH FLOW AND PRESENT WORTH AFTER TAXES

Discounted cash flow (DCF) is a technique used to arrive at *present worth after taxes* (PWAT). By setting up a capital investment for an anticipated duration, depreciating it on some permissible schedule, and taking the tax credit permitted, we establish first the cash flow itself. For example, a $1000 investment having a 3-year life, depreciated by the straight-line method, has the following cash flow:

| | Years | | |
	1	2	3
Investment	($1000)	(0)	(0)
Depreciation	$333	$333	$333
Tax credit	$160	$160	$160
Cash flow	($840)	$160	$160

These future values at the end of each year can be discounted by dividing them by $(1 + i)^n$ to get their present worth, which, because of the tax credit, are summed to PWAT. The DCF then becomes

| | Years | | |
	1	2	3
DCF	($840)	$160	$160
	1.10	$(1.10)^2$	$(1.10)^3$
PWAT	($764) +	$132 +	$120
Total	($512)		

Note that the PWAT of the capital investment is reduced by the PWAT of the future tax credits.

Table 33.1 gives a list of factors under d_n, calculated from a standard accounting procedure used in the chemical industry, based on a 48% tax rate and money worth 10%. Such factors allow us to reduce present worth to PWAT by multiplying by the factor d. It follows that

$$A = PW \times d \times r \times F_n$$

where r (rather than i) is the interest rate of return after taxes

$$r = i(1 - t)$$

with t the tax rate as a decimal.

Table 33.1   Economic Calculation Factors*

Years, n	$(1 + r)^n$	d_n	F_n
1	1.100	0.520	11.000
2	1.210	0.556	5.762
3	1.331	0.583	4.021
4	1.464	0.603	3.155
5	1.611	0.617	2.637
6	1.771	0.627	2.297
7	1.948	0.633	2.055
8	2.145	0.636	1.873
9	2.358	0.639	1.736
10	2.595	0.639	1.627
11	2.855	0.640	1.539
12	3.14	0.64	1.467
13	3.46	0.64	1.407
14	3.80	0.64	1.357
15	4.18	0.64	1.314
20	6.72	0.64	1.175
25	10.82	0.64	1.102
30	17.0	0.64	1.061

*Sum-of-digit depreciation (11-year schedule; balance in year of failure)
Maximum write-off 11 years (process equipment)
$r = 10\%$
Tax rate = 48%

33.8 PWAT AND ANNUAL COSTS

We can now sum a whole series of financial transactions (income or outgo, plus or minus), regardless of when they occur in time. They can all be expressed in terms of PWAT and, ultimately, as equivalent uniform annual cost, A.

For example, we propose to spend \$X now and \$Y a year from now, and expect to receive \$Z 10 years hence. Then

$$\text{PWAT} = -\$Xd_n - \frac{\$Yd}{(1 + r)^1} + \frac{\$Zd}{(1 + r)^{10}}$$

and

$$A = \text{PWAT} \times r \times F_n$$

Note also that the annual costs can be individually calculated and summed.

$$A = -\$Xd_nrF_n - \frac{\$Yd_nrF}{(1 + r)^1} \cdots$$

33.9 USE OF ANNUAL COSTS

33.9.1 Formulation

Annual costs permit a direct comparison between alternatives of different duration and different accounting (e.g., capital items vs. maintenance expenses), even when they occur at different times.

The annual cost of any cash disbursement or income at any time can easily be defined if we ask

1. How much does it cost (or pay)? i.e., x
2. When does it occur? i.e., $1/(1 + r)^{n'}$, where n' is the year of occurrence from now.
3. What depreciation factor applies? i.e., d_1 for expense; d_n for capital, where n is the life
4. What is the expected life?, i.e., n

Then

$$A = \pm \frac{xd_nrF}{(1 + r)^{n'}}$$

33.9.2 Examples

A stainless steel pump costs \$10,000 and lasts 2 years. The production loss associated with the shutdown costs \$10,000 also. What is the annual cost?

$$A = -\$10,000d_2rF_2 - \frac{\$10,000d_1rF_2}{(1 + r)^2}$$

$$= -\$10,000(0.556)0.1(5.762) - \frac{\$10,000(0.52)0.1(5.762)}{1.21}$$

$$= -\$3203 - \$2476 = -\$5679$$

Under these conditions, how much can we afford to pay for an alloy pump which would last 5 years? (Note that this only *delays* the shutdown cost from the second to the fifth year.) Since we must not spend more than we have already, we equate

$$-\$5679 \;=\; -xd_5rF_5 \;-\; \frac{\$10{,}000d_1rF_5}{(1+r)^5}$$

$$-\$5679 \;=\; -x(0.1627) \;-\; \frac{\$1371}{1.611}$$

$$-\$4828 \;=\; x(.1627)$$

$$x \;=\; -\$29{,}675$$

Note that \$29,675 is the *most* money we can spend for a more resistant pump under the conditions postulated. If we spent that much, we would gain no advantage. If it cost \$20,000 only, $A = \$4105$ with an annual saving of \$1574.

RECOMMENDED READING

NACE RP-02-72, "Direct Calculations of Economic Appraisals of Corrosion Control Measures," NACE, Houston, 1972.

CHAPTER **34**

Corrosion Inhibitors

Corrosion inhibitors are widely used in water, paint, oil-field applications, etc. Their use in chemical processes is of much lesser import. Nevertheless, the chemical engineer in the process industries should have at least a nodding familiarity with the subject.

34.1 DEFINITION

An *inhibitor* is a substance which, added to a bulk environment, slows down or prevents reaction *without itself taking a significant part in the reaction.*

A *corrosion inhibitor* is a substance which, added to a corrosive environment, decreases its corrosivity to a metal. (*Note:* This definition excludes treatment which radically changes the nature of the environment, such as deaeration, neutralization, or substantial additives, such as liming of soil).

34.2 ELECTROCHEMISTRY

True inhibitors (as opposed to materials which decrease corrosion by reactivity with the environment) function by adsorption on the metal surface, increasing polarization. A combination of adsorption of inhibitor and accumulation of corrosion products on the metal surface may produce a passive layer (e.g., chromates promote an invisible, protective oxide layer on steel in fresh water; small amounts of zinc cause precipitation of a protective hydroxide).

The examples mentioned represent typical anodic and cathodic reactions. *Anodic inhibitors* are dangerous because, added in insufficient amounts, they may increase general corrosion (functioning simply as cathodic depolarizers) or permit intensified attack (e.g., pitting) at sites devoid of inhibitor coverage. This is due to the large cathode (where the inhibitor has been not been adsorbed) vs. the small anodes left by incomplete coverage of the original anode surface. With *cathodic inhibitors*, insufficient additions simply let localized corrosion at the anodes proceed at a reduced rate, since the area of the cathode is at least partially diminished.

In many aqueous environments, the ideal commercial inhibitor includes a combination of anodic and cathodic inhibitors.

Successful use of inhibitors requires that the surfaces to be protected be boldly exposed so that they can adsorb inhibitor in adequate amounts, with the film readily replenished. Any crevices may lead to locally high rates of attack, particularly with oxidizing anodic inhibitors.

34.3 AQUEOUS SYSTEMS

Economic considerations effectively preclude the use of inhibitors in once-through water systems. Potable water is not particularly amenable to inhibition, because of toxicity or health considerations. However, because of the corrosivity of aerated water to steel and cast iron, many studies have been made. Complex polyphosphates and glassy silicates have sometimes been successfully used in very low concentrations (e.g., 1 to 2 ppm of sodium hexametaphosphate, the *threshold* treatment).

As indicated in Chapter 18, it is relatively easy and economical to adjust the water chemistry and inhibit open or closed recirculated cooling water systems.

Other considerations being equal, the corrosivity of water toward steel is proportional to the chloride content of the water (up to about 6000 ppm chloride ion). Oxidizing inhibitors have traditionally been preferred, from the standpoint of efficiency, when the chlorides were above about 200 ppm. Chromates have been the popular choice from the standpoint of cost and effectiveness, as nitrates and nitrites not only are quite readily reduced but are a potential source of ammonia contamination, which is objectionable in many systems. On the other hand, chromates are objectionable today, from the environmental standpoint.

The amount of chromate required to inhibit a given chloride level in water can be reduced by judicious mixing with other inhibitors (e.g., polyphosphates, zinc, organic compounds). In some cases, such chromate-type inhibitors are still employed, the toxicological and ecological objections being met by treatment of the effluent prior to discharge.

There have been new non-chromate-type inhibitors developed (e.g., polyphosphonates, phosphate esters, molybdates). Originally somewhat inadequate at chloride concentrations above perhaps 1000 ppm, the newer formulations may be more effective.

For a given water system, it is advisable to have professional input from either a reputable water-treating firm or an independent consultant.

34.4 REFRIGERATION BRINES

Solutions of about 25% calcium chloride are used in industrial processes to effect cooling below 0°C (32°F). These solutions are rendered noncorrosive by a combination of pH adjustment (e.g., 8.5+) and inhibition with about 2000 ppm chromate (as sodium chromate). Such solutions must be protected from exposure to air, to prevent absorption of carbon dioxide which will lower the pH and interfere with inhibition. If the pH drops below about 6.5, serious corrosion will occur. If caustic additions to maintain a pH of 8.5 to 9.0 are continued without excluding carbon dioxide, precipitation of calcium carbonate will occur. An inert atmosphere and good chemical control are required for these systems.

It is important not to alternate steam and calcium chloride or sodium chloride brines with austenitic stainless steel equipment, as serious pitting and/or SCC will ensue. The so-called dimpled jacket for vessels is also very susceptible to failure in chloride brines, because of the multiplicity of crevices involved in its construction and the high localized stresses.

Aqueous solutions of methanol or ethylene glycol are also used for refrigerating brines. These are less corrosive than the chloride solutions but nevertheless require inhibition, for example, combinations of borax and mercaptobenzothiazole (MBT).

34.5 ACIDS

Dilute solutions of hydrochloric acid (e.g., 5 to 15%) are used for pickling metal parts and in chemical cleaning of boilers and process equipment. These solutions are usually inhibited against corrosion of steel (*not* cast iron or stainless steel) with about 2000 ppm of a proprietary inhibitor. The useful inhibitors include amines, such as anilines and methylethyl pyridines; thiourea; sulfonated oils; etc.

These types of inhibitors are also employed with dilute sulfuric and phosphoric acid solutions (preferably augmented with iodide additions, in the latter case).

The inhibitors for steel are not effective for cast iron, probably because of the galvanic influence of the free graphite. Also, stainless steels are not to be exposed to hydrochloric acid cleaning solutions because of their propensity for pitting and SCC. The nonferrous alloys must be evaluated in terms of the specific acid and inhibitor combinations.

34.6 ACID-GAS SCRUBBING SYSTEMS

The corrosion in acid-gas scrubbing systems, such as monoethanolamine (MEA), diethanolamine (DEA), diglycolamine (DGA), needs to be appraised on the basis of individual systems. Some are corrosive and some are not, depending upon mode of operation, degree of degradation, process contaminants, etc.

Oilfield-type inhibitors (see "Nonaqueous Environments") are successfully used in some systems, while in others mixtures of inhibitors employed include sodium vanadate–potassium antimony tartrate, etc. The oxidizing inhibitors are not useful when the gas stream contains hydrogen sulfide. They are used successfully in potassium carbonate–bicarbonate scrubbing systems as well as in ethanolamines. Note, however, that *chromates* are incompatible with alkanolamines.

34.7 NONAQUEOUS ENVIRONMENTS

Inhibitors for petroleum products or oil-water mixtures usually feature an additive which is attracted to the metal surface via a polar group, and extends a water-repelling structure toward the bulk environment. These are analogous to the function of octadecylamine as an inhibitor in steam condensate, previously described.

Other inhibitors include cationic agents, like amines, and anionic agents, like sulfonates. The iodide ion apparently enhances the power of amines, such as decylamine, to function as corrosion inhibitors for steel.

Vapor-phase inhibitors (e.g., dicyclohexylammonium nitrite) are used in paper for wrapping finished machined parts as protection against atmospheric corrosion. They are also used in closing up equipment, as for dry lay-up. It should be emphasized that their throwing power is limited to short distances (e.g., a few inches), so they must be in intimate contact with (or very close to) the surface to be protected.

34.8 OTHER CONSIDERATIONS

The main considerations in selecting an inhibitor for a specific application are efficiency (because they usually only reduce, rather than prevent, corrosion), the economics of its use, and possible adverse effects. A particular corrosion inhibitor may have adverse effects on a process, even though otherwise effective, as by poisoning a catalyst or affecting final product quality. Particular components of a process equipment system may be incompatible with the inhibitor, even though it is protective of the major material of construction. It is important that valve trim, pump parts, process instrumentation, etc. be considered in making the final decision. It may be necessary to make significant changes in that area before implementing the corrosion inhibition program.

CHAPTER **35**

Paints and Coatings

A tremendous amount of steel is used in both industrial and consumer applications, and much effort is expended on preventing its spontaneous rusting. Rust and corrosion can be a problem not only from the standpoint of wastage of metal but also from the aspect of product contamination as by internal corrosion of storage tanks. Machined parts can be rendered useless by even superficial rusting. Rust is also aesthetically objectionable.

Temporary protection, as for machined parts or steel in storage, may be achieved by means of special oils, greases, or waxlike coatings. More nearly permanent protection is effected by suitable paints or coatings, properly maintained.

In common parlance, the term *paint* is commonly used to indicate a system applied to the exterior, while *coatings* more often signify systems for internal lining or external spillage or other more severe conditions. However, NACE terminology uses the word coatings in the broader sense to encompass all kinds of paints and coatings.

35.1 TEMPORARY RUST PREVENTATIVES

Ordinary oils and greases, such as those used for lubrication, are not themselves effective protection against rust. This is due to acidic components formed by the oxidation of hydrocarbons, and the fact that ordinary oils and greases cannot effectively displace water from the metal surface.

By the addition of buffering agents, corrosion inhibitors, and chemical additives which permit the oil to "wet" the metal surface (displacing moisture), common oils and greases are converted into effective rust preventatives.

These proprietary products, often called *slushing compounds*, vary in their effectiveness, depending on whether they are used for indoor or outdoor storage, for how long, and how aggressive the environment. (Note that an "indoor" environment may be very aggressive, in the vicinity of acid fumes, for example, as discussed in Chapter 20.)

The commercial rust preventatives vary in consistency from light machine oils through heavier oils, greases, and waxes to hard strippable films. Table 35.1 shows a number of categories of rust preventatives, with their characteristics and uses, covered by the American Military Specification MIL-P-116E.

35.2 PAINTS AND COATINGS

Although everybody knows in a general way what paints are, they are not always defined in corrosion texts. For our purposes, they can be defined as below.

35.2.1 Definition

Paints and coatings are a mixture of pigments with natural or synthetic resins (plus solvents, plasticizers, and extenders), which form a protective film by drying, oxidizing, or polymerizing.

35.2.2 Types of Coatings

Paints and coatings may be based on either naturally occurring compounds or synthetic materials, or a mixture of the two. Traditionally, the natural systems have been based on asphaltic or bituminous materials or on natural oils, such as those derived from rice and fish. The latter group comprise the original "oleoresinous" paints, but the term has a much broader meaning today. These older systems are much more tolerant of poor surface preparation and contamination than are the modern synthetic paints and coatings.

The modern synthetic coating systems are based on a variety of chemistries. Usually, they demand more sophisticated surface preparation and

Table 35.1 MIL-P-116E Temporary Rust Preventative Compound Chart

	P1	P2	P3	P10	P11
Type	Solvent cutback, thin, hard	Solvent cutback, thin soft	Water displacing, oily, light	Oily film	Grease, soft
Color	Black	Amber, transparent	Transparent	Transparent	Semitransparent
Use	General purpose, indoor or out, with or without cover	Indoor or under cover; limited out	Indoor or under cover; limited protection	Protection of internal surfaces of internal combustion engines	Indoor or out; must be removed
Life,					
out	2 yr	4 mo	2 weeks	None	2 mo–2 yr
in	5 yr	2 yr	1 yr	6 mo	1–5 yr
Federal specifications	MIL-C-16173	MIL-C-16173	MIL-C-16173	MIL-L-21260	MIL-C-10924
	Grade I Type P1	Grade II Type P2	Grade III Type P3	Various	Various
Drying	1.5 h	0.5 h	0.5 h	—	—
Ft²/gal	400	800	1400	4000	—
Thickness, in.	0.004	0.002	0.001	0.0005	0.16

application than the natural systems. However, their improved performance more than compensates for the incremental cost of materials and labor.

The various types of paints and coating systems in current use include the following.

Alkyds.   This nomenclature derives from the alcohols and acids used in the manufacture of the paint. Alkyds have largely replaced the original oil-base paints. They are faster drying and have better gloss retention, greater hardness, increased water resistance, good weathering characteristics, and good durability in mild exposures. Although they do not have good chemical or solvent resistance, they are the "workhorse" of much industrial painting.

Acrylics.   These are systems based on resins formulated from acrylic acid and acrylate esters. They are used to produce a high-gloss finish on house siding, automobiles, and appliances. Because they also possess good chemical and sunlight resistance, they are being increasingly used in industry both for appearance and protection.

Bituminous.   The bituminous systems comprise asphaltic or coal tar—based resins, including both natural and combination natural and synthetic mixes. Coal-tar coatings have good water resistance, which can be improved by formulating with epoxies, but are not very good in weather and have poor resistance to sunlight. Bituminous coatings are mostly used for underground protection.

Chlorhydrocarbons.   Chlorinated hydrocarbon paints are quite similar to chlorinated rubber. Having good resistance to moisture and *inorganic* chemicals, they are particularly useful for application to masonry.

Chlorinated Rubber.   These systems have good chemical and excellent water resistance, but are adversely affected by direct sunlight. They are good for splash-zone and immersion service, and are useful for coating concrete.

Epoxies.   These are formulated from polyphenols and epichlorhydrin, and require a catalyst to effect curing. The epoxies have good adhesion and are resistant to acids, alkalis, and many solvents. Good quality catalyzed epoxies are used for many severe atmospheric and water-immersion applications.

Epoxy-Esters.   These systems are compounded with drying oils to provide an uncatalyzed, single-package paint. They have good resistance to moisture, but have sacrificed most of their chemical and UV resistance.

Latex.   These water-base paints are formulated from vinyl or acrylic resins and have the advantage of lacking objectionable solvents. They are easily applied to masonry as well as steel.

Oleoresins. These are any combination of oils and resins, including oil-modified phenolics and modified epoxies as well as alkyds. Because of their slow drying characteristics and limited chemical resistance, they have only restricted application in modern industrial plant.

Phenolics. The outstanding phenolic systems are those which are *baked* at about 230°C (450°F) to provide a 3- to 5-mil coating of high chemical resistance. Although attacked by oxidants and by even dilute alkalis, they provide both corrosion and contamination protection in a wide variety of chemical and petroleum services.

Phenoxys. The phenoxy systems make excellent primers because they readily wet and adhere to steel. Because they lack good weathering characteristics, they are not used for finish coats. Their primary use is as zinc-rich organic primers.

Polyesters. Besides their use in reinforced plastics and high-build barriers, the vinyl polyesters are available as both thin- and medium-build coatings.

Silicones. The silicone systems are quite expensive, being based on organic silicon compounds (which have silicon rather than carbon linkages in the structure). They are primarily used for high-temperature service, where carbon-based coatings would oxidize. Silicone paints are frequently pigmented with powdered aluminum.

Urethanes. Several types of urethane formulations are defined in ASTM C-16. These products provide a wide range of properties characterized by excellent abrasion resistance, good chemical resistance, and outstanding gloss retention. Proper selection of the appropriate formulation for the intended service is very important.

Vinyls. The copolymers of vinyl chloride and vinyl acetate are solvent-based paint systems. While they lack solvent resistance thereby, they are outstanding in marine environments. They also have good resistance to acids, alkalis, and oxidants. An excellent combination for industrial and marine exposures is a vinyl top coat over an inorganic zinc primer.

Zinc, Inorganic. The "IZ" system is silicate-based, heavily pigmented (about 70%) with powdered zinc. When dried, the zinc content provides CP to the steel substrate at any holidays, i.e., through-film defects, or scratches. The IZ system is excellent in its own right, being resistant to high-humidity atmospheres and salt spray (although it will not withstand acids or alkalis). However, it gives its best service when top-coated with another system (e.g., vinyl, epoxy, or coal tar). It should be noted that any sulfur contamination, as by atmospheric pollution, may make it difficult to top-coat. The choice between using IZ paint systems as opposed to hot-dipped galvanized steel is primarily an economic decision, largely based on the area per ton of steel.

35.2.3 Preparation and Application

Selection of the appropriate paint system presupposes consideration of the application conditions and material problems that may be encountered (e.g., temperatures to be expected, catalyst problems, compatibility with existing paints, viscosity problems, drying rates, contamination effects, overspray, flowout, thickness, or moisture tolerance of the paint system). Certainly, the system must be durable—i.e., resistant to UV, chalking, oxidation, loss of constituents after curing, thermal shock, moisture, chemicals, and loss of adhesion.

Most modern paint systems require good surface preparation, and this can be a major part of the overall cost (usually 70 to 80%). The older traditional surface preparation (e.g., by brushing, scraping, or flame cleaning) has largely given way to mechanical cleaning.

The minimum in mechanical cleaning is derived from power wire-brushing or needle guns. Abrasive blasting is preferred to establish a suitable surface profile, at the same time cleaning the surface to promote both mechanical and ionic bonding. Abrasive blasting may be effected with sand, grit, or other materials, wet or dry. The degree of cleanliness (e.g., brush-off, commercial, near-white, or white) is determined by comparison with NACE or other standards.

Application methods vary from the traditional paintbrush or roller to spray techniques, of which the latter is preferred for large-scale industrial applications. High-pressure airless spray is commonly used. Exact procedures will vary with the paint system and application conditions, and should be based upon manufacturers' recommendations.

35.2.4 Justification

The economics of painting hinge on three factors: safety, metal replacement costs, and aesthetics. Because the corrosion rate is relatively low in many atmospheres, most current painting is done for aesthetic reasons. However, with the steady increase in materials costs and the depletion of our natural resources, the decision to achieve an adequate paint job to protect an investment is easily justified. Certainly, when safety of people is concerned, such as in maintenance of highway bridges, a considerable maintenance expense is justified.

Justification for a paint system and its maintenance program can easily be determined by the methods described in Chapter 33. The cost of rigging, surface preparation, paint materials, inspection, and other factors must all be incorporated in the calculations. An evaluation of the procedures to be used must be made prior to implementation. A decision must be made as to whether to use company personnel (if available) or contractors. Individual contractors may operate on either a bid or a cost-plus basis. Many offer maintenance contracts as well.

It is more difficult to compute the effectiveness of a painting program. Only the cost per square foot (or square meter) per year is an adequate index. Expressing the cost as percent of capital investment or of the maintenance costs is meaningless. Specifications for the entire job must be written. These will not in themselves assure a good job, however. A prejob conference should be held to ensure a common understanding among all parties involved as to what is to be done and how.

Proper application of the paint system cannot be overemphasized. Trained application personnel and competent inspectors are essential. Expediency must not be allowed to compromise the job just to meet a schedule. The final job and its service performance will be not better than the attention given to application details.

Adequate inspection can greatly aid in obtaining a better job but, in the last analysis, the knowledge and integrity of the applicator crews are essential to a satisfactory paint or coating application.

RECOMMENDED READING

Burns, R. M., and Bradley, W. W.: *Protective Coatings for Metals* (ACS Monograph No. 163) 3d ed., American Chemical Society, Washington, D.C., 1967.

Munger, Charles G.: *Corrosion Prevention by Protective Coatings*. NACE, Houston, 1985.

CHAPTER **36**

Anticorrosion Barriers

This brief chapter discusses techniques which are a combination of two corrosion control techniques, a sort of mix between changing materials of construction and interspersing a barrier layer between the material and the environment. I have deliberately elected to consider anticorrosion barriers as a separate entity from paints and coatings, for example.

This treatment of the subject derives from the fact that a change in material of construction can be partial rather than total. Corrosion may often be economically controlled by changing only the surface characteristics, e.g., by means of a fairly thick and substantial barrier (as distinct from paints, coatings, and thin electroplating or similar means). Indeed, in some cases, this anticorrosion barrier may be applied only to a localized part of the equipment, such as the bottom of a tank or vessel.

Such a barrier may be organic in nature, like a lining of a plastic or elastomeric material; inorganic, such as glass, cement, or metallic oxide; or metallic. The following discussion is divided into metallic and nonmetallic barriers.

METALLIC BARRIERS

36.1.1 Plating and Metallizing

Because of the thin deposit formed, as well as a tendency to contain defects or holidays which would expose the nonresistant substrate, electroplating is not often used for corrosion control in distinctly corrosive services. More often, electroplating (or electroless plating, in the case of the nickel–nickel phosphide deposit) is used to minimize contamination of product or to improve lubrication, as in chromium plating of rotating equipment, where the microcracked chrome plate tends to act as a reservoir for oil.

An important exception is tantalum plating, deposited from a molten salt bath. This has the unique characteristic of being *pore-free*. Tantalum-plated artifacts with a substrate of steel, copper alloys, etc. can be utilized in services which would rapidly attack the substrate. Typical applications include tantalum-plated thermowells and orifice plates.

Metallizing, as of zinc or aluminum, is effected by spraying molten metal on a steel substrate. The resultant surface is very porous but does effectively reduce the area of steel exposed, as in barge or tanker compartments handling iron-sensitive products.

36.1.2 Weld Overlays

A weld overlay is usually laid down in two or (preferably) three weld passes to deposit a surface of weld metal considerably more corrosion-resistant than the substrate. A familiar example is the deposition of S30803 or S31603 stainless steel weld overlays on carbon steel to give corrosion resistance equivalent to solid stainless steel.

The purpose of the multiple passes is threefold. First of all, they override the dilution effect inherent in the first-pass melt mixture, which loses some of its alloy content by dilution with carbon steel. Secondly, they minimize the chance of a fault or holiday giving the environment access to the nonresistant substrate. Thirdly, they tend to assure that the final surface will have a chemical composition very nearly identical to that of the weld rod itself.

It should be noted, however, that there are specialized modern techniques which can achieve these effects in a single-pass weld overlay, but their use is restricted to shop fabrication under highly controlled conditions. For maintenance work in the field especially, the multipass weld overlay is to be preferred to single-pass work.

The weld overlay may be put down manually or under machine-controlled conditions, using any conventional welding process appropriate to the weld metal–substrate combination. There is a machine available which uses a submerged-arc technique to deposit an overlay while it rotates within a vertical cylindrical vessel.

Although weld overlays are intimately bonded to the substrate material, they do contain high residual stresses. The alloy selected for the overlay deposit should therefore be neither hot-short nor susceptible to environmental cracking in the environment of concern.

One of the weaknesses of a weld overlay is that it cannot be subjected to a quality assurance test for resistance to IGC (e.g., of a columbium-stabilized or low-carbon deposit), as can the linings or claddings described below.

36.1.3 Linings

A metallic *lining* is fabricated by attaching a series of small segments of sheet or plate, usually by welding, to a less-corrosion-resistant substrate metal or alloy. A substantial amount of linear welding is involved, depending upon the size of the segments relative to the total area of the vessel or part of the vessel to be lined.

Linings have an advantage over weld overlays to the extent that the sheet or plate can be subjected to quality assurance corrosion tests prior to welding in place. To a certain extent, they share the disadvantage inherent in a multiplicity of welds, i.e., the possibility of weld defects.

Another disadvantage can arise if there is a significant difference in thermal expansion between the alloy lining and the substrate. Such a difference can result in inordinately high stresses unless the lining is very carefully designed. Austenitic stainless steel linings in carbon steel vessels are notoriously subject to failure in service for this reason.

Vacuum service is very hard on lined vessels and, unless the vessel is specifically designed for the vacuum rating, can lead to premature failure, usually in the form of weld cracking. Once a leak occurs between the lining and the vessel wall, weld repair is difficult, or impossible, because of foreign material trapped between them.

Alloy linings are usually more often specified for repair or refurbishing than for new design.

36.1.4 Cladding

Cladding is the preferred technique, from the standpoint of reliability, for the application of a corrosion-resistant barrier of a metallic nature on a less-resistant substrate.

In this technique, a sheet or plate of a resistant alloy is *metallurgically bonded* to a less-resistant substrate, whose function it is to provide the mechanical strength. Usually, the cladding comprises 10 to 20% of the total wall thickness [e.g., 3 mm ($\frac{1}{8}$ in) of alloy on a 1.2 cm (0.5 in) of steel plate]. The mechanical strength is predicted only on the thickness of the *substrate* material.

Unless there is a particular service requirement other than general corrosion resistance, e.g., having an *exterior* surface resistant to SCC, clad construction usually becomes economically competitive with solid alloy construction at about 16- to 19-mm (0.625- to 0.75-in) total thickness.

The manufacturing processes for clad steel plate include rolling, brazing, and explosive bonding. The cladding material can be subjected to prior quality assurance tests, Nevertheless, the integrity of the metallurgical bond should subsequently be verified by ultrasonic inspection. A partially disbonded cladding has the same weaknesses as a lining (in vacuum service, for example).

Cladding is commonly employed to provide a corrosion-resistant barrier of copper or nickel alloys, stainless steels, or reactive metals on steel or low-alloy steels. Because of the intimate metallurgical bond, differential thermal expansion is less of a problem than with linings.

There is, however, a problem in SCC service. Thermal stress relief is not effective for clad construction if there is a significant difference in thermal expansion between cladding and substrate (e.g., S30403 or S31603 stainless cladding on carbon steel). One can go through the motions, e.g., 2 hr per 2.5 cm (1 in) of thickness at 900°C (1650°F) and a slow cool. However, stresses will be reintroduced during the cooling process, due to the restraint imposed, and the cladding will still be susceptible to SCC.

36.2 NONMETALLIC BARRIERS

36.2.1 Organic

Organic barriers comprise both plastic or elastomeric sheet linings and heavy-duty coatings. The sheet linings most commonly employed are rubber linings of various kinds and vinyl, polyolefin, or fluorinated plastics (e.g., FEP, PFA).

Whereas paints and coatings (see Chapter 17) are usually of a 0.08- to 0.38-mm (3- to 15-mil) thickness, heavy-duty films of 1 mm (40 mils) or more may be considered barrier materials, Among these, we find vinyl plastisols, fused fluorocarbons, 0.25 mm (10 mils) per coat; PFA coatings; flakeglass-filled polyesters; and vinyl esters. Currently, special furane coatings of up to 2.5 to 3.0 mm (100 to 125 mils) are also available.

36.2.2 Inorganic

Glass linings of 1.5 to 2 mm (60− to 80 mils) have been previously mentioned. Cementitious barriers may be spray-applied on the interior of vessels. Brick linings and carbon-brick are also employed to provide very thick anticorrosion barriers on the interior of steel vessels. The conventional acid-brick is best employed in conjunction with a plastic or elastomeric membrane.

CHAPTER **37**

Cathodic Protection

There have been several mentions of CP in past chapters. Although of primary interest to "pipeliners," it behooves the process industry engineer to understand the principles and applications for interplant and intraplant underground piping, buried or mounded vessels, and water services.

37.1 DEFINITION

CP is the reduction or elimination of corrosion by making the metal structure a cathode by means of an impressed current. The dc current employed may be generated by corrosion of a sacrificial anode or by the application of impressed current from an external source.

From the electrochemical standpoint, CP is effected by polarizing the local cathodes to a potential as negative as (or more negative than) the metallic anodes on the structure to be protected.

37.2 PRINCIPLES

It has been previously noted that corrosion in natural environments is usually under cathodic control. In aqueous environments of high conductivity, this means that the principal controlling factor is the degree of polarization of the cathode.

In less-conductive waters, and for underground applications in soil particularly, the effect of electrolyte resistivity is additive to the influence of driving potential between anodes and cathodes and their effective polarization.

The relationship between voltage (E), amperage (I), and resistance (R) is given by Ohm's law

$$E = IR$$

where E is in volts, I in amperes, and R in ohms (or their values in milliequivalents).

It must also be remembered that a series of individual resistances can be summed as $R = r + r' + r'' \ldots$, while *parallel* resistances (which apply particularly in soil) are summed as their reciprocals, where $1/R = 1/r + 1/r' + 1/r'' \ldots$. Series resistance applies to structure-cable-anode connections, while parallel resistances apply to current paths in water or soil for the immersed anodes and structure, and to multiple-anode connections supplying current to a pipeline.

37.2.1 Galvanic Anode Systems

When CP employs sacrificial anodes such as magnesium, zinc, or aluminum, they function in a galvanic cell as a source of dc current. Corrosion is not stopped or slowed, but rather is transferred from the structure to the galvanic anodes, while a net current flow onto the structure effects CP. The electrochemical basis for CP by sacrificial anodes is illustrated in Figure 37.1.

Selection of galvanic anodes for a given system calls for consideration of three requirements:

1. There must be sufficient driving potential between the anodes and the structure acting as cathode to overcome local anodes.
2. The anodes must have enough contained energy to give an effective and economical life.
3. The anodes must have good efficiency (i.e., relatively little self- or autocorrosion, which does not effectively contribute to the CP system).

Efficiency is usually expressed as a percentage, but is practically evaluated in terms of ampere-hours per pound (A-hr/lb) or as pounds per ampere-year. For example, zinc theoretically would provide 372 A-hr/lb but, at its 95% (0.95%) efficiency, actually yields about 353 A-h/lb. Magnesium is less efficient but cheaper than zinc and is preferred in most soil applications. It is subject to excessive autocorrosion in seawater (where zinc or aluminum are preferred).

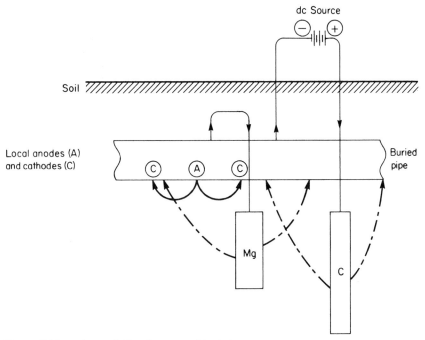

Figure 37.1 Galvanic *(left)* and impressed *(right)* current CP systems. Corrosion current: →;
CP current: - · - · →.

Replacement of galvanic anodes is predicated on figures such as these (i.e.,
how long an anode of a given weight should survive).

37.2.2 Impressed Current Systems

Impressed current systems supply energy from an external source, and the
system of structure and relatively inert anode(s) comprise a *sink*. The anodes
are connected to the *positive* lead of the dc source. The situation is the reverse
of a problem in electrolysis and is analogous to recharging the storage battery
in an automobile.

Usually, the dc source is a rectifier connected to available ac power.
However, other dc sources are also employed, such as storage batteries,
motor-driven generators, windmills, fuel cells, thermoelectric devices, and
solar panels.

Because of the way an impressed current system is connected, high-quality
cable and carefully insulated cable connections are required. Otherwise,
electrolysis *will* occur at weak points in the insulation. (Galvanic systems
cathodically protect the substrate at such defects.)

37.2.3 Geometry Effects

In terms of where the current can most easily go, all CP systems are subject to the sort of limitations previously described under galvanic corrosion (Chapter 5). However, the practical aspects are somewhat more complex, especially in underground applications.

Figure 37.2 illustrates the current and voltage distribution related to a single anode for a section of pipeline. Galvanic systems often have n anodes per mile (or kilometer) of line, for example. The current distribution and attendant voltage changes are influenced by both distance of anode from the pipe and by soil resistivity. Figure 37.3 illustrates the effect of a low-resistivity soil such as clay on the same pattern.

A foreign metallic structure in the vicinity offers the same sort of low-resistivity path and also suffers electrolysis where the current *leaves* the foreign structure to go the structure under deliberate protection (Figure 37.4). This could be corrected either with a separate anode system or, as shown, with a resistance bond (leaving the foreign structure unprotected).

37.2.4 Criteria for CP

Any current from an external source which enters the structure is beneficial, as a rule. However, there are three commonly accepted criteria which indicate that adequate protection is being effected.

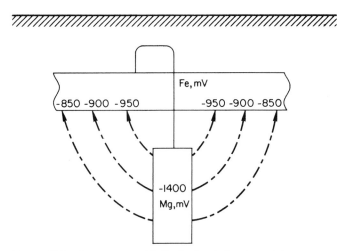

Figure 37.2   Current-potential distribution (galvanic anode).

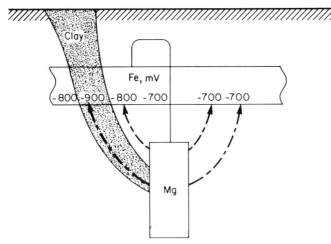

Figure 37.3 Effect of low-resistivity strata on current flow.

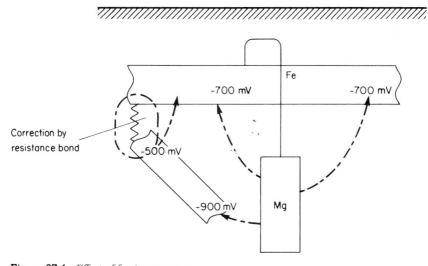

Figure 37.4 Effect of foreign structure.

Potential vs. Environment

For steel in soil, particularly (whose freely corroding potential usually lies between −300 to −700 mV to a copper:copper sulfate electrode), protection is thought to be achieved when the potential is lowered to −850 mV. If sulfate-reducing bacteria are present, a further 100-mV reduction (to −950 mV) is recommended. Pipe-to-soil potentials (an integral part of design and operation) are read directly over the line, as close to its surface as possible (usually a couple of feet, because of the earth cover). Potentials below about -1100 mV tend to generate molecular hydrogen, which can waste protective currents as well as cause disbonding of coatings.

Other materials have different criteria; for example, -700 mV for lead (as in telephone cable sheath), and -1000 to -1200 mV for aluminum. For such amphoteric metals, *overprotection* is harmful because of attack by the cathodically produced alkali.

In other situations, different reference half-cells may be employed (e.g., silver:silver chloride in seawater). Then an algebraic correction must be made to the protective value. For example, the copper:copper sulfate electrode is $+316$ mV to the SHE, while Ag:AgCl is $+246$ mV, and the SCE is $+242$ mV vs. SHE. The protective value of -850 mV vs. copper:copper sulfate is therefore -780 mV to silver:silver chloride and -534 vs. SHE.

Potential Change

There are any number of reasons why the ideal protected potential may not be achievable in some particular installation. For this reason, a negative shift in potential of about 400 mV from the original is often considered indication of an acceptable level of CP.

Direction of Current Flow

Lastly, even with less-negative values observed than described above, low readings on a line are of little concern provided it can be shown that the pipe is *gathering* current from all sides. Only a *discharge* of current from structure to soil is cause for concern.

Two other criteria are sometimes employed.

1. Corrosion coupons (or other corrosion-detection devices) can be attached to the structure, for electrical continuity, evaluation of which in the connected vs. electrically isolated condition is a measure of the efficacy of corrosion control by the CP system.

2. *Vertical* structures (e.g., well-casings) are designed on a current-demand basis derived from a plot of voltage vs. current known as an E-log I curve.

37.3 DESIGN AND APPLICATION

In designing a CP system, we must first know the current demand of the structure to be protected. (The soil resistivity is also a critical value for underground applications, determined by field measurement and calculation, using an applied current and voltage shift in the "four-pin," or Wenner, method.)

In modern practice, buried or immersed structures are *coated* with a suitable high-resistance, high-dielectric system whose purpose is mostly to reduce the *area* of bare metal to be protected. For practical purposes, this means the metal exposed at original or potential holidays.

With underground piping, the system is electrically isolated at each end (to prevent egress of current), and a dc source is used to apply current until the pipe-to-soil potential reaches the desired criterion. From the current demand and soil resistivity, the necessary galvanic or impressed current system can be designed.

37.3.1 Local Conditions Affecting Design

Local conditions which will affect the design include:

1. The availability of power (for impressed current systems).
2. Location; for example, is this location suitable for installation, inspection, and maintenance?
3. Presence of foreign structures in the vicinity and possible effects of other CP systems.
4. In plant, particularly, such unusual conditions as past or potential future acid or chemical spills, coal-pile drainage, etc.

37.3.2 Factors Affecting Design

Some of the factors affecting design decisions include:

1. Total current requirement; low current demand favors galvanic anodes, while high current demands almost always require impressed current systems.
2. Variations in structure or environment; a well-coated pipeline in good soil will have very low demand, whereas bare steel in flowing water will have a high demand.
3. The material to be protected (i.e., steel, lead, aluminum, stainless steel) must be considered in regard to protection criteria.
4. The life requirement of the installation and degree of reliability and maintainability desired enter into the economics of the design.
5. Suitable anode materials must be chosen—e.g., magnesium, zinc, or aluminum for galvanic systems; silicon iron, carbon, platinized titanium, or other proprietary materials for impressed current systems.

Details of design, sizing of anode beds, etc. should be referred to a corrosion engineer with specialized training in the CP field.

37.4 SPECIALTY APPLICATIONS

Some specialty applications are well outside the interests of the process industry engineer (e.g., submerged oceanic lines; deep ground beds; marine applications for piling, hulls, ballast compartments and propellers; CP for rebar in concrete highway bridges). However, in addition to buried lines and buried or mounded tanks or vessels, the chemical process industries engineer may become involved in water tanks, seawater flumes or piping, waterboxes for coolers and condensers, and processes themselves.

37.4.1 Crevice Corrosion and SCC

CP is sometimes employed against crevice corrosion and SCC (the latter usually via sacrificial metallic coatings). Modern practice is leaning toward potentiostatic control, derived from the laboratory apparatus and technique, to combat such phenomena, especially in the paper industry.

37.4.2 Anodic Protection

This technique, as previously noted, is the *opposite* of CP and can only be employed for special combinations of metal or alloy and environment systems. The most common applications lie in sulfuric acid storage in steel (to minimize iron contamination) and for S31603 coolers for hot strong sulfuric acid.

Because of the ever-present danger of electrolysis in the event of loss of proper control, it is even more important than for CP that these systems be professionally designed and supervised.

CHAPTER **38**

Inspection and Failure Analysis

It is necessary for reliable plant operation that process equipment be inspected on a regular basis in an effort to anticipate failures and prevent unscheduled shutdowns. But even with the best efforts, some failures will inevitably occur. This chapter addresses inspection schedules and techniques, and the methodology of failure analysis.

38.1 INSPECTION

Some plant operations schedule an annual shutdown or *turnaround*, at which time it is convenient to inspect suspect equipment from the inside. But whether or not such a shutdown schedule exists, it is helpful to divide equipment into categories which indicate both the urgency and timing for inspection. Inspection is usually divided into two categories known as ETI (equipment test and inspection during shutdown) and OSI (on-stream inspection during operation).

38.1.1 ETI Planning

Equipment can be considered as critical, i.e., where any type of failure would cause a shutdown or pose a problem to operation or to personnel safety, routine, i.e., requiring only nominal attention for unexpected attack, and long-term. With well-known operations, based upon either previous experience or with a thorough knowledge as to its low corrosivity, it is possible to schedule these categories as follows:

Category	Time to First Inspection, yr
Critical	1
Routine	3–5
Long-term	10

If the process is not so well known or understood, one should schedule a first-year inspection in any event and then recategorize or reschedule, based on the initial findings. It should also be remembered that inspection may be required for reasons other than corrosion, such as debris or mechanical difficulties, which may affect the final scheduling.

Critical items are most often heat exchangers (because of the thin-walled tubes commonly employed) and reactors (because of possible localized exotherms, side reactions, or contaminants). Routine items are other vessels. Long-term items are exemplified by "day tanks" for feed streams or storage tanks for products.

38.1.2 On-Stream Inspection

OSI does not require detailed scheduling, since it is performed while operations are in progress. It does, however, require careful planning as to what points in vessels or piping are to be monitored. OSI usually consists of corrosion monitoring by means of continuous-readout and ultrasonic techniques (see further below) for wall-thickness or cracking phenomena.

38.1.3 Inspection Techniques

The subject of recognition of corrosion phenomena was addressed in Chapter 6. It was emphasized that such phenomena can be divided into three groups: those which can be recognized by the naked eye, those which may require supplemental aids, and those which almost always demand more sophisticated analysis. Actually, inspection utilizes basically the same techniques as does failure analysis up to the point where laboratory work (chemical analysis, metallography, etc.) is required. Among the techniques routinely employed are the following.

Visual Examination

Visual examination may be made by the naked eye. However, it is often fruitful to employ other aids. A self-illuminated, low-power (10 to 30X) magnifying device is a useful tool. Dye penetrants, fluorescent or otherwise, may be used to help define and delineate defects, such as porosity or cracking. The Borescope or similar tools permit visual inspection of the bore (internal surface) of pipe or tubing, while glass-fiber optics permit one to see around corners or through small apertures.

Magnetic Flux

For ferromagnetic materials, visual inspection may also be aided by the use of finely divided iron powder under the influence of an applied magnetic field. The powder will orient itself in such a manner as to define surface and/or subsurface defects.

Ultrasonics

High-frequency ultrasound will penetrate a metal, reflecting back from the far surface (to be visible on a cathode-ray tube if desired). Ultrasound may be used either for quantitative measurement of wall thickness or to detect cracks or other surface or subsurface defects. With high gain, even differences in grain size are detectable, so the instrument must be properly calibrated for detection of flaws of the anticipated nature and size.

Radiography

The two basic radiographic techniques are x-ray and gamma radiography, both of which are recorded photographically. In contrast to dye-penetrant techniques, radiography will detect subsurface defects such as porosity in welds. Radiography is not sufficiently sensitive to detect small cracks (e.g., SCC, HAC, LMC) unless they are of an orientation which will show a low-density picture (i.e., when they lie parallel to the plane of radiography).

Eddy Current

Surface or subsurface defects will affect ac impedance, and advantage is taken of this characteristic in eddy current inspection of the bore of heat exchanger and other tubular parts. This technique is most applicable to nonmagnetic materials such as copper alloys and austenitic stainless steels. Ferromagnetic materials can be inspected, but require special techniques to compensate for the magnetic field.

Acoustic Emission

While ultrasonic devices *apply* high-frequency sound for thickness measurements and flaw detection, acoustic emission techniques listen for the high-frequency sound emitted by cracklike defects under strain. With microsecond timing and computerized triangulation, acoustic emission equipment can pinpoint the location of growing cracks or defects in a vessel, when the test pressure is varied cyclically. This is a relatively expensive technique, but it is no longer a laboratory curiosity. It is now being utilized industrially for detection of fatigue, as in structures, and environmental cracking, as in pressure vessels.

Corrosion Detection Devices

Either electrical resistance, polarization, or hydrogen probes (Chapter 9) may be considered tools for OSI, indicating the rate of attack at particular times.

38.2 FAILURE ANALYSIS

Failure is something which is unsuccessful, disappointing, or lacking to some degree. In the process and related industries, failure may consist in something as delicate (but not trivial) as a lapse in product quality (e.g., due to iron or other metal ion contamination). At the other extreme, there are fires, explosions, and/or toxic releases as a consequence of corrosion phenomena. There are all sorts of gradations in between, but we are most often concerned that we experience "leak-before-break" situations. The key concept is that failure is something *unexpected*, in contrast to the finite life one should always expect of a properly designed engineering structure.

Inevitably, there will be some failures, even with proper OSI and ETI programs. When they do occur, the inspection records are a good starting place for the investigation. In addition to the inspection techniques, the following methodology is normally followed.

38.2.1 Metallography

Low-Power Magnification

In addition to visual examination, as previously described, a *shop-type micro-scope* is useful for initial observations (e.g., from 5 to 60X). This instrument not only permits close examination of certain features of the failure but is useful in recording, as by color photography, the surface aspects of corrosion and corrosion products, pitting, cracking, etc.

Metallurgical Microscope

The optical *metalloscope* or metallurgical microscope is a *reflected* light device (unlike the medical or biochemical microscope, which uses transmitted light) designed for magnifications from about 50 to 3000X. A highly polished metal surface would simply act as a mirror, so the polished specimens must be etched (chemically or electrochemically) to diffuse the light and permit observation of metallurgical features. Most failure analysis work, unlike research-level metallography, is conducted at a few hundred magnifications to observe IGC, SCC, inclusions, and phases.

Scanning Electron Microscopy

While optical microscopy works from a surface polished and etched to define metallurgical features, the scanning electron microscope (SEM) indirectly observes the natural topography of the material (or fracture surface) at magnifications which can be varied from 100 to 30,000X, for example. Using a CRT (video screen), the electron beams readily define the difference between ductile and brittle fractures, for example, features not readily distinguishable by conventional optical microscopy. The SEM can also distinguish hot-short cracking from other forms of intergranular environmental cracking. Used with a special attachment like a microprobe, qualitative and semiquantitative analyses may be made at specific sites within the metal structure.

38.2.2 Corrosion Tests

Either quality assurance or service-related tests (Chapter 9) may be run in support of a failure analysis, in order to investigate the effects of composition, heat treatment, and/or process or service conditions.

38.2.3 Chemical Analysis

Conventional wet analyses are employed on materials, corrosion products, and samples of process streams (e.g., for composition and contaminants). Modern, sophisticated techniques have excellent capability in analyzing metals and identifying corrosion products (e.g., by x-ray diffraction). It should be remembered, however, that the analytical chemist needs guidance as to what to look for. Common mistakes include reporting "total acidity" when the titration actually includes iron salts or other corrosion products (or even hydrolyzable esters), confusing oxidizing cations with chromates in iodimetric analyses, and reporting total iron or iron corrosion products as magnetite (without regard to origin or characteristics). A team consisting of a corrosion engineer and a chemist (or at least a close liaison effort) usually is necessary for gathering reliable data, let alone proper interpretation.

38.3 PREVENTIVE AND PREDICTIVE MAINTENANCE

The ultimate purpose of both inspection and failure analysis in plant is to permit the maintenance department to develop proper scheduling of either preventive or preferably predictive maintenance.

Preventive maintenance is maintenance performed on a regular basis to forestall failure or to ensure attainment of the normal anticipated life. First applied to rotating equipment such as pumps and compressors, it has come to be applied to vessels and piping as well.

Predictive maintenance is a more sophisticated extension of the preventive maintenance concept, quantifying corrosion rates and attempting to establish schedules for refurbishing or replacement of equipment to minimize downtime and lost production.

Normally, the inspectors in the maintenance department or ETI group are perfectly capable of evaluating general corrosion (with loss of corrosion allowance) and the more obvious forms of localized corrosion. They should call on the corrosion engineer when there is any question about phenomena or when any cracking is detected.

The corrosion engineer's role consists in aiding such routine inspection as required, utilizing the equipment reports from OSI and ETI to predict the probable life of specific equipment, and running such laboratory and/or field corrosion tests as are required to monitor the life of equipment and the behavior of potential alternative materials of construction. Failure analysis, when necessary, is an essential part of this effort also.

Equipment records are the province of the inspectors. The *usefulness* of such records is limited by the extent to which other knowledgeable people (like the corrosion engineer or other professionals) use them as an aid in deriving maintenance or replacement schedules.

For corrosive processes, such records are invaluable in the writing of regular process reviews intended to document the process conditions and the performance (with materials of construction and possible alternatives) of the equipment. A *simplified* flow diagram, kept up-to-date and including materials of construction and relevant specifications, is a valuable tool for maintenance planning.

38.4 DOCUMENTS AND INFORMATION RETRIEVAL

Inspection records are usually entered on a fairly concise form and filed both by unit and by type of equipment. Modern microprocessors permit the computerization of such records, with ready access to scheduled events such as retubing exchangers, replacing seals, hydrotesting, and inspection.

However, other documents, such as reports on materials selection, corrosion studies, and failure analyses are often of the essay type, as opposed to simple forms. Two aspects of these documents are their format and the ability to retrieve the data or information.

Practical engineering documents, *even letters*, should follow an outline similar to that which follows (although letters, unlike formal memoranda, do not need section headings).

Summary.   The summary (or the opening paragraph in a letter) should be a brief abstract of the reason for the study, with its findings and conclusions. This is probably as far as the "top brass" will read.

Introduction.   This (or the second paragraph) is a more detailed statement of why the study was made, with background detail, and by whom it was made.

Discussion.   The details of the history, methods, and observations during the study. (Technical details of the methodology should be relegated to an appendix, so as not to interrupt the flow of thought.) The text should be written so that the casual reader can scan the text by reading the *first sentence* of each paragraph only. (This follows naturally from a proper outline; paragraphs are intended to expand on the details of the lead sentence.) This is very helpful to middle management.

Conclusions.   The findings of the study should be enumerated.

Recommendations.   What the author suggests the client should do about whatever resolution of the problem has been made.

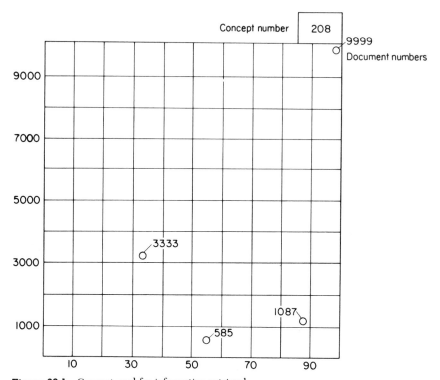

Figure 38.1   Concept card for information retrieval.

The author's peers will read the letter and reports in depth (including the detailed appendix), but the format described allows other disciplines and other levels of management to extract the necessary information either superficially or in depth, depending upon the extent of their interest.

Anybody can file letters and reports. The critical question is whether one can find, at some later date, what is in the files. In modern practice, conventional files are being replaced with data retrieval or information retrieval systems.

Although some companies use data retrieval systems just for quantitative data such as corrosion rates, a better approach is to handle *all* pertinent supporting documents, as well. G. B. Elder of Union Carbide Corporation in South Charleston, W. V.,has described such a system (see "Data Retrieval for the Corrosion Engineer," *Materials Performance*, vol. 6, no. 33). The main features of the system comprise

1. A simple sequential numbering system for all documents.
2. A numerical list of key concepts which embrace such diverse subjects as type of data, plant locations, types of equipment, materials of construction,

types of environment (e.g., steam, water, specific chemicals), types of phenomena, etc. In this numerical system, for example, the number 17 might represent S31603, 208 acetic acid, and 295 SCC.

3. A series of cards (one per concept) capable of coding 10,000 reports (i.e., lined off in 100 horizontal and 100 vertical squares).

4. A small drill-press device for perforating a stack of cards at a particular number, corresponding to that of a particular report (e.g., report no. 99 owns the bottom right-hand square).

5. An illuminated viewing device for the cards during the retrieval operation.

Each numbered letter is coded for the applicable concepts, and the relevant cards are stacked together and drilled at the square corresponding to the report number. The report is then filed in ordinary numerical sequence.

In the search or retrieval operation (e.g., what do we have in the file on *pitting* of *lead tanks* in *sulfuric acid?*), the appropriate concept cards are stacked and viewed over the light source. The numbered perforations corresponding to all reports coded for all these concepts are illuminated.

With a microprocessor, this type of system is further enhanced by the capability of using AND/OR techniques which allow one to exclude certain concepts (e.g., not to retrieve reports by a certain author; to exclude certain time periods). One can also use words instead of numbers for the concepts, e.g., key words in context (KWIC). However, there are difficulties with words which start with the same letters or are dual words (e.g., sea salt, seawater). The numbered concept approach is less ambiguous, even though a reference list equating numbers and concepts is required. A typical system might use the following concepts:

1	Laboratory test data
2	Field test data
3	Physical and mechanical properties
4	Inspection data
5−15	Plant locations or sites
16−30	Type of equipment
31−100	Materials and coatings
101−150	Specific processes
151−250	Specific environments
251−300	Specific phenomena

Modern software (e.g., DataBase II) is capable of handling this sort of information file and retrieval system via CP/M.

RECOMMENDED READING

Barer, R. D., and Peters, B. F.: *Why Metals Fail. Selected Case Histories*, Gordon, New York, 1970.

Plushkin, E. P.: *Defects and Failures of Metals*, Elsevier, Amsterdam, 1956.

Wulpi, D. J.: *How Components Fail*, ASM, Metals Park, OH, 1966.

Epilogue

The purpose of this book has been to familiarize the reader with some fundamental concepts concerning materials of construction and related corrosion phenomena, as well as the relevant corrosion control techniques. This foundation in practical knowledge is intended to enable one to recognize a problem and the possible need for professional help. It should also arouse a further interest in corrosion science, technology, and engineering.

Technology is the reduction of scientific knowledge to engineering practice. While the specific fields of CP, painting, and water treatment are continually developing specialists, there is a dearth of capable people developing as corrosion/materials engineers in the process industries. The industrial plant in chemical, petrochemical, and related processes requires guidance in a very broad field of materials design, operation, and maintenance.

Although many colleges and universities offer postgraduate degrees in corrosion and materials science, educational institutions have not yet developed an undergraduate course in corrosion control engineering.

As of this writing, the engineer who is seriously interested in specialization in this field must be self-educated to a large extent largely by technical reading. However, some short-cuts are available. NACE offers a number of courses in the several fields of corrosion control. Of primary interest are

1. Corrosion Fundamentals: An Introduction
2. Cathodic Protection
3. Corrosion Prevention by Coatings
4. Corrosion in Oil and Gas Production

   These courses are given in an intensive (1-week) mode at several locations several times a year. They are also available for purchase by a company for in-house use, e.g., on a one day per week schedule, more conducive to detailed perusal of the text). They can be taken in a home-study manner also, although this suffers the disadvantage of lacking personal instruction and examples.

   It is my sincere hope that this volume will not only fill a practical need as a compilation of information not readily available elsewhere but will encourage the chemical engineer and others in the process industries to pursue further this important and interesting field.

Index

ABOUT THE AUTHOR

C. P. (Paul) Dillon is a registered Professional Engineer and an NACE-accredited Corrosion Specialist. With more than 40 years' experience, he is a recognized authority on corrosion control in the process industries, specializing in chemical, petrochemical, and industrial water problems. A corrosion control consultant since 1976, he was formerly manager of materials engineering for Union Carbide Corporation's Chemical and Plastics Divisions, and an engineering specialist for Aramco. He has served as a consultant for UNIDO and is active in many NACE and ASTM committees.